SEARCHING THE HORIZON

A History of
Ames Research Center
1940-1976

Elizabeth A. Muenger

Infrared image of the southern end of San Francisco Bay, taken at 21,000 meters by one of Ames's U-2 research aircraft. Ames can be identified by the runway just left of center.

NASA SP-4304

SEARCHING THE HORIZON

A History of
Ames Research Center
1940-1976

Elizabeth A. Muenger

The NASA History Series

NASA Scientific and Technical Information Branch   1985
National Aeronautics and Space Administration
Washington, DC

NASA maintains an internal history program for two principal reasons: (1) Sponsorship or research in NASA-related history is one way in which NASA responds to the provision of the National Aeronautics and Space Act of 1958 that requires NASA to "provide for the widest practicable and appropriate dissemination of information concerning its activities and the results thereof." (2) Thoughtful study of NASA history can help agency managers accomplish the missions assigned to the agency. Understanding NASA's past aids in understanding its present situation and illuminates possible future directions. The opinions and conclusions set forth in this book are those of the author; no official of the agency necessarily endorses those opinions or conclusions.

Library of Congress Cataloging-in-Publication Data

Muenger, Elizabeth A.
　Searching the horizon.

　(The NASA history series) (NASA SP ; 4304)
　Bibliography.
　Includes index.
　1. Ames Research Center — History. I. United States.
National Aeronautics and Space Administration.
Scientific and Technical Information Branch. II. Title.
III. Series. IV. Series: NASA SP ; 4304.
TL565.M84　1985　629.1'072079473　85-18735

For sale by the Superintendent of Documents, U. S. Government Printing Office
Washington, DC 20402 (paper cover)

TABLE OF CONTENTS

FOREWORD

This is a book about a remarkable institution. It captures the soul of the place and the work of the people who made it what it is today.

The NASA Ames Research Center has been in business for over 40 years and during that time a great many important contributions have been made by people at Ames to both the aeronautical and space missions of NASA. In the early years, the focus of the center's work was in the area of high-speed flight and ultimately led to the creation of the superb fighter aircraft that were used toward the end of World War II and in the Korean conflict. The continuation of the effort to understand how objects move rapidly through the atmosphere resulted in the development of the blunt-body atmospheric entry concept, which was used first on military ballistic missiles and later on the Mercury, Gemini, and Apollo spacecraft. And, continuing this tradition, Ames played a large part in the development of the reusable thermal protection system of the Space Shuttle. The interest in high-speed flight and atmospheric entry created the necessity to understand the behavior of high-temperature plasmas; that, in turn, resulted in the first Pioneer spacecraft to measure the solar plasma, the later Pioneers to the outer solar system, and the Pioneer Venus atmospheric entry experiment. Finally, it was recognized very early that high-speed flight stressed the human body and that understanding biological mechanisms and human physiology was important. This led to the contributions made by people at Ames to aviation safety, space medicine, and space biology. The interest in biology also stimulated thinking about the origin of life itself and resulted in the strong participation of people at Ames in the search for biological activity on Mars with the Viking landers.

These examples of the development of various interests at Ames illustrate the astonishing versatility of the people who have worked there. It is not unusual to find someone mentioned in this book who started a career as an aeronautical engineer and completed it with a distinguished reputation in a completely different field — for example, geophysics. Fundamental to the ability to do this is a clear recognition that it is most important to seek for the explanation of things from the most fundamental theoretical viewpoint. The people at Ames have always seen to it that the atmosphere conducive to fundamental theoretical studies exists. In recent years, this circumstance caused the creation at Ames of one of the most advanced computer centers in the country.

Throughout the history of Ames, its people have made important contributions to national security. It is no accident therefore that the U.S. Army's Aviation Research and Development Laboratory is located at Ames and that this laboratory has been an important factor in the history and development of the research center.

In the last analysis, however, an institution such as Ames is, as it were, the "shadow in time" of its creator; and the shadow cast by Smith De France, the first director, is long indeed. De France understood, above all else, the importance of quality. Important technical work can only be performed by people of the highest quality. He saw to it that the quality of the staff at Ames was maintained at the highest level throughout his years as director. This resulted in the elegance and the intellectual integrity that has characterized the work of the people at Ames.

For my own part, I am proud to have had a part in the continuing growth and development of the Ames Research Center. I shall always treasure the memories of the years I spent there.

Hans Mark
Deputy Administrator
April 1983

PREFACE

For those who know Ames, this history of one of the country's most interesting and important research institutions may seem woefully incomplete. In charting the growth and expanding interests of Ames Research Center, many of its research contributions have indeed been omitted. Instead, I have attempted to sketch a broad outline of Ames's technological achievements within the context of its operational and managerial development. This perspective has produced a narrative covering almost 40 years, in which the major changes Ames has experienced are clearly defined, traced chronologically, and analyzed for their various effects upon the research center.

There are several reasons for this broad approach. First, the overriding aim of this study is to present to the lay reader as complete a picture of Ames as is possible, and to portray the research laboratory in all its complexity as a combination of personalities, management philosophies, and research needs, acted upon by the pressures of economics, politics, and military necessities. The process, mode, and directions taken in research prove as fascinating and worthwhile a subject as the products of research, and it was these elements I hoped to capture in a profile of the institution.

Secondly, the scope and sophistication of the research done at Ames is in itself daunting. Had extensive technical detail been included, the resulting book would have been double the size of the present manuscript. It would also have been, I feel, forbidding in both appearance and style to my intended audience, interested readers not necessarily acquainted with Ames or involved in its technical fields of expertise. For those needing technical details on various research projects mentioned in the book, the NACA's and NASA's Technical Notes, Memoranda, and Reports provide clearly written, technically detailed summaries of Ames's work, written by those who accomplished the research; they surpass any treatment possible within the confines of this work.

During the process of researching and writing the history of Ames, I discovered the truth of many of the assumptions people make regarding successful research. Success, continued success in pursuing new ideas and possible solutions to major technological challenges lies, of course, with the calibre of men and women involved in that research. Ames, over the years, has been continually lucky in the people who have worked there; they have been among the finest in their fields. Beyond that, however, Ames researchers impressed me with their lack of confinement to narrow areas of expertise. They emphatically did not fit into the stereotypical mold of narrowly educated, immediately unintelligible technocrats whom outsiders like to think comprise the engineering professions. On the contrary, I was constantly struck, while talking with Ames-connected people, how wide their interests spread, and how many fascinating byways they had explored in their careers. The research flexibility Ames has displayed throughout its history is, I think, a phenomenon closely connected to the intellectual flexibility of its personnel. New ideas, however unorthodox, have always been given serious attention by Ames; alternative solutions to technical puzzles have been explored in refreshingly open-minded manners. Frequently it has been the unorthodox approach that has provided the answer to major hurdles. The most striking example of this was, without doubt, Harvey Allen's blunt body solution to the temperature problem of high-speed flight. On the face of it, the idea that a rounded body could not only survive atmospheric reentry heating but also lessen its effects appears curious, yet Allen's theory developed as a result of his preoccupation with the simplicity of the natural world and his ability to escape the dead ends of conventional thinking. This talent, both in research and management, has always blessed Ames.

Ames personnel also seem to be strikingly self-motivated in their work habits. It was perhaps easier to be self-motivated in Ames's earlier decades, when much less paperwork and fewer regulations intervened between the researchers and the task they were trying to accomplish. But today's engineers have educated themselves admirably in the art of plowing past the bureaucracy to productivity, and I see this feat as evidence of the high level of commitment to research excellence. No manager, however effective, could replace the self-motivating factor in research; it inspires as well as fuels the search for solutions and answers to research conundrums.

Finally, studying Ames revealed, in ironic detail, the lack of connection between large budgets, heavily structured bureaucratic procedures, and effectiveness. The budgets under which Ames operated during its early years are a literal drop in the bucket compared to present funding. The management and research process, a seemingly simple relationship in earlier decades, is now monitored at every turn. Large budgets and accompanying bureaucracy are probably inescapable in today's context; our goals have also become far more complex and sophisticated than they used to be. It is useful to remember, however, that Ames worked equally as effectively, albeit differently, when the *modus operandi* was what we might now call primitive. Large-scale funding and the increasing involvement of bureaucracy in the daily life of research are not reasons for Ames's success; dedication to creative thinking is. There is something to be learned from the history of Ames; I believe this is it.

Many people have aided me during this project. Ames management has helped me in every possible way. I am grateful to former Ames Director Clarence Syvertson and to Director of Administration Louis Brennwald for easing my way on numerous occasions. In Washington, former Ames Director Hans Mark, later Deputy Administrator of NASA, was generous with his time and help.

I owe a great deal to many at Ames who donated their time and provided me with information I could not have acquired from printed sources. Not only did my interviewees aid in the writing of the book, many of them also read portions of the resulting manuscript, offered invaluable suggestions, and saved me from miscellaneous errors. John Dusterberry, coordinator of the manuscript's review process at Ames, accomplished a Herculean task with grace and good humor. Paul Bennett offered tangible assistance in choosing illustrations and in handling the technical production of the book's design. Darryll Stroud patiently tracked down a long list of needed photographs. Alberta Cox and her colleagues did a wonderful job typesetting the manuscript. Joyce Courtney provided needed details from Ames with professional competence. Mildred Macon, who assisted me initially in finding and retrieving necessary archival documents, became indispensable as a friend, typist, and proofreader. I owe her a great deal.

The NASA History Office has made my association with NASA a truly pleasant one. Monte Wright, former Director of the History Office, edited and much improved the original manuscript. Lee Saegesser, the NASA History Office archivist, helped with references and documents. Carrie Karegeannes coordinated details of the manuscript's completion. Sylvia Fries, present Director of the History Office, has helped greatly in coordinating the book's production. The list of friends and colleagues who helped to improve the book is long. I am especially grateful to Susan Cooper, Thomas Duesterberg, Edward C. Ezell, Linda N. Ezell, Georgie Gleim, Kenneth A. Lockridge, J. W. Mornington, the late Carl Proffer and Ellendea Proffer, Alex Roland, George and Deborah Schober, the late Michael Shaw, John Shy, Walter Vincenti, and W. E. Weaver.

E. A. Muenger
Colorado Springs
December 1984

1

THE BEGINNINGS, 1939-1945

Among the mementos in the Director's Office at the Ames Research Center is a fragment of canvas covering from the Wright brothers' Kitty Hawk biplane. It was presented in 1948 to the director of Ames, Dr. Smith J. De France, on behalf of Orville Wright, who had recently died. Wright had been a friend of De France and had wanted him to have a souvenir of the 1903 flight. Hanging nearby is an equally impressive token from the 1972 Apollo 16 mission, a small flag carried in the first exploration of the lunar highlands.

The two artifacts, so far removed from each other in terms of the visions and technologies they represent, are fitting symbols of the richness of Ames's history. When Ames was founded in 1939, man had been flying for only a few decades. The aeronautical pioneers were not only still alive, but were for the most part still active in their professions. The leap in aeronautical technology had been spectacular since the almost primitive beginnings, but the first 40 years of progress were to seem tame compared with the second 40 years. Ames was built in the midst of exciting technological challenges and a frightening international situation. The state of the aeronautical art in 1939 and the urgent need for a second laboratory of the National Advisory Committee for Aeronautics (NACA) provided double impetus for the energy and creativity that characterized the new institution.

THE BACKGROUND

The second laboratory was conceived as a junior sibling to the Langley Memorial Aeronautical Laboratory in Virginia. In existence since 1915, the NACA had since 1918 operated its research laboratory at Langley Field, an Army airbase near Hampton Roads.

The NACA had made a name for itself in its first 25 years.[1] The U.S. Congress formed the Committee in recognition of the need for governmental support and coordination of research in aeronautics. In the decade after the Kitty Hawk flight, the nation had slipped behind Europe in aeronautical progress, a fact that became embarrassingly obvious as soon as World War I began. An organized effort to make up for lost time was needed; after trying for several years, a small group of aeronautical pioneers succeeded in obtaining the legislation that created the NACA, appended to the Naval Appropriations Act of 1915.

The NACA was simple in structure. A Main Committee acted as a steering group and an official voice for the NACA. The most prestigious names in aeronautics appeared as members, among them Orville Wright, Dr. William Durand, and at a later time Charles Lindbergh. Under the Main Committee, technical committees and subcommittees provided liaison between industry and the military, beneficiaries of NACA research, and the Langley Aeronautical Laboratory, the producer of research results. Langley's early research successes had provided much of the foundation of the NACA.

For both industry and the military, and for young students of aeronautics, the technical notes, reports, and memoranda written by Langley's engineers were a major source of information in the field. The NACA's reputation for solid contributions to aeronautical knowledge became an effective way of recruiting new talent. In the normal course of events, a young aeronautical engineer interested in research sought employment with the NACA, for it was "in the NACA that the exciting discoveries were being made," as one NACA veteran put it.[2]

Industry, at least at that time, offered fewer research opportunities for young engineers. The NACA, possessing better research facilities than the aircraft industry and with interests ranging over the whole spectrum of aeronautical unknowns, offered far wider horizons. "If you wanted to do research, you went where the facilities were, and the NACA had the facilities," recalled another veteran whose career with the NACA began in the 1930s at Langley.[3] The same situation was true a decade later, when Ames was recruiting young aeronautical engineers. "I couldn't see myself chained to a drafting board [as I would have been in industry]," explained Charles Hall, who came to Ames in 1942 after graduating from the University of California at Berkeley.[4]

Once at Langley, even if one had originally planned to move on to the developing aeronautical industry, one was "hooked. Research was exciting." The average age of the staff at Langley in the 1930s was 26, and the laboratory was, by all accounts, a stimulating, creative, and productive place to work, yet relaxed and informal in atmosphere. Perhaps because of the youth of both the researchers and the field of aeronautics itself, Langley's atmosphere seemed more like a college campus than anything else. It was certainly, a former Langley employee recalled, "nothing like a company or a

2

factory." Aeronautics, the laboratory, and the staff were all in developmental stages, and the combination of forces produced exciting results.[5]

In a poignant way, Langley's attraction in the 1930s mirrored the way in which the airplane had captured the imagination of Americans with its debut in World War I. In the military, the romanticism of the now-vulnerable and impractical cavalry had been quickly transferred to the aviators. Postwar barnstorming had continued the mystique, as had Lindbergh's 1927 flight to Paris. More prosaically, however, the late 1930s brought growing industrial efforts to develop aircraft capabilities and, even more crucial, the conviction of both aeronautical experts and military observers that steady progress in the field was absolutely necessary for the military security of the United States. Visitors to Europe, among them Dr. George Lewis, the NACA's director of aeronautical research, had noted with alarm the spurt of progress made there. In its 1937 report to Congress, the NACA concluded, after describing its early experimental facilities,

> The possession of such equipment was one of the chief factors in enabling the United States to become the recognized leader in the technical development of aircraft. Since 1932 this research equipment has been reproduced by foreign countries and in some cases special research equipment . . . abroad . . . is superior to the equipment existing at Langley Field. This condition has impressed the Committee with the advisability of providing additional facilities promptly as needed for the study of problems that are necessary to be solved, in order that American aircraft development, both military and commercial, will not fall behind.[6]

As the international tensions increased, a Special Committee on the Relations of the NACA to National Defense in Time of War was established in 1936. Its chairman was Maj. Gen. Oscar Westover, chief of the Army Air Corps. The recommendation was that another research laboratory be built, since Langley was vulnerable to attack from Europe and was also outgrowing both available electric power and land. The laboratory had grown from 3 employees in 1918 to almost 500 by the end of 1938.[7] In late 1938 a successor committee on future research facilities recommended to Dr. Joseph Ames, the chairman of the NACA Executive Committee, that the second aeronautical laboratory be built as quickly as possible. The committee recommended a site in Sunnyvale, California, at Moffett Field, then operated by the Army Air Corps. The estimated cost would be $11,000,000.[8] Early in 1939, the request for appropriations went to Congress.

Meanwhile, Smith De France, the assistant chief of aerodynamics at Langley, had been sent to Moffett Field to inspect the proposed site. He spoke with Army personnel regarding the project. At the same time Lewis, assisted by the NACA's financial officer, E. H. Chamberlin, made specific estimates of both the needed facilities and the required funds.[9]

Unexpected difficulties arose in Congress, however. Although appropriations for additional facilities at Langley encountered no opposition, the appropriations subcommittees in both House and Senate balked over the second research laboratory.[10] After rejection in the second deficiency bill for 1939, the funding request was attached to the third deficiency bill, and Lewis; Dr. Charles Abbott, vice-chairman of the NACA Executive Committee; and Col. Charles Lindbergh, also an NACA member, presented the case for the West Coast laboratory. All three men possessed considerable prestige and presence and argued the case eloquently. Included in the request were additional funds for Langley and for research work at academic and scientific institutions. Both Lewis and Lindbergh, having recently returned from Europe, could attest to the growing threat of German air power.

At this juncture John Victory, executive secretary of the NACA, sensed that it might aid approval of the appropriations request to remove the designation of the California site from the bill. Legislators from other geographical areas would then, perhaps, see the request less as a plum for California than as a justifiable appropriation based on the increasingly grim international situation. Whether the deletion had the intended effect is unknown, but on 9 August 1939, the bill providing funds for a second laboratory became law. The NACA was to determine a site within a month of the bill's passage, and not surprisingly, Moffett Field was chosen.[11]

The choice of the site resulted from several considerations. Being on the West Coast would at least protect the new laboratory from the possibility of European attack, although the threat from Japan was certainly considered by the NACA.[12] Other factors, however, offset the vulnerability of the coastal site. The report of the Special Research Committee of Future Research Facilities in December 1938 had listed criteria for site selection. Moffett Field fit the requirements: location on a military base to take advantage of existing airfield facilities; low-density air traffic and good flying weather; adequate and economical electric power, which had been a problem at Langley; and accessibility to the western aircraft industry, industrial centers, and academic institutions of repute.[13]

Location near the growing aircraft companies was of prime importance. By 1939 almost half of the aircraft industry was on the West Coast, and those engineers from Langley who met regularly with the western companies were well aware of the time and energy travel consumed. A trip from Langley to San Diego took four days by train or nearly 30 exhausting hours by airplane. Another factor was the competitive relationship that had devel-

4

oped between the NACA and the Guggenheim Aeronautical Laboratory at the California Institute of Technology. Pasadena was easily accessible to the California aircraft industry, but its facilities were strained with industrial research requirements. Moffett Field both answered industry's needs and reasserted the NACA's research preeminence.[14] Though other sites were considered, Moffett Field had clearly been the preference from the beginning, and as soon as the announcement of the site was made, already laid plans were implemented.

Though officially opened only six years previously, Moffett Field already had an interesting history. It had been conceived as a base for the Navy's rigid airships in 1931. At that time, the Navy was building ZRS-4 and ZRS-5, later christened the *Akron* and *Macon*. The *Akron* was to be assigned to the Lakehurst, New Jersey, base; the *Macon* was to be based in Sunnyvale. Local communities in California had donated 100 acres for the base, and the government had bought 750 additional acres. The new base was expected to provide needed jobs both in its construction and maintenance, and local firms foresaw steady orders for supplies and materials. The Pacific Gas and Electric Company proudly announced that the electric load at Sunnyvale would be 2200 horsepower, "enough to supply a good-sized town." Nearby inhabitants were awed by circulated sketches of the giant hangar that would be built to house the airship. It would be, as one drawing conceived it, able to contain San Francisco's St. Francis Hotel four times over. The hangar's length was the equivalent of four city blocks, its width greater than one block, and its height about equal to that of a 16-story building.[15]

The giant hangar was finished and in due course the *Macon* was assigned to the base. But in 1933 the *Akron* crashed off the East Coast, leaving the *Macon* as the country's only rigid airship. Commanding the *Akron* when it crashed was Rear Adm. William Moffett, who had been influential in both the Navy's commitment to rigid airships and the selection of the Sunnyvale site for the Navy's western base. In his memory the U.S. Naval Air Station, Sunnyvale, was renamed Moffett Field. The base was considered completed in January 1935, but the next month the *Macon* crashed off the coast at Point Sur, 150 kilometers south of Moffett Field. The crash ended the Navy's involvement with rigid airships and made the base surplus to the Navy. In October 1935 it became an Army air training base. Interestingly, one of the first Army squadrons sent to Moffett Field was from Langley Field.

In 1939, as Moffett Field was being chosen by the NACA for its laboratory, the Army was busy constructing barracks and mess halls to accommodate a continuing expansion.[16] The Navy still held out hope for rigid airships in the future and requested that the NACA buildings, should they materialize, be located outside the still-present mooring circles. It was, perhaps, the last official documentation regarding Moffett Field's original purpose.[17]

In early December, the Army gave the NACA use of 62 acres of land, retaining title to the land with the War Department.[18] The NACA purchased another 40 acres from local farmers and immediately began surveying building locations.

The southern end of San Francisco Bay today bears no resemblance to its appearance in 1939. Instead of a continual stretch of suburbia intermixed with industry, small communities interrupted agricultural land in an almost rural atmosphere. The land acquired for Moffett Field was completely undeveloped, as was the additional acreage that the NACA bought. Adjoining the government property were farms, fruit trees, and dairy cattle; the pastures would be concrete in 20 years. Instead of the extensive freeway system that now crisscrosses the area, a less intimidating Bayshore Highway took one to the main gate of Moffett Field, where the construction going on appeared hive-like in its activity.

Planning was under way at Langley in the fall of 1939 for the facilities at the new laboratory. The design group was headed by Smith De France, who, it was rightly assumed, would head the new installation.[19] Through the winter of 1939–1940, however, De France remained at Langley, designing the buildings and wind tunnels to be constructed at Moffett Field, and also continuing to plan Langley's own projects.

Liaison was provided initially by a representative from the NACA Washington office, Russell G. Robinson, who had been sent to California to inaugurate the NACA's Western Coordination Office. That office was intended to be a partial answer to the problem of distance between the western aircraft industry and academia and NACA headquarters. The aim was to provide a regular two-way channel of information that would make for more efficient research and a greater awareness of mutual needs. Robinson, already on the scene, was a logical person to provide on-the-spot assistance in practical arrangements with the Army at Moffett Field and to deal with any problems that might arise during initial construction.

At Moffett Field in the last months of 1939, Robinson juggled Western Coordination Office planning with construction details at Moffett Field and maintained a steady correspondence with Langley over building eccentricities caused by Moffett Field's geography: the high water table and the possibility of earthquakes. De France requested Robinson to obtain local technical articles on earthquake construction, and building specifications were then adjusted for maximum protection. Moffett Field military buildings were closely examined for cracks that could provide information on construction pitfalls.[20]

While on the West Coast, Robinson also publicized the new laboratory at surrounding universities, with the result that the original roster of Ames employees included a fair sampling of local talent. Stanford University, one of the few institutions in the country at that time with both a wind tunnel and a widely known body of aeronautical experts, became an important source of professional manpower for the laboratory. The Stanford connection rose naturally from earlier association with the NACA. Dr. William Durand, one of the original members of the Main Committee, was a highly respected member of the Stanford faculty. Prof. Elliott Reid, another aeronautical engineer in the Department of Mechanical Engineering (which then included aeronautics) had worked at Langley in the early 1920s. The location of the NACA's second laboratory so close to Stanford was to prove important in the dynamics of the laboratory and in the continued growth of aeronautics at the university. Indeed, two of the driving forces behind Ames in its early years were Stanford graduates who had been working at Langley, but who returned to the area as staff for the new laboratory — H. Julian Allen and John Parsons.

This local connection with an academic institution, which Langley did not have in its early years, was an advantage that should not be overlooked when assessing the distinctive sense of community that seems to have characterized the new laboratory. As one early Ames employee recalled, "My roommate and I took the civil-service test together, graduated together from Stanford, and began work at Ames together on the same day."[21]

Another source of local talent, if not quite so close as Stanford, was the University of California system. Berkeley provided personnel, as did the University of California at Los Angeles and the University of Southern California. Active recruiting for Ames tended to confine itself to the West Coast, though of course anyone taking the civil service test could ask to be put on the roster for potential employment at Ames. Especially during the war, however, when Ames recruited directly and the civil service test was waived, efforts were focused on hiring engineers from nearby universities. De France, writing to an inquiring author in 1945, listed the University of California and Stanford as the two schools most heavily represented at Ames. In response to a question regarding wartime recruitment of personnel, De France named 13 universities where Ames had recruited, the farthest afield being Arizona and Washington.[22]

Construction continued at the new site, and in April 1940 it was announced that the new laboratory would be named after Dr. Joseph S. Ames, the recently retired chairman of the NACA. Ames had been influential in the conception of the NACA and had been one of the original members of the Main Committee. He was highly respected in physics, which he taught at Johns Hopkins University, and revered as an individual. The honor was both well deserved and timely; Ames died only a few years later.

As progress was made at Moffett Field, planning of the future facilities for Ames continued at Langley. The NACA, trying to make up for the time lost in obtaining congressional sanction for the laboratory, now felt that it was more advantageous to keep most of the staff at Langley until the move to California could be made with efficiency. De France, named engineer-in-charge in June 1940, thus did not arrive at Ames until August. He had been preceded by John Parsons, who had been put in charge of the various construction projects, and by a few others from the Langley group who would eventually form the nucleus of the early Ames staff. This logistical coordination eased the way greatly — planning could continue without the designers having to cope with the raw realities of the building site, and those involved in the actual construction were kept busy by continuing directives from Langley.

Until De France arrived, the day-to-day administrative details were directed by Edward R. Sharp, another Langley man. Even before he arrived in California in early 1940, Sharp had been helping with problems encountered by Parsons at Moffett Field. One of them was the rerouting of a county road that ran through the site of the planned 16-foot wind tunnel. The road was on the acreage the NACA had bought and obviously needed to be rerouted, but the contract for constructing the tunnel had been let and the county had done nothing. Sharp, still at Langley, asked John Victory, the executive secretary of the NACA, to help. Victory somehow moved the county authorities to action, and they moved the road.[23] Construction of the 16-foot tunnel, one of the first two wind tunnels built at Ames, began in May. By that time Sharp was at Moffett Field acting as De France's administrative officer. The county road is a good example of one of the Washington office's strengths. Correspondence among Sharp, De France, Lewis, and Victory during the construction phase attests to the efforts of the Washington office to expedite the planning and to lend weight where needed. Also striking, however, is the leeway given De France in making decisions and in choosing his future staff.[24]

Throughout the spring and early summer, a steady stream of correspondence between Sharp and De France dealt with the many details of construction and staffing. Specific persons were requested by Sharp and promptly sent by De France in a continuous transfer to Ames as the new laboratory was able to absorb personnel.[25] Travel involved more adventure then than now. Even so, H. Julian Allen, who arrived in April, perhaps had more than his share: "He burned out a bearing in the middle of the Arizona desert but found an old Scotch machinist who turned out a bearing on a wobbly old lathe. This enabled him to proceed to Bakersfield where he had a brother, and from there he wired New York to send him a new bearing airmail. This was a little slow in coming and so he only arrived here after driving all night."[26]

Sharp happily reported that the military personnel at Moffett Field were most cooperative in all matters. The commanding colonel had provided storage space for NACA tools and had promised more space when needed. Sharp reported, "Relations with the army are as sweet as you could ask for.

8

I think they have gone far out of their way to receive us well and to assure us of their fullest cooperation. . . . I certainly hope we can keep these fine relations and never 'get in their hair.'"[27] This was a better start than had been made at Langley, where the laboratory's early years had been colored by several misunderstandings with the Army.[28] At that time, of course, the NACA itself was so young as to be regarded by some in the military as an upstart civilian group whose function might better be performed within the military organization.

Back at Langley, De France had his hands full coordinating the various design projects. Although Sharp at Moffett Field continued to request more staff, De France needed to juggle his personnel into locations where they could work most effectively. As he wrote Sharp in late June 1940, "It is expected that we will start transferring the remainder of the engineering force on July 15, but all of the personnel will not come at the same time. In other words, the departure from Langley Field will be staggered so as to continue the engineering work and have people familiar with the contracts available to handle any correspondence either from Langley Field or Moffett Field." The problem was complicated because De France's design staff was not only busy with plans for Langley's new wind tunnels and those at Ames, it was also planning the NACA's new engine research laboratory near Cleveland. Indeed, De France intended to continue designing for Cleveland after his staff moved to Ames. His closing lines had almost a harried note:

> We are so busy here at Langley Field that we do not know which way to turn. The design work . . . is more than can be handled with the present organization. It will be necessary to organize this design work in sections and increase the design and drafting force. We are planning on doing some of the design for the new engine research laboratory at Moffett Field; therefore it is evident that the force which we are planning on having at Moffett Field by August 1 or shortly thereafter will not be any too large for handling the extra design in addition to that at Moffett Field.[29]

The Move to Moffett Field

By the end of August 1940, however, one could speak of a real staff at Ames. De France and 22 others had arrived from Langley. The NACA had hired, through the usual civil service procedures, additional junior engineers and support staff. The entire contingent assembled at the end of the summer for the first Ames staff picture, taken outside the new Flight Research Building. Of the 51 people in the group, half had worked with each other at Langley. A few of them were Stanford graduates. This academic connection

January 1940. The first building erected at Ames, the construction shack served as head-quarters for the engineers and crews fighting California's winter mud as they laid out and built an aeronautical laboratory.

should not be overemphasized, but it doubtless strengthened ties, both organizationally and individually. Both institutions would gain from the relationship. One should note, however, that it has, over the years, made for a subtle feeling of exclusion among more recent employees who lack such academic ties.[30]

What of the Langley people now building the new laboratory? Langley was, by all accounts, still small enough and informal enough to be tightly knit. Camaraderie had been reinforced by its isolated location in rural Virginia; closeness had probably been an act of desperation. Despite its growth over the years, however, the sense of small community had remained, so it must have been a hard decision for those who moved to California. Those who did, however, had actively wanted to go, and morale among them was high. H. Julian Allen, who was to head the Theoretical Aerodynamics Section, had demanded transfer on threat of resignation. At Langley it had

10

August 1940. The Langley contingent arrived and was joined by other newly hired junior engineers. The group, still remarkably small, gathered outside the completed Flight Research Laboratory for the first staff photo. (1) Smith De France, (2) Harry Goett, (3) Harvey Allen, and (4) Jack Parsons.

been "considered a plum" to be chosen by De France as part of the design team for the new laboratory, and selection led almost certainly to transfer. Those who went were excited by the opportunity to "make a name for yourself or fall flat on your face," as one employee put it.[31] The sense of urgency to get the laboratory into operation seems to have been common to the group.

If the feelings implied in the phrase *the Ames family* had positive results, there were also negative implications. Previously, whatever competitiveness had existed at Langley was either self-contained within small groups or was directed toward the Army's research and development laboratory at Wright Field in Ohio, or the Guggenheim laboratory in Pasadena, or Headquarters. Now the Langley staff was split, and the California contingent reassembled with a new identity. With the creation of the new laboratory came a sense of rivalry between those who remained at Langley and those who came to Ames, as well as the extremely rapid development of a strong sense of Ames's own identity. This sense of identity and feeling of community, especially among the first employees, led one later director to refer repeatedly to the "Mayflower group" at Ames. Even today, the sense of the "inner circle" is strong among the more recent employees, who express a certain resignation to what they see as permanent exclusion.[32]

The sense of separation from Langley seems to have been almost immediate. Though Edward R. Sharp, who returned to Langley in the fall of 1940, referred for a while to Ames as "my other laboratory,"[33] his attention too was quickly diverted to planning the new facilities for the Cleveland laboratory, which he later headed. But many of those involved in Ames's early stages of construction and growth stayed there for the rest of their careers. Those who helped build the laboratory identified strongly with it. Langley Field and Washington were a continent away. Not only did geography reinforce a sense of separation, but the rivalry inherent in the relationship between Langley and Ames emphasized the distance between Ames and the Washington office of the NACA. If Ames officials felt less hampered by Washington's bureaucracy than their counterparts at Langley, the Ames staff was also in a less favorable position to campaign for pet projects and funds. In any event, it is clear that among the early characteristics of Ames as an institution were a strong sense of community, a competitive aspect to it's relationship with the Langley laboratory, and a slightly independent attitude with regard to Washington.[34]

Also significant in the formation of a distinctive personality within the new institution was its first head. Smith De France had been in charge of the early planning for the laboratory and had been sent by Washington to inspect the Moffett Field location long before the bill establishing Ames had gotten out of congressional subcommittees. George Lewis, the director of aeronautical research in the Washington office, probably selected De France. His choice seems to have been a wise one. Older employees who worked under De France invariably mention his name when describing the sense of unity at Ames. During his long career, De France's character and strict standards permeated the laboratory, and if employees stood in awe of his uncompromising attitudes toward excellence and frugality, the respect and affection they also felt for the man were genuine.

De France was born in Michigan in 1896. He left college during World War I to train as an aviator with the Canadian Flying Corps. When the United States entered the war, he flew with the 139th Aero Squadron. Subsequently, he completed a degree in aeronautical engineering at the University of Michigan and went to work for the NACA at Langley. After early work with dirigibles, he was assigned the task of designing a full-scale wind tunnel capable of testing actual airplanes instead of models. With a test section of 30 by 60 feet, the tunnel became the largest in the world. De France was put in charge of it, and in 1939 held the title of assistant chief of aerodynamics.

He was regarded by those who worked with him at Langley as a fine engineer, a hard worker, and a thoroughly professional civil servant. By the time he was named engineer-in-charge at Ames, De France already had a reputation for making sure the government got its money's worth. Neither manpower nor facilities were ever wasted under his supervision, and if this made for a somewhat strict and sober atmosphere at times, it was one those associated with him could respect. De France stood by his own standards, demanding equal devotion to those standards from others, and apparently he received it. One Ames veteran has compared him to a strict parent: "He demanded obedience to his rules, but you knew what the rules were and they were good rules. Since you knew what was expected of you, you obeyed the rules."[35]

The Ames family was very much a De France family, held together by his idea of what a research laboratory should be, how it should be run, and how its employees should perform their duties. An interesting perspective on De France's uncompromising attitude is given by an incident in 1943. Ames was running on two shifts for the war effort, paper was in short supply, and employee time was, obviously, at a premium. Nevertheless, De France issued a memorandum requesting the entire staff of Ames to read an address that had recently been given at the Cleveland laboratory by the director of research there, because he felt it "applies also to this laboratory." Since the address was lengthy — 23 pages — De France must have felt strongly about the material in it.[36]

Much of the circulated address was a history of the NACA and referred to the planning and building of the Cleveland laboratory. But De France's philosophy was reflected in the address. The best of facilities, the speaker remarked, would not produce results without the best in workers: "An excellent laboratory staffed by mediocre personnel will yield mediocre results. A mediocre laboratory staffed by excellent personnel will give excellent results." De France had been adamant about getting the best facilities and personnel for the new laboratory. The care he took in planning paid off as construction remained remarkably close to both cost estimates (at least initially) and to scheduled operational dates.[37]

The same speech also defended regulations: "Rules of procedure and regulation are required. . . . If you think they are unnecessary or that they hamper you . . . in your work, discuss the matter with your supervisor or with me." De France's rules were known to everyone, and they were respected. He also demanded from his workers a great deal of self-reliance and self-motivation. "Each man is expected to supply the drive to keep his project going. Don't expect either the men who supervise your work or those you supervise to supply the push necessary to get your work completed."

The result was a self-disciplined laboratory, and if its organization sometimes seemed vague to outsiders, the work did not suffer.

Another of De France's traits also helped shape the character of the laboratory. In 1924, soon after De France went to Langley Field, he was flying a new engineer around the laboratory in a Curtiss Jenny. The newcomer, in the copilot's seat, froze at the controls while De France was beginning a landing approach. The plane crashed into the marshy land surrounding Langley Field, and the young engineer was killed. De France spent a year in a Washington hospital; he lost an eye and sustained multiple facial fractures. He never flew again, honoring a promise to his wife. Thus the head of one of the country's aeronautical laboratories denied himself the efficiency air travel afforded. The significance for Ames, however, was that De France's lack of rapid transportation to the East Coast reinforced any tendency toward isolation that location and independent outlook already encouraged. A journey from coast to coast in the 1940s was certainly more time-consuming by any mode of travel than it is today, but by train it was particularly inconvenient. As a result De France did not go east, either to Langley or to Washington, often. In April 1942, when he *was* planning a trip, it was remarked that it was the first time he had left the laboratory since he arrived in August 1940.[38]

Three other original Ames employees were also influential in the formation of Ames's personality. One was John Parsons, a Stanford graduate who had gone to Langley shortly after his graduation. He had worked with De France in the 30- by 60-foot tunnel.[39] Parsons's health was uncertain, and early 1940 correspondence between Parsons at Moffett Field and De France back at Langley indicate that Parsons was driving himself almost past his physical limits, and that De France was concerned about him. Despite his health, Parsons projected such enthusiasm and energy that he inspired others. He was tireless in pursuing construction details and in reporting almost daily to De France in long, handwritten letters. In the early years Parsons acted as a real catalyst in keeping up construction momentum and, like De France, in setting uncompromising standards of quality. The example of Parsons added greatly to the energy generated at Ames in its early period.[40]

Another striking influence on Ames was H. Julian Allen, also a Stanford graduate and Langley veteran. Allen's force of personality and ability to inspire his co-workers is still spoken of by all who knew him. At Langley, Allen had acquired his nickname, "Harvey." With a nearly total incapacity for remembering names, he greeted one and all jovially as "Harvey," and the name stuck, in return, to him.

Allen had distinguished himself in his early work at Langley, where he had been since 1936. He became legendary for his ability to generate exciting, often brilliant aerodynamic theory. The best-known work from his

14

Langley period was the development of a general theory of subsonic airfoils. The ability to calculate the distribution of pressure on airfoils made low-drag characteristics easier to obtain. In 1940, Allen requested transfer to the new California laboratory, and though Langley was undoubtedly reluctant to lose him, he was put in charge of the theoretical aerodynamics research group at Ames. This group, though not attached to any of the wind tunnels, was very much involved in planning research facilities, carrying out sophisticated aerodynamic and structural design, and supplying calculations and specifications to the contractors.

Allen provided an especially good contrast to De France, balancing De France's sobriety with a hearty enthusiasm that never failed to encourage those around him. Where De France provided a steadying paternalistic influence, Harvey Allen's talent lay not only in his own work, but in his gift for rallying people to enthusiastic involvement in whatever puzzle lay before them. While Ames personnel respected "Smitty" De France, they loved Harvey.[41] In getting the laboratory off to an energetic start, Allen's role was decisive. In producing sparkling theoretical work spanning both aeronautical and astronautical decades, his genius added greatly to Ames's reputation.

Harry Goett, who was the first head of the two 7- by 10-foot wind tunnels at Ames and later the division chief for the Full-Scale and Flight Research Division, had an equally strong influence on Ames's research atmosphere. Allen and Goett had been at Langley together, and indeed had lived together in bachelor quarters noted for loud classical music and Allen's imaginative cooking. At Ames, the close friends were in frequent competition, Allen controlling the high-speed area of research and Goett in charge of low-speed investigations.[42]

Both men, by all accounts, inspired their subordinates to research excellence in completely different ways. While Allen nudged and chivvied with avuncular good humor, Goett rigorously demanded. Where Allen was effusive with praise, Goett was restrained and could sometimes be overwhelming, especially to young engineers who were cowed by his often brusque manner. "Is your brain frozen?" demanded Goett of a newly hired engineer who had plotted data without allowing for necessary approximations caused by a poor scale system.[43] Like Allen, however, Goett was determined to force his research team to think creatively. The combination of the two men and the competition between them, as Goett's startled young engineer reflected years later, were real elements of strength in Ames's early years.

Early Facilities

The Flight Research Building was put into operation in August 1940, only two weeks behind schedule. It housed not only the flight research engineering staff, which was about to resume the deicing research started at Langley, but also doubled as an airplane hangar and maintenance shop.

In the fall of 1940, three wind tunnels were under construction. In May work had started on one of two 7- by 10-foot wind tunnels and a 16-foot tunnel.* In August, the second 7- by 10-foot tunnel was started. The construction would take over a year and involve all the technical staff in some way or another. For many of the young research engineers, the challenges were real and involved problems they had not been trained for. "I was asked to go monitor the pouring of the concrete for the flight apron, to make sure the contractors were proceeding correctly," recalled Walter Vincenti, whose specialty was theoretical aerodynamics. "I had never been involved in concrete pouring before in my life. But we found ourselves doing all kinds of practical, applied engineering which we had no training for. When something came up, you did it." Equally removed from the Theoretical Aerodynamics Section's normal activities were jobs such as stress-analysis of reinforced concrete beams used in constructing the laboratory's buildings. It was a standing joke, Vincenti recalled, "for a while we were known as the Reinforced Aerodynamics and Theoretical Concrete Section."[44] If assignments at Ames were varied, quick changing, and sometimes unconventional, it was because the major concern was to produce working wind tunnels as quickly as possible. Through the 1940–1941 winter, construction continued in a quagmire of mud with no roads.

The 7- by 10-foot tunnels[45] presented no particular problem — Langley had one in use at the time, so the designers at Ames were familiar with the construction details and, indeed, had begun working out the specifications while still at Langley. The practicality of the Langley 7- by 10-foot wind tunnel, at the time in heavy demand for military testing, had made approval of two that size at Ames easy to obtain. The 7- by 10-foot tunnels at both laboratories were the workhorses,[46] highly useful for stability-and-control testing, and utilized for both industry and the military. Eight-foot wing-span models were used, and tests were run for drag, lift, lateral force, and pitch, yaw, and rolling moment. The airspeed in these tunnels was usually 400–480 km/hr. In April and August 1941, the two new Ames 7- by 10-foot wind tunnels were put into operation.

The 16-foot tunnel was a new design, and to no one's surprise, the designers encountered problems. Sixteen-foot tunnels had been approved for both Langley and Ames and were built simultaneously. Their size permitted the testing of full-scale aircraft components; the higher speed range was also essential as flight speeds continued to increase. Otherwise similar to the

---

*Wind tunnels are measured by their test section size. Thus the test section of the 7- by 10-foot tunnel was a rectangular 7 feet high and 10 feet wide in cross section, while that of the 16-foot tunnel was circular, with a 16-foot diameter.

tunnel at Langley, the Ames 16-foot tunnel was to be powered by a larger motor, which would produce a speed of 1100 km/hr. The tunnel was put into operation in October 1941. "At every stage," an early employee recalled, "we were doing things we didn't know how to do, because the field was developing so fast. We were working beyond the limits of our knowledge; . . . you couldn't learn it in a university."[47] Calibration tests on the tunnel extended into 1942, and eventually the fan-support struts had to be reshaped. Later, the 16-foot tunnel was to prove invaluable in complementing flight research to investigate the problem of aileron flutter. Oscillating shock waves, producing pulsations in the airflow over a wing, were a serious problem in high-speed flight. The pulsations caused both a buffeting of the aircraft and a buzz, or flutter, of the ailerons. Flight research using the Lockheed P-80, one of the earliest jet fighters, showed that the intensity of aileron flutter increased with speed; it was feared that if the speed were high enough, the wing might fail. The 16-foot tunnel research, in conjunction with flight research, produced significant data that eventually resulted in effective aircraft modifications.[48]

While construction and initial tests on the first three wind tunnels progressed, De France and his staff were also designing a tunnel similar to the one he had built and directed at Langley, a low-speed, full-scale tunnel in which an entire airplane could be tested. The 30- by 60-foot tunnel at Langley was the largest in the world, but the new tunnel at Ames was to have a test section of 40 by 80 feet. The tunnel, begun in March 1942 and completed in June 1944, is still the largest wind tunnel in the world. Its bulk on the western boundary of Moffett Field balances that of the equally huge rigid-airship hangar on the east. Supporting facilities had also been constructed during the first year, including an electrical substation to supply the needed 40,000 horsepower. By autumn 1941, there were also buildings to house technical services, utilities, and a science laboratory.[49]

Early in 1941 Ames was already being termed "part of the national defense system" in local newspapers, and it was obvious that the laboratory would quickly be used to full capacity with defense-related work.[50] By the fall Ames had used up the original appropriation of $10 million, which had been, admittedly, $1 million less than the NACA had requested in 1939. Though no changes had been made in the original plans for the facilities at Ames, construction costs had greatly increased and were fluctuating widely. Many companies were reluctant to commit themselves to such a long-term project as the 40- by 80-foot tunnel with the uncertainty of prices.[51] The lone bid on the tunnel — a staggering $6,164,000 — was made by the Pittsburgh–Des Moines Steel Company; in October it was being considered by the NACA's main office. A request for an additional $6 million was approved in October, and the cost of the laboratory rose to $16,200,000. By the end of 1945 the cost of facilities at Ames had passed $22 million.[52]

The organization of the Ames staff was beautifully simple. There was one division — the Research Division. Subordinate groups were defined as facilities became available, following the Langley pattern of organizing research groups around the various wind tunnels. As the three tunnels neared completion, therefore, a 7- by 10-foot tunnel research section was created, as was a 16-foot tunnel group. A third section, Theoretical Aerodynamics under Harvey Allen, was designing facilities and the equipment to be used in them, while continuing theoretical aerodynamic studies that would eventually generate the need for added facilities. One staff list, probably dating from late 1940, showed the majority of personnel as "unassigned to section."[53] In addition to the three research sections, a small flight research unit consisted of two test pilots, a research engineer, and a few aircraft maintenance men.

The improvisations that would be needed during the war were probably achieved more easily because of the flexibility of the early Ames organization. If the need arose, men and jobs could be shuffled for maximum efficiency. As more facilities became operational and yet more planned, the organizational structure became increasingly differentiated and complex; but in the early years the main division was between theoretical high-speed aero-

September 1941. After a year of operation, Ames boasted the Flight Research Laboratory (in foreground), two 7- by 10-foot wind tunnels, and behind them, a 16-foot tunnel. The field directly behind the center triangular plot would soon become the site of the 40- by 80-foot full-scale wind tunnel.

dynamics and applied research focused around the growing set of wind tunnels.

As the 40- by 80-foot tunnel began to take shape, the original Research Division was split. The new Theoretical and Applied Research Division included all the earlier wind tunnels. John Parsons, who had been in control of construction at Ames from the very beginning, became head of the new Full-Scale and Flight Research Division, which encompassed the incomplete 40- by 80-foot tunnel and the Flight Research Branch, with its test pilots, research engineers, and aircraft.[54] This reorganization represented little change in operations. Since Parsons was in charge of construction, he had always been responsible for the 40- by 80-foot tunnel, and since the tunnel was not yet complete, his job remained primarily that of construction engineer. The intent, however, seems to have been to differentiate between low-speed, full-scale research and higher-speed aerodynamic research and testing. Interestingly, Harvey Allen, whose specialty was high-speed theoretical aerodynamics, was one of the designers of the huge, low-speed tunnel, a typical example of the versatility of both the researchers and the functional structure of the laboratory. Organizational charts, even when they existed, did not necessarily present a true picture of daily operations. As an early employee remembers, "it was all very loosely organized. . . . After the war, when the civil service people came out to try to regularize things, [they] were driven crazy trying to write job descriptions. They were completely baffled [when] they encountered this mad research organization. . . . I don't remember seeing an organization chart the whole time I was at Ames."[55]

The War

The entry of the United States into World War II in December 1941 came as a surprise to very few. Much of the anxiety regarding construction at Ames had come from the expectation that demands on defense-connected organizations could only increase, whether the United States became formally involved in the war or not. The two 7- by 10-foot tunnels were in operation when war was declared, and calibration tests were in progress on the high-speed 16-foot tunnel, which the military was anxiously awaiting, since it would be used in testing of new military aircraft.

In terms of research being done or contemplated, the war brought one immediate change. The basic research through which the NACA had made its reputation was virtually phased out as all the laboratories concentrated on specific, immediate problems. The aircraft companies and the military asked the NACA for information and testing. The Washington office in turn assigned these tasks to one or more of the laboratories.

Deicing research became even more critical. Ice forms on all aircraft that enter certain weather conditions. It increases the gross weight of aircraft, puts a burden on propellers and power plants, changes the aerodynamic properties of wings, and hampers radio reception and visibility. For years commercial operators had canceled or rerouted flights to avoid such hazards, to the detriment of their schedules. Bombers, transports, and troop carriers operating worldwide would encounter icing conditions somewhere every day, and their missions could not so easily be canceled or rerouted. The aircraft companies and the Army and Navy were eager to combine forces with the NACA to solve the many-faceted problem.[56]

Research into thermal methods for deicing had been started at Langley Field as early as 1927. Early experimentation with steam, piped through the leading edge of the wing, had showed that method to be impractical. Direct heating with engine exhaust gas had proved more successful, and both branches of the military had donated aircraft to be converted to carry experimental wing-and-tail systems.

When construction of facilities was just beginning at Ames, the decision was made in Washington to transfer deicing research to the West Coast. The principal reason was to be near a sure source of ice-carrying clouds, which California's geography was expected to provide. The Langley engineer who had been most heavily involved with the deicing work, Lewis A. Rodert, moved west with the initial group from Langley and continued his work with the small flight research section — himself and two test pilots. Typical of the informality then existing within the organization, Rodert continued his research at Ames a year before the official research authorization came through.[57]

A C-46 Flying Laboratory, used for deicing research at Ames. Deicing research at Ames during the war resulted in immediately applied aircraft modifications that saved lives and airplanes and quickly made the reputation of the new aeronautical laboratory.

The electrically heated shoes on the propeller blades of the C-46 removed ice as it formed and increased the speed of the C-46 by 16 mph.

By early 1942 the Ames researchers had moved to colder country and established what became the Minnesota Ice Research Base for flight testing of aircraft equipped with deicing apparatus. The Army contributed two bombers, a B-24 Liberator and a B-17 Flying Fortress, and later a C-46 transport. The Army, the NACA, and the aircraft companies worked closely together experimenting with various methods and devices. While Ames was involved in testing in flight, the new engine research laboratory at Cleveland had built a wind tunnel to be used in deicing research. Research in the tunnel, which became operable in 1944, assisted the Minnesota team by checking test results under controlled conditions and by adding to the general body of information on the subject. The data that were obtained made it possible to install deicing equipment on most military aircraft, with satisfactory results. But as Edwin P. Hartman noted, the deicing research was "not at all representative of NACA research projects. Seldom before had

21

NACA's work been carried so far into the hardware stage or so far in achieving a complete and satisfying solution to a major operational problem."[58] After the war, the research continued as the NACA sought more precise data on the various characteristics of the equipment they had developed.

For Ames, though, the early success of the deicing research was particularly welcome. Atypical though it might have been as a research story, the very fact that a workable solution to a hardware problem was achieved went a long way to impress both industry and the military with the effectiveness of the new laboratory. It was a dramatic way to enter the scene, and if far removed from the type of research Ames would usually deal with, in terms of publicity and acclaim there could not have been a better debut. The coordination among the NACA, industry, and military personnel, by all accounts, was of the best. The wind-tunnel research at the Cleveland laboratory also illustrated the way in which the NACA could marshal additional forces when necessary. Though the NACA perhaps wished for more exact solutions and considered the research still "in progress" even as deicing equipment was being built into military aircraft,[59] the successful research established Ames in the most favorable light with the rest of the aeronautical world. After the war, the NACA received the Collier Trophy for its deicing work, impressive public recognition of its contribution.

Though the deicing research done by Ames was perhaps the most dramatic of its early research tasks, the laboratory assisted the war effort in other less dramatic ways. The wind tunnels, as soon as they were operational, lent themselves to preliminary design testing of aircraft prototypes, a process that made it possible to evaluate aerodynamic characteristics and handling qualities and to refine designs. Once a model had been produced, the wind tunnels were used in "clean-up" jobs requested either by the military or by their industrial contractors. Often wind tunnel research on existing aircraft accompanied flight research. The technique was the same as that used in the deicing research; wind tunnel testing added detailed measurements under controlled conditions and investigated alternatives to optimize design and improve performance. A constant stream of requests resulted in round-the-clock wind-tunnel use, as models were tested, adjusted, and retested. Wartime needs carried Ames far from the basic aeronautical research for which it had been built, perhaps establishing early a continuing dialogue between the institution and the aircraft industry. It is interesting to speculate on possible different turns in the relationship established with industry, had the wartime tradition not been established.

Good relations with the military were not an accidental by-product of the icing research. Quite early Langley Field had established an Army liaison office to ease relations between NACA personnel and the Army. A Langley historian has noted that the laboratory's major hurdle, in its earliest years, had been its relations with the military.[60] Though time and the liaison office had done much to establish more cordial relations, care was taken to prevent any incivility from developing at Ames. When the first tunnels were about to go into use, therefore, the Army established a liaison office at Ames, staffed with personnel from Wright Field. The liaison office not only opened a regular channel for Ames-military communication, but also served as a buffer for any problems Ames might have with the Army's industrial contractors. The liaison office, juggling scheduling difficulties, was therefore kept constantly aware of commitments and priorities, also removing some of the pressure from Ames in dealing with industry's demands on Ames expertise and facilities.[61]

Ames enjoyed another institutional aid in external relations. In 1940, while the laboratory was materializing, the Washington office had laid plans to form a Western Coordination Office to deal with industry and academia on the West Coast. This development was perhaps overdue, for the NACA had developed the reputation of being "an eastern organization . . . not responsive to the needs of western industry."[62] The Western Coordination Office, energetically and perceptively headed by Edwin P. Hartman, became an invaluable source of information for the head office in Washington. Very often the reports Hartman made to Washington resulted in Ames being detailed to a requested research task because of a specific need of the industry coupled with Hartman's awareness of what was currently happening at the Laboratory.[63] Ames from the first avoided strains in its relationship with industry and the military.

In April 1942 the Army left Moffett Field and the Navy returned. With responsibility for Pacific coast security, the Navy planned to patrol the coast using nonrigid airships, or blimps. The Moffett Field hangar was the logical place to moor them. The transfer was accomplished routinely, and relations with the Navy proceeded as cordially as had those with the Army.

Aside from influencing the direction that early investigations took, the war very visibly affected Ames in other ways. Clothed in blackout window shades ordered early in 1942,[64] Ames continued its mushroom growth in facilities and personnel. From the original 51 people at work in September 1940, the laboratory had grown by February 1943 to 341. In August 1945 the wartime high of 844 people was reached.[65]

In atmosphere, however, the laboratory remained almost as informal as it was the day Charles Hall first reported for work in 1942:

> The day I showed up, I went down to personnel to sign forms. Helen Davies was head of personnel, and the ad building in those days was in the old hangar. As Helen was about to take Brad Wick and me out to the 7- by 10- and the 16-foot wind tunnels, De France walked by and said hello. Davies introduced us, and

said she was taking us over to the tunnels. He said [he'd take us] so he [did] and gave us a tour of each wind tunnel. He [dropped] Brad off at the 7- by 10- and took me over to the 16-foot. When I got to know the people better a year or two later [I found out] they thought I'd really had an in and was a good friend of De France. . . .[66]

Selective service also came to Ames, as to all NACA laboratories.[67] The NACA had been designated an "essential industry" before the war began. This implied that deferments for the staff would be almost routine. In the early days of the war, Langley had also fought to retain some of their young model-makers, who lacked the professional legitimacy of engineering degrees but who were increasingly irreplaceable.[68] Indeed, most of the staff of both laboratories remained at their jobs under "essential occupation" status for some time. In February 1944, however, state control of deferments was ended. California's Selective Service Board had been extremely cooperative in granting continued deferments to the Ames staff, and the NACA Washington office had been helpful, providing conservative timetables showing when particular staff members would be available for the draft. In 1943, for example, the executive secretary of the NACA proposed to the state board that only 16 out of 97 eligible men be released over the next year.[69] Ames had been, until 1944, more successful than the other laboratories in getting deferments from the board.[70]

In the end most laboratory personnel were inducted into military service and continued in the same jobs. Those at Langley and Cleveland joined the Army; but because Ames was on a Navy base, Ames personnel joined the Navy. There were some complications. Civilian superiors at times became military subordinates, and reports one had written in one's civilian identity were sometimes too confidential to be read in one's military identity. The Ames staff, one veteran admitted, made life as difficult for the Navy as the Navy made it for them. Ames's nonchalance in the face of military regulations and protocol became a source of frustration to the Navy.[71] The Selective Service Board's solution, however, was the best alternative under the circumstances. In the event that there was an immediate emergency, the Ames staff, which had received basic training, could have been of use at Moffett Field. Also, Navy morale was undoubtedly a consideration — the position of Moffett Field and the role of the Navy in protecting the Pacific shores would have made it difficult to justify continued civilian status for those at Ames.

To help ease the manpower shortage at Ames, the Navy assigned some 200 men, from machinist mates who had seen combat to engineering students from the Navy's V-12 college programs, to the laboratory. Alfred J. Eggers was one of the V-12 Navy men. Years later he remembered his dawn arrival at Moffett Field as part of the "Ames detachment," still slightly puzzled about his assignment. His introductory tour of the wind tunnels by Harvey Allen opened a new "wild Buck Rogers world"; he was to remain at Ames almost 20 years as one of its most imaginative and productive researchers.[72]

The pressure to build a laboratory quickly in wartime and its distance from Washington were potential areas of tension in the relationship that developed between Ames and the Washington office. Quite early one detects an impatient note running through correspondence. Whether this impatience was shared by the other laboratories is difficult to know, but within the Ames staff, it is marked.

A specific issue that created sharp and vocal annoyance was small-purchase authorizations, which had to be cleared by the Washington office. Ames personnel argued that the delay in obtaining authorization from Washington was handicapping them in obtaining materials. In July 1941 Ames received a very conservatively couched permission to make emergency purchases where it was impossible to take the time to receive authorization from Washington.[73] This was the result of a sternly phrased letter from Ames to Washington pointing out the handicap under which they operated.[74]

Later in the year, after what was evidently a reprimand from Washington for Ames's indulgent use of that emergency authorization, one administrative assistant at Ames wrote a heated memorandum on behalf of his superior berating the Washington office. The reprimand from Headquarters, he maintained, was based on "procedure standpoint," not "supplies and results." It must be "thoroughly understood," he went on to say, that "neither I nor any member of the purchase section can be held responsible for our failure to obtain items needed by the various sections of the Laboratory, under our present purchase procedure." That they had overstepped their authorization he was prepared to admit, but only "to get results. . . . We are in a better position to know what the Laboratory needs and what are fair prices."[75] In 1944 the Washington office granted authority to all laboratories to make routine purchases for amounts up to $500. Any repair or alteration cost, however, still had to be cleared through the Washington office, and the paperwork for even the self-authorized purchases was extensive.[76]

Another example, probably from the immediate postwar period, concerned the issue of pay and travel vouchers. Originally these had been processed in Washington, but Headquarters had decided to delegate at least part of the work load to the laboratories. Ames objected, though it expressed willingness to cooperate in the plan. "The Committee," an Ames reply pointed out, "will be operated more efficiently if the final actions of certain functions and procedures are centralized." Ames, it seems evident, felt that its function as a research laboratory was being undermined by bureaucracy, from which it wanted protection by the Washington staff. Even more evident in this memorandum, however, was the subtly expressed conviction that Ames was unique and that Washington did not understand that uniqueness. There was a slight tone of aggrieved isolationism in the conclusion of the memorandum:

> Uniformity in these matters can be satisfactorily obtained only by having someone in the Washington office work with and study thoroughly the problems at each laboratory and to then set up a procedure that is workable for all. It cannot be obtained by taking the ideas of one laboratory and attempting to apply them to the other two without first studying the problems of all three. It cannot be obtained by someone in Washington arbitrarily determining the policy without visiting each laboratory and carefully studying the problems of each laboratory.[77]

The problems of bureaucracy, of course, are always present and the NACA was certainly no worse than any other government agency. It was probably better than most. But what is striking is that Ames, early in its history, seems to have asserted its distance, differences, and self-determination. Whether Ames was truly burdened by the Washington office is moot; it seems to have believed itself so.

The end of the war saw Ames with five wind tunnels. Both the huge 40- by 80-foot tunnel and the high-speed 1- by 3.5-foot tunnel were completed in 1944. At the opening of the 40- by 80-foot tunnel in June 1944, a formal dedication of the Ames Aeronautical Laboratory was held. In a way the late dedication was symbolic of the very conditions and circumstances through which the laboratory had come into existence; the energy demanded in establishing Ames and in dealing with the crisis of almost immediate war had left little time or concern for traditional formalities.

SOURCE NOTES

Chapter I. The Beginnings, 1939–1945

[1] See Alex Roland, *Model Research: The National Advisory Committee for Aeronautics, 1915–1958*, NASA SP-4103 (Washington, 1984).

[2] Similar statements have been made by several ex-NACA researchers, among them Walter Vincenti, Russell Robinson, and Harry Goett.

[3] Harry Goett interview, 3 Dec. 1981.

[4] Charles F. Hall interview, 10 Aug. 1982.

[5] I am grateful to Russell Robinson for valuable accounts of the atmosphere at Langley Field in the 1930s and for an insider's perspective on the relationship between Langley and the Washington staff of the NACA. See interview, 4 Nov. 1980. The unpublished manuscript by Michael Keller, "A History of the NACA Langley Laboratory, 1917–1947," written in 1968, also yields similar description of Langley. NASA History Office Archives.

[6] Quoted in J. C. Hunsaker, *Forty Years of Aeronautical Research* (Smithsonian Institution: Washington, D.C., 1956), p. 261.

[7] Personnel statistics, Langley Field, 63-A-224, V-6631, San Bruno Federal Record Center (henceforth SBFRC).

[8] See the 25th Annual Report of the NACA, 1939 (Washington, D.C., 1940), p. 38.

[9] Smith De France to Langley engineer-in-charge, 23 Feb. 1939, 75-A-1324, 21896, box 5, SBFRC.

[10] See Edwin P. Hartman, *Adventures in Research: A History of Ames Research Center, 1940–1965*, NASA SP-4302 (Washington, 1970), pp. 11–12. Hartman's official history of Ames's first 25 years is an invaluable source, especially for technical details on many of the research investigations conducted by Ames. Hartman, for many years head of the Western Coordination Office of the NACA and NASA, had a unique vantage point for understanding both technical and administrative perspective. See also Alex Roland, *Model Research: The National Advisory Committee for Aeronautics, 1915–1958* (Comment Edition, April 1980), pp. 238–240.

[11] See Hartman, *Adventures in Research*, p. 19, for a description of Victory's rewording of the appropriations request.

[12] See Roland, *Model Research*, p. 233. As Roland notes, both Dr. Lewis and John Victory felt that the new laboratory should be located inland, presumably as extra protection against attack.

[13] See the *Report of the Special Committee on Future Research Facilities*, 30 Dec. 1938, app. D. Quoted in Hartman, *Adventures in Research*, pp. 20–21.

[14] See Roland, *Model Research*, pp. 233–236, for a detailed examination of the issues regarding the GALCIT–NACA relationship.

[15] *P. G. and E. Progress*, vol. 8, no. 5, Apr. 1931, p. 1.

[16] See typescript memorandum on Moffett Field, in 74-A-1624, box 163100, SBFRC. See also *From Lighter Than Air to Faster Than Sound: The Silver Anniversary of Moffett Field, 1933–1958* (U.S. Navy, 1958).

[17] Smith De France to Langley engineer-in-charge, 23 Feb. 1939, 75-A-1324, 21896, box 5, SBFRC.

[18] See Hartman, *Adventures in Research*, p. 25. Hartman notes that the assistant-secretary of war issued a permit to the NACA for the construction of a research laboratory on 7 Dec. 1939.

[19] De France was not formally named engineer-in-charge at Ames until mid-1940, but it was generally assumed by all concerned that he would be the choice of the Main Committee.

[20] Russell G. Robinson to Smith De France, "Information Desired on Moffett Field Station," 20–21 Dec. 1939, 75-A-1324, 21896, box 5, SBFRC.

[21] Walter Vincenti interview, 31 Oct. 1980.

[22] Smith De France to George Gray, 28 Dec. 1945, 74-A-1624, V-1624, SBFRC.

[23] Edward R. Sharp to John Victory, 12 Feb. 1940, 63-A-224, V-6630, SBFRC.

[24] Correspondence among Sharp, John Parsons, De France, George Lewis, and Victory during the early construction period in 1940, 75-A-1324, 21896, box 5, SBFRC.

[25] Memoranda between Sharp and De France attest to the efficiency of the building and staffing process, May–July 1940, in 75-A-1324, 21896, box 5, SBFRC.

[26] Sharp to De France, 15 Apr. 1940, 75-A-1324, 21896, box 5, SBFRC.

[27] Ibid., 15 Apr. 1940.

[28] Keller, "History of Langley Laboratory," chap. 2, p. 16.

[29] Smith De France to Edward Sharp, 29 June 1940, 75-A-1324, 21896, box 5, SBFRC.

[30] In conversations with younger Ames employees, many spontaneously mentioned the "closed club" atmosphere there.

[31] Russell G. Robinson interview, 4 Nov. 1980.

[32] See n. 30.

[33] Correspondence between Arthur B. Freeman and Sharp, 1940–1941, 63-A-224, V-6630, SBFRC.

[34] This impression is based on interviews with Mildred Cardona Macon, Walter Vincenti, and Russell Robinson, and in the tone of correspondence among those involved in the early activities. See correspondence of Arthur B. Freeman in 63-A-224, V-6630 and correspondence of John Parsons, 75-A-1324, 21896, box 5, SBFRC.

[35] Mildred Cardona Macon interview, 11 Sept. 1980.

[36] The address was given in Jan. 1943 by Addison Rothrock; the entire address was retained in De France's files, 63-A-224, V-6630, SBFRC.

[37] See various construction contracts, 1940–1941. Especially interesting is a report, "Cost on All Job Orders through Nov. 1944." Estimates and actual costs are surprisingly close, in 63-A-224, V-6630, SBFRC. See also construction correspondence of Smith De France in 75-A-1324, 21896, box 5, SBFRC.

[38] Ruth Scott to Arthur B. Freeman, 7 Apr. 1942, 63-A-224, V-6630, SBFRC.

[39] See Hartman, *Adventures in Research*, p. 26, for biographical information on Parsons.

[40] Additional information on John Parsons from Walter Vincenti interview, 7 Nov. 1980.

[41] Both men are unfailingly mentioned by interviewees as key figures at Ames, as is Harry Goett. The affection felt for Allen is striking, and seemingly universal.

[42] Goett interview, 3 Dec. 1981.

28

[43] Charles Harper interview, 10 Sept. 1982.

[44] Vincenti interview, 7 Nov. 1980. See also Hartman, *Adventures in Research,* p. 45.

[45] Much of my descriptive information on the early wind tunnels I owe to George Gray, *Frontiers of Flight* (New York: Alfred A. Knopf, 1948), whose clear description of NACA research and facilities provides an excellent introduction for the layman to the field of aeronautical research. See also Hartman, *Adventures in Research,* for descriptions of the 7- by 10-foot tunnels and the 16-foot tunnel, pp. 45–46.

[46] See Hartman, *Adventures in Research,* p. 31.

[47] Vincenti interview, 31 Oct. 1980.

[48] Hartman, *Adventures in Research,* p. 66–68.

[49] See the memorandum prepared by John Parsons, Chief, Construction Div., for De France, May 1945, for a listing of the specifications regarding Ames's early facilities, in 74-A-1624, V-4823, SBFRC.

[50] *P. G. and E. Progress,* vol. 18, no. 2, Feb. 1941, p. 2.

[51] *San Jose Mercury News,* 3 Oct. 1941, p. 4.

[52] See Note 9, construction memorandum.

[53] See "Organizational Breakdown, Ames Aeronautical Laboratory," in 74-A-1624, V-4823, SBFRC.

[54] Hartman, *Adventures in Research,* p. 41.

[55] Vincenti interview, 31 Oct. 1980.

[56] See Gray, *Frontiers of Flight,* chap. 14, for a detailed description of both the problem and the solution. See also Hartman, *Adventures in Research,* chap. 9, in the World War II deicing research.

[57] Hartman, *Adventures in Research,* p. 35.

[58] Ibid., pp. 76–77.

[59] Gray, *Frontiers of Flight,* p. 324.

[60] Keller, "History of Langley Laboratory," chap. 2, pp. 16–22.

[61] Wright Field, the Army's aeronautical research laboratory, was the logical source of liaison personnel for the office at Ames. See also Hartman, *Adventures in Research,* pp. 37–38.

[62] Hartman, *Adventures in Research,* p. 39.

[63] Robinson interview, 4 Nov. 1980. Hartman's role as Western Coordination Officer was discussed from the perspective of the Washington office in the 1940s. At that time Robinson was working in the office of the coordinator of research, S. Paul Johnston.

[64] See correspondence of Arthur B. Freeman, "Job Orders, 1941–44," in 63-A-224, V-6630, SBFRC.

[65] See "Personnel Statistics, 1940–45," Also see De France to George Gray, 8 Nov. 1945. In correspondence of De France, 74-A-1624, V-4823, SBFRC.

[66] Charles F. Hall interview, 10 Aug. 1982.

[67] The Ames details occur in a letter from De France to Gray, 28 Dec. 1945, in 74-A-1624, V-4823, SBFRC.

[68] See file on "Selective Service – Langley," in 63-A-224, V-6630, SBFRC.

[69] Victory to Col. Kenneth Leitch, state director of Selective Service, 4 Feb. 1943, 63-A-224, V-6631, SBFRC.

[70] De France to Gray, 28 Dec. 1945, 74-A-1624, V-4823, SBFRC.

[71] Vincenti interview, 18 July 1980.

[72] Alfred J. Eggers interview, 6 Oct. 1982.

[73] E. H. Chamberlin, financial officer, Washington office, to A. B. Freeman, Ames administrative officer, 30 July 1941, 63-A-224, V-6631, SBFRC.

[74] Freeman to Chamberlin, 28 July 1941, 63-A-224, V-6631, SBFRC.

[75] E. C. Braig to Freeman, 22 Oct. 1941, 63-A-224, V-6631, SBFRC.

[76] Chamberlin to Freeman, 29 June 1944, 63-A-224, V-6631, SBFRC.

[77] Unsigned memorandum on pay vouchers, undated, in a file that covers 1941–1945, in 63-A-224, V-6631, SBFRC.

2

THE POSTWAR PERIOD, 1945-1952

In November 1944, when it was becoming obvious that the war would soon be over, President Roosevelt asked Vannevar Bush, director of the Office of Scientific Research and Development (OSRD), to recommend policies that would ensure continuing governmental encouragement of and financial aid to scientific research. The war, Roosevelt observed, had been responsible for a great mobilizing of the scientific and technological resources of the country. Bush's OSRD, a wartime innovation, represented "a unique experiment of team-work and cooperation in coordinating scientific research and in applying existing scientific knowledge to the solutions of the technical problems paramount in war."[1] Roosevelt intended that lessons learned in managing research during the war not be forgotten during peace.

Roosevelt asked the right person, for Bush's career had involved just such relationships of research and management. A New Englander, Bush had engineering degrees from Tufts University. During World War I, he had been a junior faculty member at Tufts and had done submarine-related research for the Navy. In the next decade he attained prominence at the Massachusetts Institute of Technology. In 1938 he was appointed to the NACA, and in late 1939 succeeded Joseph Ames as its chairman.

In June 1940 Bush had obtained Roosevelt's approval to form the National Defense Research Committee, a civilian organization involved in the development of new weapons. A year later the committee was absorbed into the Office of Scientific Research and Development, and Bush resigned his chairmanship of the NACA to devote himself to the OSRD. The OSRD reported directly to the President and had its own funds to work with.[2] Such assets produced remarkable technological results: workable radar, the proximity fuse, fire-control mechanisms, amphibious vehicles, and, of course, the atomic bomb.

In his varied capacities, then, Bush had been on both sides of government-sponsored research. A renowned engineer and scientist himself,

Bush was sensitive to the problems of research and the difficulties in bureaucratizing the process of scientific work. As a director of research organizations — the Carnegie Institution of Washington, the NACA, and the OSRD — he experienced the opposite side of the coin in confronting the need to form broad organizational policies to govern research.

With the aim of perpetuating the wartime achievements in scientific and technological research, the President asked Bush to turn his attention to four major questions:

1. What could be done to publicize, for the public good, the contributions to scientific knowledge made during the war?
2. How could the government aid a continuing effort in the war against disease?
3. How could the government aid research by public and private organizations?
4. What could be done to discover, encourage, and develop scientific talent in the younger generation to assure that scientific research would continue to progress at the same level it had during the war?[3]

The questions Roosevelt placed before Bush had a certain refreshing simplicity to them, but they were timely, and timeless, questions. They embraced many facets of national concern: national security, health, the issue of government aid to private institutions, the relationship between public and private research organizations, and federal support for the development of scientific talent.

That Roosevelt addressed himself to such questions in the closing days of the war, even before peace had brought time for reflection, is testament to his wisdom. The answers that Vannevar Bush and his committee framed in June 1945 for President Truman reflect both sound judgment and the context of the times. Science, properly funded and inspired, could solve the problems and insecurities of the coming decades. It was indeed an "endless frontier," as Bush was to call it. The policies that grew out of the report Bush submitted formed much of the federal attitude toward research and development for the next 20 years, and the history of Ames during that period reflects this.

Bush's recommendations were plainly worded and pragmatic. First, science is a proper concern of government, and the government should take steps to nurture science in the best possible environment. The government should support the universities generally, as well as those scientific areas where large outlays of funds were crucial. The wartime advances against disease were possible because of "a large backlog of scientific data accumulated through basic research in many scientific fields in the years before the war."[4] The key to continued scientific progress was a strong foundation in basic research that was helped, not hampered, by federal intervention. Guiding policies were necessary: to ensure support where needed, to encourage the current generation in scientific directions, to develop programs at universities not necessarily geared toward specific problem-solving, but toward building strong foundations in basic research. Medical schools should be heavily supported, the continued scientific education of those who had just served in the war should be financed, and measures should be taken by a civilian-military advisory board to disperse the results of wartime research that were no longer crucial to national security. Better liaison among the military, universities, industry, and the government should be developed to coordinate research and to promote mutual awareness of both needs and accomplishments.

Bush's final recommendation was for the formation of an agency with a broad base of power and intellect and stable funding to further basic research in sciences. Five years later the agency Bush had envisioned, the National Science Foundation, was formed, underlining the national commitment to support science. It was in this postwar period of faith in the potential of basic research and the government's dedication to the solid advancement of science that Ames reached maturity as a research laboratory.

The issues of advance planning, efficient management, dedication to basic research, proper liaison among concerned groups, coordination of research efforts, encouragement of supporting institutions, and continual attraction of new talent are themes running through the postwar period at Ames. The first years of its existence had been highly colored by the circumstances of its inception and the abnormal conditions caused by World War II. As the war drew to a close, the Ames staff was turning toward new concerns.

HIGH–SPEED RESEARCH

At the somewhat tardy dedication ceremony in 1944, Ames had five wind tunnels — the 7- by 10-foot tunnels, the 16-foot tunnel, the 40- by 80-foot tunnel, and the high-speed 1- by 3.5-foot tunnel. The last two were the newest and represented, in a sense, the two diverging directions of research undertaken at Ames. The 40- by 80-foot tunnel proved highly useful for testing full-scale aircraft during the last year of the war. One of the first aircraft tested in it was the Ryan XFR-1, which was powered by a reciprocating engine and an auxiliary jet engine. The first U.S. aircraft with a jet engine, the Navy fighter lacked stability and control under certain conditions, and as such was unusable. Testing in the 40- by 80-foot tunnel and in flight identified the flaws and led to modifications that corrected them, to the delight of the Ryan company and the Navy.[5]

1. Electrical Substation	8. 12-Foot Pressure Wind Tunnel
2. 16-Foot Wind Tunnel	9. Flight Research Laboratory
3. 1- by 3.5-Foot Wind Tunnel	10. 40- by 80-Foot Wind Tunnel
4. 7- by 10-Foot Wind Tunnel No. 2	11. Technical Service Building
5. Paint Shop	12. Science Building
6. 7- by 10-Foot Wind Tunnel No. 1	13. Auditorium and Cafeteria
7. Utilities Building	14. Administration Building

1943. Ames continued to construct wind tunnels even as it ran triple shifts to keep up with wartime demands for aircraft testing. The 40- by 80-foot tunnel was completed in 1944, and the 12-foot pressure tunnel was completed in 1946.

It had been planned, however, that Ames would concentrate on high-speed problems, and it was toward those questions that aeronautics was turning. One of the major projects at prewar Langley had been the development of airfoil shapes that would allow airflow close to the wing surface, the so-called boundary layer, to remain laminar, or streamlined, over the entire wing. This became especially critical at high speeds. In the late 1930s a Langley research group had also experimented with various airfoil shapes to reduce as far as possible the detrimental compressibility effect of shock waves forming adjacent to the wing surface at transonic speeds. (The transonic region is usually defined as flight speeds between roughly 0.8 and

1943. The giant entrance cone of the 40- by 80-foot wind tunnel under construction. For almost 40 years a closed-system tunnel, a 1979-1982 expansion created an additional 80- by 120-foot test section with an open-intake air system. The wind tunnel remains the largest in the world.

1.2 times the speed of sound, which itself varies, according to altitude and temperature, from 960 to 1230 km/hr.) As it turned out, the method for calculating airfoil shapes for laminar flow was also applicable for delaying the formation of shock waves on wings at transonic speeds. However, these research questions were for the most part shelved during the war as both laboratories dealt with the day-to-day clean-up work on aircraft.[6]

That basic research on high-speed problems was about to become crucial was made increasingly obvious by another major development in aeronautics. The jet engine, which was still in the experimental stage in Britain and Germany when war broke out, operated most efficiently at higher speeds. Therefore, if jet engines were to achieve their highest potential, aircraft that could operate at much higher speeds would have to be developed as well. Both the development of the jet engine and the accompanying problems of high-speed flight were issues that the NACA, involved

35

as it had been in the increasingly frantic requests for new aircraft designs by the military, felt it could not devote itself to wholeheartedly. In March 1941, however, a special committee on jet propulsion had been appointed by the NACA's Main Committee. Stanford's Dr. William Durand was named chairman. At 82, he had come out of retirement and rejoined the NACA at the request of Vannevar Bush.

Under the aegis of the special committee, investigation of current jet propulsion research led NACA to sponsor specific projects. In 1943 a testing facility went into operation at the Engine Research Laboratory in Cleveland. Research was closely guarded and only those directly involved in the work knew any details. By 1945, however, jet-propulsion research had become a major activity at Cleveland. Aerodynamic and thermodynamic problems related to the higher speeds were being attacked simultaneously at both Langley and Ames.

The NACA has been condemned for its laggard development of the jet engine. Especially after the war, when German progress had become known, the NACA was criticized for not throwing all its resources into producing a workable jet airplane for the war.[7] Though there is an element of truth in the contention that the NACA "missed the boat," in the prewar context of the late 1930s, exploration of jet propulsion may have seemed a luxury those preparing for the expected crisis could not afford. It was, perhaps, less a question of stodginess in outlook than a decision to work in directions that might be more immediately productive. In beginning research in new areas, there is, of course, no way to predict how long it will take to produce useful results, and myriad problems remained to be solved in the field of propeller-powered aircraft. In 1939 the NACA's facilities at Langley were stretched almost to capacity, and even though the two new laboratories, Ames and the Cleveland engine laboratory, would in time relieve pressure on Langley, their planning created new demands on the NACA.

In the Langley aerodynamics group, Eastman Jacobs had done early research on a multistage axial-flow compressor that would be more efficient than a centrifugal compressor, the path being followed by the British in jet propulsion. Jacobs was working on a somewhat unofficial basis, and his early leads were not pursued by the NACA. With the war, however, and the mobilization for action by the Durand Committee, the NACA attempted to catch up with the British. After the war, in the opinion of one NACA official, the Washington office of the NACA felt "a little sensitive about it, in light of the British example. There was a wish that the NACA had worked continuously on the axial-flow jet-engine concept."[8] The NACA should not be held solely responsible for the late start on jet-engine research in this country. Neither the military nor the aircraft engine companies had urged continued investigation of jet propulsion.

In any event, with the field developing as it did toward the end of the war, jet propulsion and high-speed aerodynamics were the major concerns of those involved in aeronautical research in the postwar period.[9] As one Ames employee observed, though propulsion had not been within his laboratory's field of research, the staff regretted that the NACA had not been at the forefront of research in that area.[10] High-speed research, however, was specifically one of Ames's specialties, and it was important, as the demands of wartime clean-up work receded, to move in that direction. There was a sense of urgency, both within the NACA as a whole, and specifically at Ames, as other research groups were beginning to explore the problems of supersonic flight. At the Aberdeen Proving Ground, the Army was organizing a ballistics research group to investigate supersonic phenomena; work had begun on the study of airflow over projectiles at supersonic speed. An engineer at the Guggenheim Aeronautical Laboratory (at the California Institute of Technology (Cal Tech)) had built a small supersonic tunnel to provide data upon which to base the design of a larger tunnel at Aberdeen. The Ames staff was anxious to waste no time in assembling the necessary facilities to proceed with transonic and supersonic research.

POSTWAR FACILITIES

The original plans for facilities at Ames had included a supersonic wind tunnel,[11] but the increasing cost of construction coupled with the other demands of war had delayed it. Toward the end of the war, however, as it became obvious that supersonic tunnels would be needed in the near future, Ames engineers began designing what would eventually materialize as two 1- by 3-foot supersonic wind tunnels. As was true of so much of the NACA's prudent financing, economy played a large role in the construction plans. One of the new tunnels was designed to use compressed air being discharged from the adjacent 12-foot pressure tunnel. In this way two supersonic tunnels were built — one a continuous-flow tunnel and the other an intermittent blow-down tunnel attached to an existing tunnel — one relatively cheaply. The cost for both was $1,250,000, most of which was spent on the continuous-flow tunnel.[12] Because of the high pressure drop available from the 12-foot pressure tunnel, the blow-down tunnel could achieve higher Mach numbers than could the continuous-flow tunnel.

Even before the tunnels were approved, however, Ames was planning for them in a typically enterprising way. It was the kind of foresight that Vannevar Bush would have subscribed to, for it looked to the future with imagination and energy. Harvey Allen, then head of the Theoretical Aerodynamics Section, was largely responsible for the advance planning of the new supersonic tunnels. As one of his subordinates recalled,

We needed information on supersonic flow through nozzles. We also needed information on the pressure drop required across a nozzle to establish the supersonic flow through it. This information was essential to determine the horsepower needed, so that we could then choose the proper compressors and drive motors. . . . So Allen put a couple of young engineers to work on the job of making a small model converging-diverging nozzle, running some experiments and getting some data, and the only place where there was a supply of compressed air was in the Technical Service Building where . . . compressed air [was used] to drive pneumatic tools. So they designed the equipment in an ad hoc, hurry-up way and set it up next to the compressed-air tank in the boiler room. . . . But since they could only have use of the air when it wasn't being used for the shops, they had to come in after midnight — the shops at that time were running on two shifts — and run their tests, which had to be designed to use the little bit of space left between the boiler and the wall. . . . It was strictly a bootlegged kind of operation. I'm not sure if Allen even had official approval from Washington to do it, but it was something that had to be done so we did it.[13]

With the information so gained, Ames was ready with specifications as soon as the two supersonic tunnels were approved. Construction began in February 1945 and was finished by September, De France playing a strong role in holding construction to its deadlines. Again foresighted, Ames engineers and the construction contractors had provided for possible difficulties in the flexible-throat apparatus of both tunnels. The flexible throat made it possible to vary the configuration and curvature of the throat to change the test Mach number. Because the flexible throats were difficult to build and make function properly, the design contractor had been asked to furnish two fixed throats, each designed for a different Mach number, so that the tunnels could function on schedule. As it happened, problems with the flexible throat did arise; but the fixed throats allowed the tunnels to operate on schedule at two supersonic speeds.[14]

With equal foresight, the continuous-flow tunnel had also been pressurized. Allen felt that the Reynolds-number effect, which made pressurization necessary to obtain accurate test results on models at subsonic speeds, would continue to be important at higher speeds. This opinion contradicted that of the influential Theodore von Kármán of California Institute of Technology's Guggenheim Aeronautical Laboratory, but, as it turned out, Allen was correct. This lucky hunch saved much trouble later, and probably considerable expense. Intuition was significant in the history of aeronautics and the NACA — and the very necessity of occasionally resorting to the informed guess kept the work exciting to young researchers. As a section head of the 1- by 3-foot tunnels commented, "As I look back on it, the way we went ahead and designed things and spent for those times fairly sizable sums of money on the basis of such rudimentary knowledge is sort of staggering. It was only because of everybody's ignorance that we went ahead and did some of the things we did. You simply didn't know what the problems were, and you found out as you went along.[15]

While the small 1- by 3-foot tunnels were being planned and built, Ames engineers were also planning another supersonic tunnel, this one a larger facility. Ames had submitted plans for it to Lewis in the Washington office in 1944, but the war was still in progress and the cost of the projected tunnel was quite high, over $4 million. The plans, legend has it, disappeared into Lewis's desk drawer. Months later, the chief of the Navy's Bureau of Aeronautics came to see Lewis to discuss projected research facilities for the NACA. The Navy's position was that a large supersonic facility was needed; had the NACA given any thought to this? Lewis rummaged through his desk and produced the Ames plans, no doubt impressing his Navy colleague with the NACA's foresight. Lewis explained that they had not proceeded because of the prohibitive cost, at which point the admiral said the Navy could pay for the tunnel. In January 1945 the NACA received the funds from the Navy, and by May construction of a 6- by 6-foot supersonic tunnel had begun at Ames. The somewhat accidental — in timing at least — conjunction of interests produced a needed research tool.

This example of civilian-military cooperation illustrates the personal role that was often necessary for such transactions to occur. Throughout his career in the NACA, George Lewis often obtained approval and funding for new facilities on the strength of his solid reputation for conscientious management and wise forecasting. Lewis made a point of visiting the Langley and Cleveland laboratories once a week to keep abreast of progress on various projects, as well as to be aware of their future needs. Although he was not able to take such a direct role in the day-to-day activities of Ames, the case of the 6- by 6-foot tunnel — "hip-pocket" administration at its best — indicates that he did not neglect Ames. That the NACA had the desired plans already at hand must have contributed to continued good relations with the Navy.[16]

EXTERNAL RELATIONS

Official relations between Ames and the Navy remained extremely pleasant and cooperative throughout the years, possibly because the Navy — despite its own Bureau of Aeronautics — was never a direct competitor with the NACA. With the Army, the situation was different. It had not only its Air Corps to sponsor, but also its own experimental laboratory at Wright Field. From the inception of the NACA, Army Air Corps concerns and research interests and those of the NACA sometimes collided, causing a real difference in tone between Army-Ames and Navy-Ames relations.[17]

Another aspect of the Navy-Ames cordiality was the marked lack of tension that always accompanied the sharing of Moffett Field. Ames was barely two years old, and still very much in the developing stage, when the Navy returned to Moffett Field. De France, and before him Edward Sharp, had taken great pains to cultivate frequent, pleasant exchanges between Ames and the military,[18] and De France continued to display great tact in dealing with the Navy. Correspondence between Ames and the Navy concerning items of mutual interest is complimentary to both De France and the successive commandants.[19] In 1948 Ames transferred its first building, the wooden shack used in 1940 to house equipment and personnel, to the Navy, and moved it just outside the main gate of Moffett Field, where it became the Chief Petty Officers' Club. Ames also arranged the arrivals of its industrial and military clients so as not to conflict with the Navy's take-off and landing schedules, a courtesy that did not go unappreciated. Another exchange of letters arranged for Ames to procure dry ice for the Navy; the laboratory was the bigger consumer and dealt daily with the dry-ice supplier.

The Navy returned such favors in a number of ways that made life easier for Ames. In the early years the Navy newspaper gave the laboratory a substantial column in the *Moffett News.*[20] More important, the Navy continued the Army practice of providing Ames with aviation fuel. Two 25,000-gallon tanks were reserved at the naval air station for the use of the NACA. This made it unnecessary for Ames either to construct storage tanks or to order fuel.[21]

When Ames needed an air compressor in 1948, it borrowed one from the Navy. The loan was to run for six months, but Ames kept the compressor for almost three years before the Navy really insisted on its return. The same civility accompanied the loan of a naval crane. Its transportation from the Alameda Navy Shipyard necessitated considerable inconvenience to the Navy. Eventually, the crane too was recalled, but not before it had been used for some time by Ames.[22] That these loans of equipment were accomplished so agreeably speaks for the courtesy of individuals on both sides and for the larger context of the Navy-NACA relationship.

During the war, there was some concern that the NACA was being too helpful to the military, at the expense of its own affairs. In 1942 George Mead, vice-chairman of the NACA and a former vice-president for engineering of United Aircraft Corporation, wrote J. C. Hunsaker, the committee's chairman:

> I am rather afraid that most of our facilities are tied up in what you might call "service" engineering jobs on current models. It is a shame the industry hasn't its own aerodynamic tools, in order to free ours for forward-looking work. It will be just too bad if some other country has been able to do this, as there seems plenty of opportunity of developing ways and means of improving performance of more or less orthodox equipment which could be utilized during this war.[23]

Toward the end of the war, Mead again voiced the same worry to Hunsaker:

> I feel strongly that NACA should confine its work to research of a fundamental nature in both planes and engines. . . . Our national safety, as well as commercial leadership in the air, depends upon straight thinking on research and carrying forward a constructive program at all times. You haven't had much opportunity of doing this as NACA's forehandedness had provided the vital equipment needed to perfect designs that neither the services nor the manufacturers had had the wisdom to make available for the job.[24]

The end of the war brought relief from the feeling that the NACA existed to solve specific military problems. At the same time the NACA needed to redefine its goals.

In 1946 the NACA initiated discussion within the government for a policy that would delineate the areas of responsibility of the various aeronautical factions. Obviously the NACA was most concerned about its role vis-à-vis the military. There was rancor on both sides. The Army Air Forces felt let down by NACA's failure to develop the jet engine in time for use during the war, and the NACA felt it had neglected just that type of basic research because it had been overwhelmed doing testing and clean-up for the military. The attempt to clarify positions was only partially successful. As might have been expected, and as the NACA had desired, its main province was defined as "fundamental research"; the military would explore and develop for military use the results of such research. Where, exactly, the line was to be drawn was still moot. In July 1947 the Army Air Forces became a separate service as the United States Air Force, and thereafter was the NACA's main competitor.

An Ames historian has remarked that two of the notable features of the Ames staff in 1946 were "a nucleus of extremely competent men and . . . the general lack of knowledge about transonic and supersonic aerodynamics."[25] If there is truth in the statement, it is also true that Ames had no monopoly on ignorance. Research opportunities beckoned. The challenge was to begin and to lead the field. Ames was in a position to follow new directions and exploit the opportunities.

In July 1945 the importance of high-speed research was recognized at Ames by reorganization. Harvey Allen, who had been head of the Theoretical Aerodynamics Section, became head of the new High-Speed Research Division and responsible for the work done in the 1- by 3.5-foot tunnel (called "high-speed" when built but subsonic nevertheless), the about-to-be-completed 1- by 3-foot supersonic tunnels, and the 6- by 6-foot supersonic tunnel. There were now three research divisions, the other two being the Theoretical and Applied Research Division and the Full-Scale and Flight Research Division. The divisions were still organized around existing and planned facilities, but the organization was becoming more complex. The more formalized organizational structures really began with the end of the war, with attempts to "normalize" operational practices. For Ames, which had known nothing but abnormal conditions, the transition from war to peace also brought adjustments in procedure that involved both increasing size and complexity and increased documentation and justification both locally and in Washington. This was accompanied, not just at Ames but throughout the aeronautical profession, by a general taking-stock as to where things stood in research, what could be learned from Europe, and where the first priorities lay.

As Vannevar Bush had noted, one of the great needs in science and technology was the rapid dissemination of research results to those who might make use of them.[26] On an international level, this concern for knowledge of the latest aeronautical developments had naturally been focused on Germany, where aeronautical engineers rivaled those in the United States. As the war ended, the Alsos mission of American scientists and engineers had been sent to study German laboratories and to retrieve useful research results.[27]

One discovery of the mission was that the Germans had made little progress in transonic research. Though the Allies had little to gain from German research in this respect, it was comforting to know that the same difficulties the Americans and the British had encountered in this field had been experienced also by the Germans. Another product of the Alsos mission was information on the revolutionary German swept-wing research.

42

Illustrative of the concept of coordination and dissemination urged by Bush, the models and test results on swept wings in Germany enabled the Boeing Aircraft Company to proceed quickly with a swept-wing bomber. A Boeing engineer was a member of one of the groups surveying German developments, and he relayed the information back to his company, which gambled, with happy results, and produced the B-47.[28]

But, interestingly, the German research on the swept wing had been paralleled in the United States. A NACA researcher, R. T. Jones, who at the time worked at the Langley laboratory, had been doing theoretical research on the swept wing for transonic flight. The concept was not new; in Germany, Adolph Busemann had proposed a swept wing in 1935.[29] However, as Jones later noted in a letter explaining his contribution, Busemann "did not make the point that a subsonic type of flow would appear if the wing were swept behind the Mach lines" — i.e., more obliquely.[30]

Thinking back to a NACA paper written by Max Munk in 1924 ("The Relative Effects of the Dihedral and the Sweepback of Airplane Wings," TN-177), Jones took the idea further: "I remembered Munk's paper and wondered if it would also apply to compressible flow, and I saw no reason why it didn't. Other people seemed to think compressible flow much more complicated than that."[31] The ramifications of sweeping the wings behind the Mach lines were crucial; sweepback could delay the compressibility phenomenon that was such a problem at transonic speeds.

Jones and his colleagues were of course unaware of the work that had been going on in Germany at the same time.[32] The Messerschmitt 163, with swept wings, did not reach production before the end of the war.[33] Working at Langley, Jones developed the theoretical principles for sweepback in February 1945; they were tested experimentally in Langley wind tunnels in March. Jones recalled the first tests: "It seemed to suggest what I was predicting, but it was pretty crude." Robert Gilruth, later head of Langley's Space Task Group and the Apollo program but in 1945 a research engineer, did more decisive tests. He attached model wings to the upper surface of the wing of the P-51 and got more satisfactory results. "When I went over to find out what the results were, they said something was wrong with the balances," Jones remembered. "About the third try they began to believe the results — the drag was much lower than they would believe!"[34] When von Kármán's Army Air Forces Scientific Advisory Group was in Europe investigating German aeronautical research a short time later, they questioned Busemann on Jones's research, which had been the topic of conversation during the long flight to Europe. Busemann corroborated Jones's findings. It was, as one member of the Alsos mission recalled, "a scientific coincidence. . . . Another example of the case where a background of common knowledge may lead to identical, important theories pursued independently and simultaneously by warring centers — the United States and Germany — even though isolated from each other in the intervening six years by security classification."[35]

For Ames, the sense of being on the verge of a new era became even sharper when Jones transferred there from Langley in July 1946. After John Stack and others at Langley devised the slotted-throat tunnel, making the first truly transonic wind tunnel possible, the Ames 1- by 3.5-foot tunnel was quickly converted for transonic testing by the expedient of drilling holes in the walls. At almost the same time, the NACA proposed to carry transonic research into the upper atmosphere with the Bell X-1 and the Douglas D-558.[36]

Not only was aeronautics more exciting, but the role of an aeronautical research laboratory had become more complicated. Ames had to deal with more agencies, and more closely, than during the war. Some way had to be found to meet the legitimate needs of the military, industry, the universities, and the NACA with minimum duplication. The solution was the Unitary Plan written by a committee under Dr. Jerome Hunsaker, the chairman of the NACA. After considering the needs of aeronautics as a whole and the desires of the various groups, the committee produced a scheme for research and development facilities for the Air Force, the NACA, and the universities. The appropriations, when finally passed in 1950, gave the NACA $75 million for facilities at each of its three research laboratories.

For Ames, the Unitary Plan produced not the 8-foot, Mach 0.7–3.5 tunnel originally planned, but a giant complex that linked three tunnels, one transonic and two supersonic, to an impressive power plant that could generate 240,000 hp. Begun in 1950, the complex took over three years to construct and, as E. P. Hartman noted, "represented perhaps the end of the line in large, continuous-flow wind-tunnel construction." The cost was over $27 million, a leap from the $7.2 million spent in 1944 on the 40- by 80-foot tunnel. The difference in cost reflects not only the general difference in prices and complexity of equipment over the eight years, but also a real change in attitude regarding the necessity for major financial commitment, on the part of the government, to basic research.[37]

By 1950 more than 1200 persons were employed at Ames.[38] Unavoidably, the close-knit atmosphere of the early war years had changed, reflecting not only the larger population, the greater range of facilities, and the implied specialization, but also the increased bureaucracy that accompanied that growth. Albeit with difficulty, some of the spirit of a small community remained, where persons felt bound to common goals and loyalties. Many ideas were discussed and perhaps even decisions made on them, as one veteran remembers, "in the cafeteria line."[39] Employees felt drawn not only to their own particular jobs, but to the institution as a whole. The standards of Ames were still very much those of Smith De France, who while wielding

44

an iron hand as the engineer-in-charge also commanded great personal loyalty. De France was committed to excellence and periodically circulated memoranda that recognized achievement. Especially when outsiders complimented the NACA or Ames, De France let the staff know, so that "you will take great pride in knowing how much this work is appreciated."[40] Thus from an internal standpoint, Ames continued to display the early characteristics that had made it such a desirable and exciting place to work.

AMES AND HEADQUARTERS

In its relations with the Washington office, however, Ames was not completely comfortable. The problem of distance was multiplied by the increasing complexity of both the laboratory and the NACA itself. Another problem came from the inevitable clash of personality that accompanied many dealings with the secretary of the NACA, John Victory. For Ames, Victory personified the worst of bureaucracy and pomposity. From the West Coast the very real services he performed for the NACA were not so apparent. Instead, Victory announced himself in a series of terse bulletins that tended toward petty detail and general complications for the recipient. He was cordially disliked at Ames, and most administrative communications from Washington came over his signature. A typical Victory directive informed Ames that the NACA now had a "lighting consultant," attached to the Cleveland Laboratory, who should be consulted on any proposed lighting installations. An attached Ames comment observed, "Don't like to see this, but guess we will have to like it. Pretty soon we may be like some of the large industrial companies and be afraid to make a move unless we consult the home office first."[41] When Victory's official title changed from secretary to executive secretary, defined as "the assistant head of the agency, supervising and directing its administrative work," the memorandum was greeted at Ames by a penciled "wow!" and "not that!"[42]

In addition to the personal annoyance embodied by Victory, Ames in the late 1940s and early 1950s suffered the effects of a general tendency on the part of government agencies to encourage greater efficiency — or at least to document efforts toward that end. In late 1949 Ames was instructed to name a "Policy and Procedure Officer," to be "charged with the responsibility of continuously studying policies and procedures and collecting information in an orderly manner for discussion from time to time with representatives of the other laboratories and of the Headquarters Office." Evidently Ames did not respond favorably to this, for a second letter from Washington observed:

It appears that there is still some lack of clarity in our letters attempting to convey to you the objective and *modus operandi* of our policy and procedures group. Uniform functioning of all branches of NACA is really secondary. Improvement of the efficiency of the organization is the primary objective. . . . I don't believe that personnel at Ames is any more susceptible to confusion than is the personnel in other parts of the organization. We have a job to do. Let's get along with it. . . . Please submit the name of the individual you recommend for designation as Policy and Procedure Officer of the Laboratory.[43]

Of the same era is the Headquarters-instituted Management Improvement Program, which attempted through periodic reports and conferences to cut inefficiency and costs and to save time and equipment. Reading the reports now, one cannot help but feel they were headaches that the Ames staff dispensed with as summarily as possible. The detail illustrates the growing amount of paperwork and the increasing man-hours spent in management analysis. One conclusion to such a report announced, "Following a detailed analysis of the report on Langley's survey, Ames and Lewis agree to undertake a study at the time of preparing the Annual Motor Vehicle Report and to forward information copies of their reports to all offices."[44]

An interesting contrast to the Management Improvement Program is a memorandum from a group of Ames engineers to De France. They were concerned that they had insufficient knowledge of industry's wider needs and concerns. They worried about "the necessity for the research aerodynamicists of the NACA becoming acquainted with the complex interrelationship of problems that the aircraft designers must face." As the Ames researchers pointed out, their specialization, as those concerned with intricate aspects of aerodynamic problems, often made it unlikely that they had the larger design perspective fully in view. The situation existing in previous years, they pointed out, had reversed itself — no longer was information dispersal solely a NACA function. Now the NACA researchers also needed to know industry's needs in a very specific manner.

A lecture series was suggested. Company engineers would be invited to brief Ames, in a technically detailed manner, on larger aspects of their aeronautical projects. The memorandum was sent by Harvey Allen to De France, to be followed up three months later by another even more specific letter by one of the concerned engineers.[45] Thus, in a very real way, a part of the staff tried to cope with the laboratory's growing size and complexity, as well as the complexity of the research field. But the request for the lecture series was not granted.

As Ames entered the 1950s and the United States faced another war, the changes that had occurred since the end of World War II were visible to all. The Ames staff had doubled in six years, the number of facilities had also doubled. Aeronautical research now dealt with speeds that had increased substantially since 1945. Unavoidably, and unsurprisingly, the daily routine at the laboratory had increased in complexity also. Ames was no longer the new, developing institution it had been during the war, and the field of aeronautics, having reached a stage of maturity, was burgeoning into new sophistication.

SOURCE NOTES

Chapter 2. The Postwar Period, 1945–1952

[1] Roosevelt to Bush, 17 Nov. 1944. Quoted in Vannevar Bush, *Science: The Endless Frontier: A Report to the President on a Program for Postwar Scientific Research* (Washington, D.C., 1946), p. 3.

[2] Vannevar Bush, *Pieces of the Action* (New York: William Morrow and Company, Inc., 1970), p. 31.

[3] Bush, *Science: The Endless Frontier*, pp. 3–4.

[4] Ibid, p. 13.

[5] Edwin P. Hartman, *Adventures in Research: A History of Ames Research Center*, NASA SP-4302 (Washington, 1970), p. 105.

[6] Ibid., pp. 50–53.

[7] See Alex Roland, *Model Research* (unpublished manuscript, Apr. 1980), Chapter 8. Roland argues that the NACA's failure to pursue jet propulsion soon enough was not only eventually fatal to the NACA, but was a product of the committee's very structure.

[8] Russell G. Robinson interview, 17 Dec. 1980.

[9] See John V. Becker, *The High-Speed Frontier: Case Histories of Four NACA Programs, 1920–1950*, NASA SP-445 (Washington, 1980). Becker's book is a fascinating study, though limited largely to Langley's role in transonic work.

[10] Walter G. Vincenti interview, 31 Oct. 1980.

[11] Smith J. De France interview by Michael Keller, 16 June 1967. See also De France interview by Walter Bonney, 23 Sept. 1974. Transcripts are in the NASA History Office Archives.

[12] "Memorandum for Engineer-in-Charge — Construction of Ames Aeronautical Laboratory," May 1945. 74-A-1624, V-4823, San Bruno Federal Record Center (henceforth SBFRC).

[13] Vincenti interview, 3 Oct. 1980.

[14] Hartman, *Adventures in Research*, pp. 61–62.

[15] Vincenti interview, 31 Oct. 1980.

[16] I am grateful to Russell Robinson for reminiscences of Dr. Lewis and for details on the 6- by 6-foot tunnel's sponsorship. Also see Hartman, *Adventures in Research*, pp. 63–64.

[17] This opinion has been expressed by many Ames employees, with the usual reason given being the lack of competitiveness between the Navy and Ames.

[18] See chapter 1, p. 9.

[19] 74-A-1624, box 163100, SBFRC.

[20] H. J. E. Reid to De France, 27 July 1944. 66-A-301, V-1677, SBFRC.

[21] A. B. Freeman to Capt. A. C. Olney, May 1948. 74-A-1624, box 163100, SBFRC.

[22] Correspondence regarding both the air compressor and the crane is in the personal papers of A. B. Freeman. 63-A-224, V-6630, SBFRC.

[23] George J. Mead to J. C. Hunsaker, 22 Dec. 1942. George W. Lewis's personal file, NACA History Office Archives.

[24] Mead to Hunsaker, July 1944. George J. Mead's file, NASA History Office Archives.

[25] Hartman, *Adventures in Research*, p. 121.

[26] Bush, *Science: The Endless Frontier*, p. 28.

[27] Much publicity was accorded the Alsos mission, especially as it touched upon the V-1 and V-2 launching site at Peenemünde and the possibility of advanced research in the nuclear field. Much less mention was made of the mission's aeronautical investigations. Samuel A. Goudsmit, Alsos (New York: Henry Schuman, Inc., 1947).

[28] For information on the aeronautical aspects of the Alsos mission, I am grateful to Russell G. Robinson.

[29] Busemann had suggested the concept in a paper he had given at the 1935 Volta Congress. See George Gray, *Frontiers of Flight* (New York: Alfred A. Knopf, 1948), p. 343-344.

[30] R. T. Jones to Ernest O. Pearson, Jr., 2 Feb. 1960, NASA History Office Archives.

[31] Interview with R. T. Jones, 9 Sept. 1982.

[32] R. T. Jones to James J. Strebig, 18 Apr. 1946, NASA History Office Archives.

[33] Gray, *Frontiers of Flight*, p. 344.

[34] See the report by R. T. Jones, "The Shaping of Wings to Minimize the Formation of Shock Waves," witnessed by the liaison officer of the NACA, Langley Field, 27 Feb. 1945. This was an informal memorandum; shortly thereafter Jones wrote also to Dr. Lewis in Washington, explaining the principle. NASA History Office Archives. Jones interview, 9 Sept. 1982.

[35] George Schairer, "Evolution of Modern Air Transport Wings," p. 62. A paper given at the AIAA Evolution of Aircraft Wing Design Symposium, 29 Mar. 1980, Air Force Museum, Dayton, Ohio. Robinson interview, 17 Dec. 1980.

[36] Hartman, *Adventures in Research*, pp. 146-149; Gray, *Frontiers of Flight*, pp. 334-338; Becker, *The High-Speed Frontier*, pp. 61-82. See the announcement of the transonic flight program in *The Moffett News* 4 (11, 30 May 1947): 1. 66-A-301, V-1677, SBFRC.

[37] Hartman, *Adventures in Research*, pp. 137-139, 194.

[38] See personnel figures, 1949-1950, in 70-A-1261, V-4823, SBFRC.

[39] This feeling has been stressed, notably, by Mildred Cardona Macon and Edie Watson Kuhr. Vincenti interview, 18 Aug. 1980.

[40] De France in memorandum for staff regarding speech by Congressman George P. Miller, 20 July 1953, 70-A-1261, V-4823, SBFRC. See also a memorandum from De France to division and branch chiefs regarding the esteem in which NACA was held in foreign countries.

[41] Victory to Ames, 20 Feb. 1950; Ames annotations 3 Mar. 1950. 70-A-1261, V-4823, SBFRC.

[42] NACA to all laboratories, 19 May 1949. 70-A-1261, V-4823, SBFRC.

[43] E. H. Chamberlin at NACA to Ames 29 Dec. 1949. 63-A-224, V-6631, SBFRC.

[44] Notes on the Management Improvement Program Conference at Lewis Flight

Propulsion Laboratory, 5–6 June 1951; reports on the Management Improvement Programs for FY 1951, 1952, and 1953. 63-A-224, V-6631, SBFRC.

[45] Memorandum for De France, annotated by Robinson, written by Wallace Davis, Walter Vincenti, Dean Chapman, Jack Nielsen, Richard Scherrer, and Edward Perkins, 4 Mar. 1952. 70-A-1261, V-4823, SBFRC. All of the engineers were members of the 1- by 3-foot supersonic wind-tunnel staff. Wallace Davis to R. G. Robinson, 4 June 1952. 70-A-1261, V-4823, SBFRC.

3

THE LEAN YEARS, 1952-1957

Until 1958, budget limits necessitated careful and frustrating choices both at Ames and in the NACA as a whole. Research alternatives, facility utilization, and priorities of time and financing had to be weighed and compromises effected. Though the government had made a commitment to sponsor and coordinate scientific research, appropriations were not unlimited and salaries of civil-servant researchers were not competitive with industry. The financial realities encouraged a conservative approach to planning on the part of the NACA. At the same time, however, the budgeting process for the individual laboratories remained simple enough to make it easy to reallocate funds between projects.

By the early 1950s facilities at Ames had increased substantially, but the laboratory remained small enough to be relatively free of bureaucratic complexity. Operational limitations resulted primarily from an overload of obligations compared to personnel strength. This no doubt hampered the staff in conducting Ames-originated research. Even more, it delayed developmental tests requested by the aircraft companies. John Dusterberry, who had come to Ames in 1943 with a degree in electrical engineering, remembered the early 1950s as a period of "doldrums" for those involved in the design of new facilities. "Nobody seemed to have any money to do anything, and as a result, I think people . . . lost motivation and spirit to do things."[1]

Lack of money meant the inability to hire the manpower needed to operate the wind tunnels at maximum use. As Harry Goett explained it,

> You spent men and time. . . . Washington said, "Now look, Smitty, we'll give you 1500 people for next year; now how many people will it take you to run your wind tunnels?" Then [De France] would come back and talk to Ferrill Nickle, the budget officer, and they'd make the first cuts, and then they'd call in Harvey Allen and myself, the major contenders. Harv had more facilities planned and would get more people, and I'd fight.[2]

Lack of "tunnel time" often created a backup of work and potential tension with industry. That this tension seldom developed is noteworthy. Harvey Allen, head of the high-speed division, put the problem clearly to NACA headquarters when describing a proposal made by North American Aviation. Allen supported the proposed research, but admitted: "Of course, the addition of the investigation of this missile to the 1- by 3-foot tunnel program will further overload this facility. This wind tunnel section is not up to full complement at present so that only single-shift operation is possible, hence there is no hope of speeding up the tunnel program unless the staff can be brought up to that commensurate with two-shift operation."[3] Allen added that the company had volunteered its own employees to build and maintain the model during testing.

The same staffing problem was mentioned by De France to a visiting congressman over a year later. In a typically polished way, De France explained that the situation at Ames was common throughout government-sponsored research.

> I pointed out to him that we have in operation at present and will have, in the additional equipment to be constructed under the Unitary Plan, the best facilities for high-speed research that can be found any place in the world. I explained, however, that it was difficult to operate these facilities to their full capacity with the manpower made available to us, and that if we needed anything, it was a greater appropriation for personnel. Congressman Crawford asked if the industry was proselyting our trained technicians. I told him that they did to a certain extent and cited one case which had occurred within the past week in which a GS-14 of the Laboratory had been offered a position at $15,000 a year with the Northrop Aircraft Company to take charge of their guided missile work. I told him that we had had other similar cases but that in most instances, because of the interest of the men in the work of the Laboratory, we were able to keep them from taking positions with the industry.[4]

The attraction of the research at Ames was a very real advantage in keeping the staff surprisingly stable. "At the beginning," as one veteran put it, "Ames had a little edge in salary, but by 1950–1952, a person had to ask himself if it was worth 25% in salary."[5]

Part of Ames's success in keeping researchers lay in the continuing postwar approbation enjoyed by aeronautics. Aeronautical research had reached enviable stature during World War II. Its worth was firmly established in the public mind, and the very obvious advantage of continuous, conscientious research had endowed the aeronautical laboratories with a certain prestige. During the supersonic decade that followed the war, it was easy to be excited by the possibilities for continuing progress and discovery. Harry Goett described the 1950s as a "continuing technological revolution," as aeronautics moved to the problems of transonic and supersonic flight and on to a new challenge — automatic control of aircraft. Challenge and competition kept Ames full of vitality.

> [Langley was] doing somewhat the same kind of stuff. That kept us on our toes. We'd go back and meet not only our counterparts at Langley, but the Air Force people, and the people from industry. We would present to these outsiders our own programs, and [it was] rewarding . . . to find that [we weren't] in a vacuum, that there [was an] outside use for our projects.
>
> [We'd get] 50% of the top people in the field around a table talking — it was very stimulating! [We'd] take back the list, circulate it [and develop] a program that was going to be helpful to them. . . .[6]

For those actively involved in the research process, belief in the NACA as a nonpartisan pursuer of research excellence and a crucial troubleshooter for the aircraft industry evidently kept many of the Ames staff from being tempted by higher salaries offered by private companies.

This enthusiasm was perhaps not surprising among the research staff itself, but it also seems to have been a part of the auxiliary services at Ames, from the administrative staff to the clerical workers. A partial explanation is surely found in the smallness of the original group that established the laboratory. Because of the academic ties among Ames personnel, and the imported camaraderie contributed by the people from Langley, the initial atmosphere of high motivation in an extended-family context seems to have continued as Ames grew. By example, older employees initiated new personnel into high levels of job-involvement. Equally important, however, was the habit of strict discipline set by De France. Because all knew De France would not tolerate negligence or sloppiness, professionalism at all levels was high. Pride in one's work was a real part of the Ames personality. As one employee put it, "We knew we'd hear about it from De France himself if our work wasn't satisfactory. So we learned to pay attention. And we were proud of the fact that we were required to meet [his] standards."[7]

ORGANIZATIONAL CHANGES

Another factor in the spirit of the institution in the early 1950s was the relative simplicity with which Ames was organized and the lack of bureaucracy with which it ran. In 1947 De France's title changed from engineer-in-charge to director. The change was symbolic, connoting the finished laboratory rather than a project under construction. In one sense this was certainly true. Ames was one of the most versatile aeronautical research facilities in the world, and it had settled into the research routine for which it had been designed. But it is also true that Ames was far from finished. A backward look at the organization of the laboratory in the early 1950s reveals a model of simplicity that appears almost unbelievable today.

From the earliest days at Ames, De France's right-hand man had been Jack Parsons, who initially was in charge of construction. The two men worked well together, and De France moved Parsons into a variety of jobs with confidence that he could manage a number of major functions simultaneously. During the time Parsons was still head of the construction division in the mid-1940s, he was also head of the Full-Scale and Flight Research Division, supervising all work done in the busy 40- by 80-foot tunnel. In Parsons De France had an informal assistant who kept him informed in a number of realms. Reporting daily to De France, Parsons served as liaison between the director and the rest of the laboratory. Parsons was, by all accounts, an inspiration in dedication, hard work, and quiet competence. The devotion told on his health, however. In 1947, after a leave of absence because of sickness, De France made him an assistant to the director, with Carlton Bioletti, another Langley transferee, in a parallel position. These two men relieved De France of some of the burden of research supervision; but the positions represented, in a sense, the beginnings of insulation between the director and his laboratory. The situation was mitigated by the strong hand with which De France governed the laboratory, which made his constant involvement with the daily issues and problems a certainty.

In 1949 Parsons became responsible for coordination of the Unitary Plan wind tunnels that the NACA expected to build at Ames, Langley, and Lewis. This position took him out of the post of assistant to the director, but in 1952 De France appointed him associate director. For the rest of his career at Ames, Parsons was second in command, continuing to facilitate communications between research and administration within the laboratory. He remained the coordinator of wind-tunnel construction under the Unitary Plan until 1956 when those facilities were completed.[8]

In 1950 Carlton Bioletti's title of assistant to the director evolved into that of assistant director. Russell Robinson was also appointed to a parallel position. Robinson, who had broken ground for the first construction at Ames in 1939, had been in a technical management position at the NACA's Washington office since 1940. His transfer to Ames in 1950 fulfilled a promise made him during the war by George Lewis, the NACA's director of aeronautical research. "Exciting things were happening out there and I wanted to be in on them," said Robinson, "to be involved with research and

54

research people more directly."[9] Robinson was not only rejoining old Langley colleagues, but also reestablishing relationships as a Stanford alumnus. His return illustrated the network of personal and professional ties that was so common among the Ames staff.

As assistant directors, Bioletti and Robinson managed current and projected research at the laboratory. Both men played a crucial role in considering the advantages and disadvantages of particular research programs, consulting with the research divisions and NACA headquarters as to the feasibility of various projects. In this way De France was able to make decisions for the laboratory after Robinson and Bioletti had studied the options and presented their recommendations. Supposedly, a distinction was made between planning and operations in the two posts, but in reality the distinction was not observed. As Robinson recalled, it would have been difficult to draw a clear dividing line between the jobs. It was equally unclear whether the two positions were line or staff appointments, and it would seem that they were a little of both, and an effective liaison between line and staff.[10] Robinson had the additional task of reviewing and editing much of the published material emanating from Ames research, an important detail De France felt needed constant attention.

Thus the assistant directors, and after 1952 the associate director, provided high-level assessment and filtering of information for the director. As buffers, they made it possible for De France to avoid becoming bogged down in much of the day-to-day detail, while at the same time they provided the information he needed to make informed decisions.

When Ames was formed, Donald Wood had the all-inclusive title of director of research. By 1943, however, the volume of research and its differentiation made two research divisions desirable: the Theoretical and Applied Research Division under Wood and the Full-Scale and Flight Research Division under Parsons. Wood's early responsibilities as director of all research had probably been less complicated than his later duties as division chief because of the new laboratory's limitations. As chief of the Theoretical and Applied Research Division in 1950, Wood was responsible for the 7- by 10-foot tunnels, the 12-foot tunnel, the 16-foot tunnel, and the Theoretical Aerodynamics Section. In 1943 that division represented the main thrust of Ames's planned specialty — high-speed research and theoretical aerodynamics. The focus of activities within the divisions was to change over the years, as was their proportional importance in terms of the laboratory's total research.

During the war the Full-Scale and Flight Research Division had concentrated on the deicing problem and on solutions to various performance problems in fighter aircraft. In addition to that, the division was responsible for planning the 40- by 80-foot tunnel and the full-scale research that it would make possible. The division dealt with the most crucial demands that were laid on Ames — problems in actual aircraft operations. The late 1940s saw significant work on wing research, as well as the load and stability studies and flight-testing of the F-86. In the 1950s, however, low-speed research and the Full-Scale and Flight Research Division lost that preeminent position. Perhaps it was not unusual that this occurred, since Ames, despite its capacity for full-scale research, had been originally conceived as more of a high-speed laboratory. In high-speed aeronautics, with theories still being hammered out, applications to structures had not yet become as important as in low-speed aeronautics. Many thought, as Hugh Dryden did, that Ames was "a little more purely scientific. . . . Langley aerodynamic studies were always done with an eye to the structural problems in mind, whereas Ames took it as a purely aerodynamic problem . . . and let other people worry about the structures."[11]

Harry Goett, who succeeded Jack Parsons as chief of the division, was not about to let the Full-Scale and Flight Research Division wither on the vine. He organized flight engineering, flight operation, flight research, and the 40- by 80-foot tunnel into interlocking sections. Goett's abrupt style contrasted greatly with that of Harvey Allen, yet Goett too is remembered for his ability to keep his sections running smoothly while also encouraging the spontaneity that must be a part of successful research. Like Allen, Goett had come from Langley, where he had worked under De France.

The third research division was formed in 1945: the High-Speed Research Division under Allen. By 1950 the division, with six transonic or supersonic wind tunnels, could claim the most exciting frontiers of research for its own. This division had grown out of the Theoretical Aerodynamics section of Wood's division. As high-speed flight moved from theory to actuality and the possibilities for experimental testing expanded, the need to redefine the field and organize its facilities had resulted in the creation of the new division. The breakthroughs that made transonic flight possible — the jet engine and the swept wing — rapidly elevated the division to a position of prominence in the laboratory. In addition, of course, the personality of Harvey Allen kept the sections under his control lively. The division included sections organized around the 1- by 3-foot supersonic tunnels, the 1- by 3.5-foot transonic tunnel, the 6- by 6-foot supersonic tunnel, the 10- by 14-inch hypersonic tunnel, and the supersonic free-flight tunnel.

Other divisions provided both administrative services and auxiliary expertise to keep the research facilities running smoothly. The available records, including some unofficial organization charts, suggest that the administrative division included clerical, financial, personnel, purchase, warehouse, and library sections. A construction division handled the continuing building, a technical services division ran the mechanics shops and serviced aircraft, and the research instrumentation and engineering services division dealt with engineering design, instrumentation development, photography, electronics, and illustrations for reports and publications.[12]

Although the administrative division had a financial section, the budget officer for Ames was not a part of this section. Instead, the financial section supported the budget officer, who reported directly to De France. As one Ames employee has described it, Ferrill Nickle, the budget officer, kept track of Ames's financial standing for the year by the "scratchpad" method. At any time, De France could find out exactly how much money the laboratory had left for the year and could reallocate money originally earmarked for a project that was proving less expensive than expected. Decisions in the financial management of the laboratory, once the funding had been approved for the year, were very much the director's, and little bureaucracy intervened between Ames and the NACA Washington office. It was, indeed, a period when the main office trusted their directors and left many major decisions in their hands.[13] As one scholar observed, "The laboratory director [had] almost complete freedom in deciding *how* the job [would] be done and *when* it [would] be done."[14]

The organization at Ames was certainly clear enough to those within the laboratory at the time. Difficulties arose, however, in outside assessment of organization and decision-making processes. In 1950 a student submitted a major paper to the Stanford Business School on management and procedural practices in the NACA.[15] For convenience he concentrated much of his study on Ames. When he attempted to obtain organizational charts from the Washington office of the NACA, he found that none existed, though he was referred to several "unofficial" organizational charts constructed by other sources. The same situation existed at Ames, and the scholar was forced to draw his own diagram of the lines of authority there. Greatly bothered by the lack, he recommended that the situation be immediately remedied and charts drawn up, both at the laboratory level and in the head office.

The reason for no published charts seems to lie primarily in the administrative philosophy of George Lewis, the NACA's director of aeronautical research from 1924 to 1947. According to a colleague, Lewis disliked organizational charts because he did not wish to encourage contacts from the outside directly with organizational subdivisions or specialists. Lewis preferred to be the sole route by which the NACA could be approached. He wanted to remain aware of all aspects of NACA concerns, and as he saw it, organization charts unnecessarily complicated matters.[16] Though Lewis retired in 1947, his style of management, in this regard at least, was passed on to the laboratories and outlasted his tenure.

ADMINISTRATIVE METHODS

Ames almost certainly inherited Lewis's disdain for organizational formality through De France, who had worked almost his entire career under Lewis. As the laboratory grew in size and complexity, De France's solution was to create the posts of assistants to the director, occupied originally by Bioletti and Parsons, and later the position of associate director. In delegating responsibility, however, De France did not relinquish final authority for major decisions, nor did he create a chain of command that would hinder his going directly to the divisions or sections and bypassing his immediate subordinates. In this way De France, like Lewis in Washington, was able to maintain informed control even after the laboratory's activities became far more diverse. The lack of clearly defined organizational functions and lines of command, at least at certain levels, was probably quite conscious on the part of De France.[17] It did not bother those on the staff nearly so much as it did an outsider attempting to analyze the workings of Ames. As the Stanford scholar rather plaintively noted,

> The exact status of the assistants to the Director is not clear to me. . . . the organizational structure appears to be highly unorthodox. I have had the distinction between the duties of these positions explained to me at some length, yet this distinction is still not clear to me. There are borderline cases wherein it is difficult for me to judge which position has the responsibility.[18]

But lack of clear organizational definition did not hamper the efficiency of the laboratory,[19] as the scholar admitted: "it is not readily apparent that the lack of organization charts had hindered managerial relations."[20] On the section and division levels, one obviously took problems to one's immediate superior, who himself might suggest a higher-level consultation. At times, one suspects, the relative smallness and informality of Ames would find issues being hashed out among various echelons of staff and line, a fine disregard for hierarchy being displayed.

By contemporary lights, Ames in the early 1950s appears to have been almost haphazardly organized and run. The outward appearances, however, are deceiving, for the laboratory had the advantage of a strong and conscientious director whose control was both constant and informed. Formal organization and the checks and balances of bureaucracy were less needed because of De France's reputation as an uncompromisingly honest, hardworking, and sensible manager and because the times themselves were simpler. The staff fluctuated between 1200 and 1350 in 1950-1955. By 1957 it had reached approximately 1450, but the gradual increase seems to have diluted staff familiarity only slightly. Operating costs for the laboratory climbed gradually also, from approximately $3 million in 1945 to $10 million in 1955.[21] Harry Goett recalled an episode from the postwar period that illustrates De France's management philosophy. Its similarity to Lewis's attitude toward organization charts is striking:

> The NACA had a pretty good reputation for managing its money, so the [Office of Management and Budget] sent some men out here to find out how we [worked]. One of them came to see me, and I [explained] how decisions were made to undertake research. . . . Decisions obviously involved cost decisions, but the decision to do a test in the 7 X 10 or the 40 X 80 was made on the basis of which tunnel you decided better fit the problem, not on the money it would cost. When De France found out I'd told the OMB man all this he hit the ceiling: "You told them how we work! I'm never going to let you talk to the budget people again!" Boy, he was mad![22]

Another factor making for relatively simple, informal operations was constant discussion and feedback among all levels of employees. Though difficult to document, the low turnover rate of the staff and the various long-standing relationships deriving from old Langley employment, university experiences, and friendships built through the early years at Ames all contributed to the laboratory's ability to function with a minimum of organizational formality and bureaucracy. It was a joke among Ames employees that "once at Ames, always at Ames."[23]

The flexibility displayed in the administration of Ames is interesting for several reasons. First, while the casual attitude regarding bureaucracy and formality dated from the original wartime context in which the laboratory was established, it continued after the war. Second, this "family" attitude toward administration seems to have been as much a product of De France's personality and management philosophy as it was a result of Ames's early years. Last, it must be admitted that even for 1950, when rigid chains of command, bureaucracy, and paralyzing paperwork were not so developed as today, Ames was atypical. The Stanford scholar was hard pressed to contain his disbelief at the lack of clearly defined administrative channels and regularized procedures he discovered at Ames.

The De France method of administration worked extremely well during its time. Perhaps, too, the nature of research contributed to the success of the system. The thought processes upon which inspired research depend need a certain leeway and protection from rigid definition and pigeonholing. To escape losing impetus in a forest of nonessential detail, a researcher needs to be free to discuss, consult, and make decisions relatively easily and quickly. This was possible at Ames partially because of the lack of black-and-white distinctions and job definitions, and because of the pervasiveness of informal discussion.

GENERATING RESEARCH

In the early 1950s aeronautics enjoyed high status as a field of research. Visible advances were being made all the time, and there was a general awareness of the research frontier. Aeronautics was a field of endeavor one could believe in — it was free of the moral ambiguities that attached to most military-connected research. The technology of the ever-faster-and-higher airplane was seen as, and for the most part was, a "clean" technology, so it was easy to remain enthusiastic about one's work. The happy climate at Ames in the early 1950s, therefore, must be seen not only in terms of personnel and management, but also in the context of the nature of its research and the prevailing atmosphere of the time.

To analyze life at Ames, one must consider how research projects originated and were accomplished. The means by which Ames became involved in a research effort varied as widely as the projects themselves. An outstanding characteristic, however, was a flexibility that made it possible for research to originate from any of a number of sources. Only sometimes did work derive from a dictum of the Washington office. Just as frequently Ames itself initiated the process by which a research authorization was eventually issued. An idea that evolved into an extensive investigation might begin with a single engineer or a group discussing a persistent problem. Conversely, the suggestion for a specific investigation might come from one of the special subcommittees of the NACA, to be assigned to a laboratory depending upon work under way there at the time or upon areas of specialty. Between these two extremes was a spectrum of possible origins for projects, some within the laboratory itself, some outside.

The investigations undertaken by Ames, and indeed by most aeronautical laboratories, fell into two broad categories. The NACA and its facilities were primarily designed for basic research in aeronautics; that is to say, the pursuit of answers to broad questions within the discipline. Examples of this type of research were the various efforts to minimize the compressibility effects of transonic flight and research into the characteristics of different wing shapes. Basic research might also deal with problems of experimentation itself, like the work at Langley that led to the slotted-throat solution to transonic choking. A research idea along broad lines such as these might originate anywhere. After conceptualization and discussion at various levels, the Washington office issued a research authorization, which was formal

60

approval for work to begin.[24] Sometimes the actual work began before formal approval was issued. This had been true, for example, in the case of the deicing work done at Ames by L. A. Rodert and his flight research section; Rodert simply continued, before the research authorization came through, work he had started while at Langley (p. 20).

Sometimes research elsewhere that had come to the attention of a NACA researcher provoked a memorandum or proposal for further investigation. This was true in the case of a very long-lived research authorization that a young Langley engineer originated in 1926.[25] Having read a NACA technical memorandum on boundary-layer-control research being done in Germany, he proposed to the enginer-in-charge at Langley that the various methods for delaying boundary-layer turbulence be investigated further. The idea moved from Langley to the Washington office, where George Lewis, director of aeronautical research, wrote a research authorization.

Other projects grew out of barriers encountered by research. The ballistics work undertaken by Ames in the immediate postwar period was a response to the inherent limitations of wind-tunnel research at transonic speeds. It was one of the logical directions to proceed, at least until the choking problem in the tunnels could be solved.

The various technical subcommittees of the NACA were sources for research directives. Either through their own expertise or through the concern of an outside interest — industry or the military — the committees identified areas where work was needed, and the appropriate laboratory was consulted and eventually detailed to handle the research. The technical committees and subcommittees served both as sources for research ideas and as reference authorities when proposals were advanced by one of the laboratories.

Occasionally a new project grew out of meetings of the interlaboratory panels. Beginning in 1944 and continuing into the 1950s, both the High-Speed Panel and the Research Airplane Projects Panel met at one or another of the laboratories to exchange ideas. Often research was informally apportioned by the researchers themselves and plans were made to seek formal authorization to continue along the directions discussed. In 1944 the High-Speed Panel was composed of Russell Robinson from the Washington office, Harvey Allen, John Stack, and Eastman Jacobs. The airplane panel was active from 1948 to 1957, with a membership that remained approximately the same throughout the years, including representatives from all major NACA installations. The panel reviewed the work done in flight research, discussed new undertakings, and hashed over problems. Decisions reached at the meetings went directly to the main office for final approval.[26]

Another source of research ideas was the individual whose current work sparked a spinoff. If an engineer was able to convince his section head and then the division chief that the idea was worthwhile, the proposal would be taken up the administrative ladder. The division chief reviewed the research plan and consulted with one of the assistant directors. De France then received the recommendations of the assistant directors, and the plan was submitted to Washington with the hope of receiving a research authorization. The assistant directors at Ames also played an important role in providing informed technical liaison between the laboratory and the NACA technical committees that reviewed the proposals.

If the originator of the idea was someone like Harvey Allen, who an associate said "could keep us supplied with research projects indefinitely,"[27] the approval process could be automatic and informal. As division chief, Allen could do a certain amount of work on a new idea, sometimes even delegating a preliminary investigation to one of his subordinate sections, without getting official approval. Again, being able to pursue an idea without step-by-step authorization from above was probably of great benefit to the research process. The leeway granted by De France was an extension of the leeway granted *to* De France, and it created a fertile atmosphere in which new ideas could be tried without prior commitment to their long-term support. Barren leads could be abandoned without embarrassment. When initial work proved promising, then the formalities leading to a research authorization were begun.[28]

Applied research, that is, research directed more specifically at a practical need or problem, could also begin almost anywhere. Applied research projects most often resulted from a need of the military or the aircraft industry. The route taken by the idea before the research authorization appeared varied widely. In the case of the military, the need was usually expressed at the top first — the problem was brought to the attention of the Washington office. When George Lewis was the NACA's director of aeronautical research, his close ties with the armed forces usually meant that a military official came to him with a written request. Lewis then consulted one or more laboratories and issued the research authorization. Hugh Dryden, who succeeded Lewis in 1947, depended heavily on the technical bureaucracy of the NACA to aid in decision-making. Dryden renovated the technical committees and subcommittees, equipping them to take a much more active role than they had previously exercised.[29]

With the aircraft industry playing an increasingly important role on the technical subcommittees, it is also likely that many industrial problems were initially aired there, either directly or indirectly. The ethics of membership on one of the technical committees by a company officer supposedly prevented lobbying for specific, company-concerned interests, but certainly the NACA became more aware of industrial concerns after the war. Often industry made formal application for specific work. The problem was then referred to a subcommittee for consideration, and the research, if approved, was delegated to the most appropriate laboratory. The procedure served the eastern companies well, but the western companies depended heavily on the NACA's Western Coordination Office for relaying research results to the main office.

Geography and the timing of Ames's establishment helped to forge close links between the Western Coordination Office, Ames, and the aircraft companies on the West Coast. At the same time the laboratory was being planned, the Western Coordination Office was established; its head, Edwin Hartman, had been at Langley along with many of the new Ames staff. Hartman and De France were friends, and both men wanted to establish strong ties among Ames, the WCO, and industry.

Officially Hartman served as the liaison between western industry and the NACA. Even here, however, personal relationships and geography helped to keep Ames immediately abreast of developments in the field and of any issues or problems that might become of interest. Hartman visited the various companies frequently to confer with company officials and researchers, and then reported to the NACA what he had learned. He sent copies of his reports to Ames also, so that the local laboratory was always aware of his findings as soon as the main office was, if not before.[30] Ames had a slight advantage in dealing with western industry, in that the informal communication network worked extremely well and that the laboratory was on the spot and usually eager to help. When industry made formal requests to the NACA, therefore, Ames could sometimes lend additional weight to the request, because of prior knowledge of and interest in the company's problem. This was true, for instance, in the case of the missile testing that Harvey Allen became interested in (p. 52). Although taking on the work for North American would further overload his staff, Allen was obviously excited by the research possibilities.[31]

After one of the laboratories was launched on a new research project, it was important that the others be kept informed of results. To a certain extent, communication among the laboratories was constant and informal. On a more formal level were conferences, such as meetings of the Research Airplane Projects Panel, to discuss successes, failures, and new directions for investigation. On an intermediate level, however, the research divisions of the laboratories submitted quarterly reports to their own laboratory directors, advising them on the status of current research. These detailed reports also went to the other laboratories for the benefit of researchers working in related areas. In the Ames files are years of Langley and Lewis reports, with copies for the laboratory's main files and for the individuals at Ames most closely connected with such research.[32]

Though for the most part communication among the research laboratories and the Western Coordination Office appears to have been quite good, sometimes information was less effectively dispersed than it might have been. In 1953 J. W. Crowley, Dryden's deputy, asked all the laboratories to send the Western Coordination Office "progress reports prepared at the laboratory for the various NACA subcommittees, . . . memorandums covering visits of people west of the Mississippi to the laboratory, . . . and official announcements dealing with changes in personnel and organization."[33] He went on to remind the laboratories what the WCO could do for them in the way of obtaining West Coast information and military clearance for visiting NACA personnel. Crowley's memorandum indicates that cooperation among the NACA's subordinate units needed some attention.

A similar complaint was voiced a year later by an Ames engineer whose Langley counterpart had not received some Ames data of mutual interest. The Ames engineer had transmitted the test data to headquarters, as was standard procedure, but NACA apparently had dropped the ball. De France took the matter up with Crowley and received permission to send research data to the other laboratories and the head office simultaneously. But headquarters did not surrender its perquisites absolutely. The liberal procedure was "not to be used except in special cases."[34]

Research at Ames during the last years of the NACA emphasized fundamental investigations, although the relationship of the laboratory to industry became much more complex during this period. With the completion of the three Unitary Plan wind tunnels in 1952, industry was able to buy testing time in the tunnels on a regular basis. The obligations implied in the plan guaranteed that Ames would do applied research for outside concerns. Nevertheless Hugh Dryden* continued to stress, in his many articles and speeches of the early 1950s, the absolute necessity of keeping the NACA strong in fundamental research, warning that "the trend toward short-term specific investigations must not occur again to the same degree as during World War II."[35] And the problems posed by transonic and supersonic flight continued to provide Ames with impetus for work in fundamental research.[36]

RESEARCH DIRECTIONS

As transonic and supersonic flight became practicable, investigators found it desirable to reconsider the shape of aircraft. Wing and fuselage shapes had to be revised in light of new phenomena discovered at the higher speeds. The general shape of the wing came under investigation with regard

---

*Lewis retired in 1947. J. W. Crowley was acting director of aeronautical research until September, when Dryden took the job. Crowley continued as associate director, undoubtedly easing Dryden's way.

to drag and lift, and the wing's placement on the fuselage was also crucial to performance. The shape of the fuselage underwent much rethinking, as researchers sought ways to minimize drag at both transonic and supersonic speeds. Langley's Richard Whitcomb had been responsible for the experimental development of a transonic area rule — the "coke-bottle" shape — that reduced the cross-sectional area of the fuselage where the wings and engine components began, thereby decreasing drag.[37] At Ames, R. T. Jones extended Whitcomb's ideas by devising a theoretical supersonic area rule. The area rules led to continued refinements in aircraft configurations, as researchers attempted to increase efficiency of operation and handling qualities.

In flight research, as in aerodynamic theory, high speed opened new areas where information was lacking and sorely needed. Speed itself made for control problems that had not been present in slower aircraft. In addition, the new shapes of aircraft created unusual control and stability characteristics that had to be investigated. The complex ways that component shapes affect maneuverability and control is a classic example of the often simultaneous sets of questions with which theory and actual flight are involved. The swept wing, for example, delayed or reduced shock waves occurring during transonic flight, but it also created stalling problems in low-speed flight. Flight research on these problems was necessary, and Ames aerodynamicists and pilots worked together on various possibilities.[38] In the same period, stability and control concerns resulted in much work being done on high-speed tracking methods, the means by which an aircraft keeps its weapons trained on a moving target. At Ames in the early 1950s, tests on the tracking qualities of various aircraft led to refinements not only in the aircraft, but also in the methods used for tracking.

With regard to both aircraft stability experimentation and performance aspects of flight such as tracking ability, the 1952–1957 period saw the introduction of a new element into aerodynamic research. The computer was slowly coming to be used as an auxiliary method of theoretical and flight research and as a tool in the operation of aircraft. By computer-based studies, countless combinations of component shapes and associated flight characteristics could be analyzed. Tracking equipment using automatic, computer-directed responses was developed. In the area of flight research, the first automatic control devices began to be used. Remote control of experimental aircraft lessened dangers to test pilots and also canceled out the human factor in tests, creating another means by which information could be obtained, analyzed, and evaluated. The advent of the computer in the various areas of aeronautical research was accompanied by its spreading use in administration, a development that eventually was to change the running of the laboratory.[39]

Two other major areas of research during the period would later be of major significance for Ames. One was vertical and short take-off and landing (V/STOL). In the light of the increasing commitment Ames was to make to V/STOL studies, the first attempts now appear to have been primitive in the extreme,[40] but the early recognition of the potential use of V/STOL aircraft placed Ames securely in the vanguard of this new branch of aeronautics.

The second and dramatic set of investigations and discoveries grew out of the developing importance of ballistic missile research. To launch and direct a heavy ballistic warhead, sending it at high speed into the upper atmosphere, presented several challenges. Control was a problem, but even more worrisome was aerodynamic heating upon reentry. Problems in aerodynamic heating were by no means confined to missiles, but were most

1957. Harvey Allen explains his 1952 blunt-body theory. Allen's calculations showed that the bow-shock wave created by the movement of the blunt body through the atmosphere served to dissipate much of the aerodynamic heat away from the body itself. Allen's discovery solved the problem of aerodynamic heating during a spacecraft's reentry into the atmosphere. The shape of the Mercury space capsules reflected the blunt-body theory at work.

critical in missiles because nothing else approached such speeds. In the early 1950s Harvey Allen turned his attention to ballistics reentry. His thinking completely changed the approach to the reentry heating problem. Previously researchers had taken as a given fact the slender needle-nosed shape of the intercontinental ballistic missile (ICBM). The engineering problems associated with cooling such a slender body seemed insurmountable. Allen, discussing the problem informally, observed that "meteors get through the atmosphere, [so] the problem *can* be solved."[41]

The key to the puzzle came from an equation Allen developed; the solution was a blunt-shaped entry body. A blunt body moving at extreme speed generates a bow shock wave, which dissipates heat to the air. Only a small portion of the total heat remains in the boundary layer near the body. Allen subjected the idea to professional scrutiny among his colleagues; it was accepted as an ingenious solution to a problem that had stumped the aero-

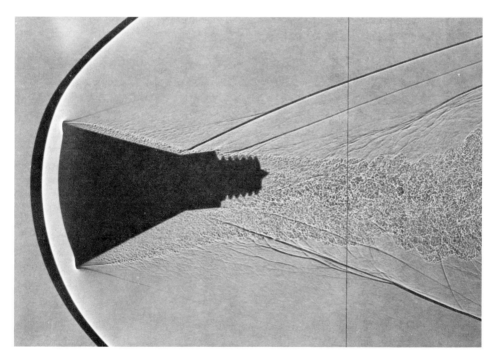

1959. Allen's principle illustrated. A shadowgraph of the Project Mercury reentry capsule, showing the bow-shock wave in front of it and the flow fields behind the capsule. At reentry speeds, radiative heat became a serious problem, leading researchers to explore also the process of ablation, the means by which a body absorbs heat by melting, evaporation, and sublimation. Ablation experiments were done in the Ames Atmospheric Entry Simulator.

nautical research community. The blunt-nose principle was crucial not only for missile design, but later became even more well known when combined with ablation for heat shields. The design of essentially all reentry vehicles — ICBMs, the early manned spacecraft, the Space Shuttle — has been significantly influenced by the blunt-body concept.[42]

In a way, the early V/STOL research and the blunt-nose principle illustrate both ends of the spectrum of Ames's research strengths. Allen's discovery, being revolutionary, practical, and readily comprehensible, at least on a superficial level, to the layman, elevated him to national prominence. The V/STOL research of the period represented the quieter, less recognized, less immediately profitable research that remains the backbone of a good research laboratory. V/STOL was to become a major research field for Ames and a means by which aeronautics remained exciting in the age of astronautics. Both types of research were necessary — the full-blown output of individual imagination and the slower, more tentative steps taken by teams of research workers. That the laboratory supported both types of work strengthened its reputation and the morale of its personnel.

In 1947 J. C. Hunsaker, the chairman of the NACA, had been questioned about the results of a national poll that had just been taken. He expressed astonishment that 26% of the respondees expected orbital and interplanetary adventures within 10 years and observed rather drily that "this . . . poll indicates that people who know about rockets like them. The same is no doubt true with regard to helicopters, alcoholic drinks, and chamber music."[43] But of course, exactly 10 years later *Sputnik* was in orbit. The Russian satellite was the visible goad that brought radical changes to the United States scientific and engineering programs, and especially to astronautics.

The furor created by the Soviet Union's surprise of October 1957, however, invites the conclusion that the American space program was only a response to Russian pressure. As Ames's work in the early 1950s illustrates, this was not true, although it is certainly accurate to say that a response to the Soviet achievement was a major investment of American energy, personnel, and funds in the following years. A realistic survey of American space history begins earlier and deals with the research laboratories of the NACA. The space frontier was approached less by a series of leaps than by a continuing effort in basic research that included the technological ingredients necessary for the push into space. The foundations of knowledge for satellites and manned spaceflight were being laid in the early 1950s. During that period, despite the hostilities of the Korean conflict and the Cold War with the Soviet Union, the space frontier was still a scientific frontier, an intellectual and technological challenge. Ames was moving toward that frontier — if at a pace that subsequently seemed too slow.

SOURCE NOTES

Chapter 3. The Lean Years, 1952–1957

[1] John Dusterberry interview, 21 Apr. 1982.

[2] Harry Goett interview, 3 Dec. 1981.

[3] H. J. Allen to J. W. Crowley, "Memorandum on Proposal of North American Aviation, Inc., for Investigation of Factors Affecting Center-of-Pressure Movement throughout the Mach Number Range," Jan. 1948, 61-A-565, V-7209, San Bruno Federal Records Center (hereafter SBFRC).

[4] Smith De France to Hugh Dryden, 12 Dec. 1949, 255-77-0020, RMO 5/62, box 81780, SBFRC.

[5] Goett interview, 3 Dec. 1981.

[6] Ibid.

[7] Mildred Cardona Macon interview, 20 Sept. 1980.

[8] Biographical detail on John Parsons was provided by personnel files collected by Edie Watson Kuhr.

[9] Russell G. Robinson interview, 13 Apr. 1981.

[10] Ibid.

[11] See Edwin P. Hartman, *Adventures in Research: A History of Ames Research Center,* NASA SP-4302 (Washington, 1970), pp. 162–164.

[12] I have consulted organization charts of Ames drawn up for personal use by Merrill H. Mead and used his terminology for the non-research divisions. Another source of unofficial organization charts is the study of B. R. Luczak, "A Management and Procedural Analysis of the National Advisory Committee for Aeronautics," written for the Graduate School of Business, Stanford Univ., 21 Apr. 1950.

[13] Information regarding the financial running of the laboratory was received from Alan E. Fayé, Jr., interview, 1 Apr. 1981. Fayé also repeated the opinion that De France's position represented one of trust vis-à-vis the main office of the NACA.

[14] Luczak, "Management and Procedural Analysis," p. 22.

[15] Luczak, "Management and Procedural Analysis."

[16] This theory regarding Lewis's dislike of organization charts, provided by Russell G. Robinson interview, 4 Nov. 1980, has been repeated by other NACA employees.

[17] Robinson interview, 13 Apr. 1981.

[18] Luczak, "Management and Procedural Analysis," p. 21.

[19] Walter G. Vincenti interview, 31 Oct. 1980; Russell G. Robinson interview, 13 Apr. 1981; and Alan E. Fayé interview, 1 Apr. 1981.

[20] Luczak, "Management and Procedural Analysis," p. 21.

[21] Hartman, *Adventures in Research,* app. A, p. 515.

[22] Goett interview, 3 Dec. 1981.

[23] This information has been given by several NACA-Ames employees. Out of 51 persons listed on the staff in 1940, at least 30 were still at Ames in 1950.

[24] For a fascinating discussion of the life of a research authorization, see Alex Roland, *Model Research: The National Advisory Committee for Aeronautics, 1915–1958,* NASA SP-4103 (Washington, 1984), Appendix F.

[25] Ibid.

[26] See reports of the 1944 High-Speed Panel and the 1948–1957 Research Airplane Projects Panel in 61-A-565, V-7209, SBFRC.

[27] Vincenti interview, 13 Aug. 1980.

[28] The relationship between De France and his division chiefs and the freedom accorded them by De France have been mentioned by Walter Vincenti, Russell Robinson, and Alan E. Faye, Jr.

[29] This conclusion is based on inference. Lewis's personal style and many connections with the military have been stressed in many interviews. This does not seem to be true of Dryden. See Roland, *Model Research,* pp. 334–337.

[30] Hartman's reporting procedure was explained to me by Edie Watson Kuhr. She was not sure if Hartman sent simultaneous copies to the other laboratories.

[31] See no. 3.

[32] See 61-A-565, V-7209, SBFRC for these reports. The most complete set is from 1950–1957 and concerns Langley's research airplane projects. Lawrence Clousing of the Full-Scale and Flight Research Div. was the recipient of the reports.

[33] J. W. Crowley to labs, "Memorandum on Information To Be Supplied to the Western Coordination Office," 19 Mar. 1953, 74-A-1624, box 163111, SBFRC.

[34] Memorandum by Charles W. Frick, 12 Aug. 1954, and memorandum by Smith J. De France, 23 Aug. 1954, 74-A-1624, box 163111, SBFRC.

[35] Hugh Dryden, "Trends in NACA Research and Development," speech to SAE National Aeronautics Meeting, 5 Oct. 1951, 255-77-0020, RMO 5/62, box 81780, SBFRC. This speech is typical of the many Dryden gave during this period.

[36] For a detailed discussion of the work undertaken at Ames during this period, see Hartman, *Adventures in Research,* pp. 199–215, 245–272.

[37] Ibid., pp. 199–200.

[38] Ibid., pp. 210–211.

[39] The importance of the computer in the way Ames operated was stressed by Alan E. Faye, Jr., who sees the presence of the computer in Ames's administrative practices as an unavoidable but complicating factor in the history of the laboratory.

[40] Hartman, *Adventures in Research,* p. 252.

[41] Observation of Victor Stevens, 16 Jan. 1983.

[42] Ibid.

[43] Quoted in a biographical abstract made by Walter Bonney, May 1972, for the J. C. Hunsaker papers, box 8, in the Smithsonian Institution.

4

THE FORMATION OF NASA, 1958

The period 1957–1959 was a transition in American aeronautics. Ames was very much affected by the events that propelled the country into the space age, though at the time technical and administrative developments seemed to produce little change in the work or atmosphere of the laboratory. For those who had been employed there since its beginnings, however, Ames had become very different.

AMES IN 1957

By 1957 Ames had grown immensely, was much more complex organizationally, and in a way was perhaps not as exciting as it had once been. The mid-1950s were a quiescent time before the advent of major changes that would transform the institution in the 1960s. Researchers who left Ames in the 1950s perhaps left because they found the challenges less exciting than during the war or in the immediate postwar period, when transonic problems were confronted. Another problem was comparable pay; industry succeeded in luring some engineers away from the NACA.

Though still a stimulating place to work, Ames in 1956–1958 was almost too established. In some respects its very successes created a certain complacency often characteristic of a mature research organization.[1] Its reputation established early and its niche in the NACA hierarchy secure, Ames continued, under the firm hand of De France, to run smoothly. The growth of personnel was slow, the addition of more sophisticated facilities was steady, and the laboratory functioned efficiently with little red tape. As one former administrator at Ames recalled, "Smitty used to like to keep as few men at the top as possible, to save most of his forces for creative research."[2] Though the research challenges had shifted and size had brought unavoidable administrative complexities, Ames continued to produce excellent research contributions with completely in-house personnel and little bureaucracy. Those who had watched the laboratory change over its first 15 years of existence would be astonished at what the next 15 would bring.

The organization of the laboratory illustrates the degree to which it had expanded since the 1940s. De France, as director, still retained direct control, aided by Jack Parsons, the associate director. In 1957 there was only one assistant director, but he was aided by two technical assistants. Parsons also had a technical assistant. The assistants, while taking some of the research expertise burdens from the associate and assistant directors, also represented another level of bureaucracy between the researchers and the administrative decision-making of De France.

Reporting directly to De France was the budget officer, as had always been the case. The administrative, instrument, research, technical services, and engineering services divisions also reported directly to Parsons or De France. De France had acquired the beginnings of what would become a public affairs office, though in 1957 it consisted of only one man, called the information specialist. Hired from Langley, he provided requested information on Ames to outside organizations and the surrounding community. It is easy to imagine that De France recognized the beginnings of public relations as a necessary evil. Reputedly, the new man was refused a secretary when he first arrived, on the grounds that he didn't need one. Once the outgoing correspondence on his desk piled up to eye level, De France took the hint and a secretary was provided.[3] De France was thrifty with public funds.

The nonresearch divisions had increased their branches and complexities as Ames grew, and the same was true of the research divisions. The research divisions, reporting to the Assistant Director Russell Robinson, reflected changes within the field of aeronautics as well as intricate relations with industry and the armed forces. The Theoretical and Applied Research Division, still under Donald Wood, had by 1957 added a machine computing branch. Primitive computers had been used at Ames from the very beginning, but by the end of the 1950s the glorified adding machines were being superceded by computers that could undertake much more complicated tasks. The machines were to bring with them greater organizational complexity, since their increased sophistication invited more elaborate record keeping and finer breakdowns in financial planning.[4]

In the Full-Scale and Flight Research Division, under the direction of Harry Goett, the flight operations, flight research, and 40- by 80-foot tunnel branches had been joined by three others: low-density tunnel, heat-transfer tunnel, and dynamics analysis. The new tunnels had been needed to deal with the new aspects of flight at high altitude and supersonic speed. Both were useful in investigating heat transfer to flight vehicles from laminar or turbulent boundary layers, the effects of heat transfer to the vehicle, and the effect of boundary-layer heating on skin friction. Earlier tunnels having proved too small and limited in scope, funds had been obtained in 1951 to

72

build two new tunnels — an 8-inch low-density tunnel and a 10- by 10-inch heat-transfer tunnel. The tunnels were housed in a new building adjacent to the 12-foot pressure tunnel, enabling the borrowing of supplementary air power from existing compressors.[5] When the new tunnels were completed in 1954, the old ones were shut down. Eventually, formal ownership of the old heat-transfer tunnel passed to the University of California at Berkeley. The 1- by 3.5-foot tunnel was deactivated and eventually dismantled and the 7- by 10-foot tunnels, seldom used, were operated by the 40- by 80-foot tunnel section. The new low-density and heat-transfer tunnels became ever more important as research grew in the areas of boundary-layer studies, skin friction, and aerodynamic heating.

The dynamics analysis branch, the other new addition to the Full-Scale and Flight Research Division, held the components of important future Ames research. Using newly procured analog computers, the branch marked the beginning of Ames's research in ground-based flight simulators. Crude early studies left much to be desired, but by 1957–1958, Harry Goett was encouraging his dynamics analysts to plan more sophisticated simulators. This natural extension of high-speed flight research, which studied the handling of qualities of aircraft under specified conditions and pilot responses to flight conditions, was to dovetail easily into simulation studies as high-speed flight became flight into space and pilots became astronauts. It is argued that the United States did not enter the space race until it had begun; but studies undertaken in the years immediately preceding *Sputnik* and the formation of NASA would be directly applicable to research needs once that race was in progress. The NACA may be criticized for its lack of dynamism in pushing for more space research funding, but it cannot be faulted for failing to move in the right directions in its last years.

The High-Speed Research Division under Harvey Allen had also gained new branches by 1957. In addition to the earlier facilities, the division had acquired the 2- by 2-foot transonic tunnel, which replaced the dismantled 1- by 3.5-foot transonic tunnel. It had also added a hypervelocity ballistic range branch, which had evolved from a growing concern with aerothermodynamic research. As research in the heat-transfer tunnel was a product of concern with the heating of vehicles at higher altitudes and speeds, so too was ballistics research, which was useful in stability studies. (Aerodynamic stability could not easily be studied in wind tunnels, since models were by necessity firmly fixed in place. An exception was the supersonic free flight tunnel.) The hypersonic ballistics range was made possible by the light-gas gun, developed by a group of researchers working under Alex Charters, who had come to Ames from the Aberdeen Proving Ground's ballistics ranges. The gun launched a test model on a charge of highly compressed helium. Gunpowder-powered rifles generally could not launch models faster than 2,135 m/sec, whereas Charters's early helium and gunpowder combination attained speeds of 3,965 m/sec. (Subsequent light-gas guns produced speeds up to 9,150 m/sec.) The light-gas gun was first tested in Ames's Janus range, a gas-filled cylinder only 21 ft long, built in the first stages of ballistics research.* The NACA then approved a much larger range for the light-gas gun, to be located near the Janus range in a new building on territory originally reserved for a seaplane towing basin. Such a research tool was no longer much in demand, and in any event, Langley already had one. The new range was in use by 1957.[6]

A fourth major research division had been added by 1957. This division managed the wind tunnels constructed under the unitary plan: the 8- by 7-foot supersonic tunnel, the 9- by 7-foot supersonic tunnel, and the 11-foot transonic tunnel. An operations branch coordinated the running of the tunnels and scheduled tests for the military, industry, and universities. The unitary plan tunnels were much in demand, and placing them in a separate division was an administrative necessity.

Although a fourth research division had been added, the range of research had also greatly expanded and many areas of research still overlapped between divisions. The problems that could have resulted were avoided, or at least alleviated, by routine and informal exchange of information between divisions. To the extent that all the research engineers were aware of their colleagues' projects, all research benefitted.[7]

The last NACA inspection was in 1958, when a big space effort was about to be mounted. No one should be surprised that Ames emphasized to its distinguished visitors the work that was most obviously related to problems of spaceflight. The booklet presented to attendees described high-temperature shock tubes, used to duplicate the high temperatures encountered by a satellite on reentering the Earth's atmosphere. Attention was given to particle accelerators, which directed oxygen and nitrogen particles traveling at speeds of 9,300 km/hr at various metal surfaces. The purpose was to study the erosion effects, or surface pitting. Ames also emphasized its studies on stability control for satellites and its investigations of satellite equipment that would perform tasks of measurement, observation, and directional control. Space vehicles, the various methods of propulsion, reentry problems, and landing problems were named as projects under study. The heating problems of high-speed, high-altitude flight were narrated, and attention was drawn to the hypervelocity ballistic range and the atmosphere-entry simulator. The new pebble-bed heaters, which made possible the study of aerodynamic heating on larger models, were proudly described.[8]

It is interesting to compare the inspection booklet of 1958 with the more balanced treatment accorded Ames research of the period by Edwin

*The Janus range had been named after Charters's light-gas gun, which ejected a reaction piston from the rear of the driving tube as the compressed helium, bursting into the launch tube, fired the model.

Hartman's history of the laboratory. While the inspection sought to emphasize the space-oriented direction of Ames research — indeed, that of the entire NACA — Hartman makes clear that the space-connected research was part of a continuum that had logically followed the increase in speed and altitude. Equally important was research into problems of lower speeds and altitudes. While the NACA was insisting on its ability to lead the new space agency and was therefore underlining its many contributions in space-related research, Ames and the other NACA laboratories were also pursuing less dramatic projects, such as the V/STOL studies, which would be of importance long into the space age.

Two research projects of 1956–1958 deserve particular attention. The first was the Air Force's Dynasoar project, an intriguing and farsighted design to put man into space. It illustrates the combination of research ideas, some from the military, some from the NACA, in the search for solutions to the problems of upper-atmosphere flight. As the next step beyond the X-15 research airplane, Dynasoar was to have been rocket-launched and powered to the upper limits of the atmosphere. Then it would glide, being equipped also with wings — hence the designation *boost-glide vehicle.*

At Ames, Harvey Allen, Alvin Seiff, and Alfred Eggers were involved in some of the many advisory groups that worked with the Air Force, investigating the possibilities of the idea. Allen's earlier ballistics work had interested him in the boost stage of the project, while his blunt-body work had also involved consideration of reentry.

Ames had already produced, in 1955–1956, a study on the alternatives under consideration for high-speed, high-altitude, manned flight.[9] Three general directions seemed feasible: a ballistic missile combined with a nonlifting reentry body; a boost-glide vehicle, such as Dynasoar; or a supersonic airplane with greater speed than had yet been produced. The Ames study, which influenced Air Force commitment to the Dynasoar project, suggested many advantages for the boost-glide idea. Compared to a ballistic vehicle, boost-glide gave greater lifting ability and a high lift-drag ratio. This would allow it to achieve greater range for a given initial boost velocity. Being able to control its angle of attack gave control over the rate at which the vehicle would heat, while maneuverability was an advantage in landing the vehicle. The boost-glide vehicle could be kept in the atmosphere or boosted beyond it, opening further possibilities for variation in the concept. The study participants visualized a vehicle with blunt, highly swept wings, hoping to control the reentry heating problem by controlling the rate of descent.[10]

In 1957 the Air Force initiated Project Dynasoar, and Ames personnel were to remain involved until the project was abandoned in 1963, when attention turned instead to a manned orbiting laboratory. Dynasoar illustrates a very successful civilian-military collaboration that used the results of research already initiated to provide a possible answer to very practical problems posed by military needs. Though the project itself was eventually dropped, the boost-glide concept was important to future research.

At the same time, Ames engineers began their own research on lifting bodies. This work grew out of the old problem of reentry heating, combined with the additional problems that accompanied manned flight. It was necessary to control, by some method, the hurtle through the atmosphere that produced such tremendous heat acting upon the flight vehicle. As one of the main researchers explained, "the idea really was to get enough drag ratio into the entry body to permit it to move laterally."[11] This characteristic would control the rate of deceleration during reentry. Clarence Syvertson, one of the earliest researchers involved, described the evolution of the lifting-body research that eventually resulted in the M2F2 reentry vehicle:

> The Dynasoar . . . was conceived to be a manned vehicle. But the experience that Al [Eggers], Harvey [Allen], and others had gained in the study of ballistic missiles indicated . . . that there

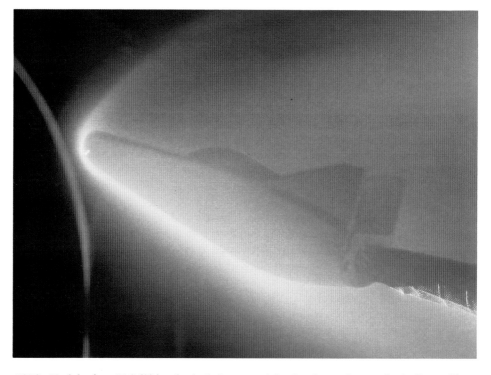

1962. Model of an M-2 lifting body being tested in the Ames Atmospheric Entry Simulator. Obviously, reentry heating would be a problem for the M-2; the tests illustrated the areas of most intense heat and the airflow patterns around the lifting body.

76

would be advantages of having a manned vehicle that didn't have wings, that didn't have a lot of surface area you had to protect from entry heating. . . . if you could find a way to combine . . . lift and high drag, lift to reduce the decelerations under reentry, . . . and bluntness to keep the heating problem under control, . . . you'd have something that would be fairly attractive.[12]

Early studies produced the M-1 shape, considered but not chosen for the Apollo vehicle. Work on the M-1 and Dynasoar led to development of the M-2 lifting body, a shape that had been studied for some time before NASA was created. As Syvertson remembered, "at the first meeting of the Center directors that we had, we prepared a demonstration model and a little pitch for Smitty [De France] to use when he went to it. It was based on the M-2 and we were pretty well along."[13]

In designing the M-2, the researchers first determined the lift-drag ratio necessary to permit the body to move laterally between two paths. Having arrived at that, a shape was calculated that would produce that ratio. The original shape was subsequently modified to make the lifting body landable. The shapes that were produced were imaginatively named:

One they called the African Queen . . . because it had a retractable wing that popped [out] on the back end and when it was up it looked like the boat . . . that Humphrey Bogart and Katharine

1969. An M-2 F-2 lifting body in flight at Edwards Air Force Base, with an F-104 in chase. The lifting body remained an attractive concept in the assortment of spaceflight possibilities for a number of years.

77

Hepburn had used in that movie. . . . Finally, they came up with . . . boat-tailing the back end of the body, making the top surface shape somewhat like an airfoil and putting the vertical fins on as end plates. That was known as the Cadillac version because it looked like the tail fins on a Cadillac at that time. From that evolved the M-2.[14]

Ames was an early proponent of the lifting-body idea for use in space-craft. As space ventures became more complex, after the formation of NASA and the first efforts in space, the idea became ever more attractive. A major advantage was that it permitted a wider entry corridor, thereby simplifying the navigation task. Providing control over heating and acceleration, it would also widen choices for landing sites, making possible a solid-earth landing. Ten years after the first work on lifting bodies began, Ames collaborated in the building of a low-speed prototype.[15]

Both Dynasoar and the lifting bodies illustrate the cross-fertilization that often occurs in research, when ideas or findings from one investigation are successfully applied in another. The involvement of Ames engineers in Dynasoar influenced Ames's own work on lifting bodies. The lifting-body research was a logical progression of building upon past knowledge, and though not specifically mission-oriented at the time, was undoubtedly part of the 29% of Ames's research that the NACA categorized in 1957 as "space-related."[16]

The thin line drawn between space-related and non-space-related aeronautics is similar to that drawn between civilian and military concerns in the field. Though the NACA had always stressed its civilian purpose and character, its inception (as later that of Ames) coincided with a military crisis. Because the line *was* a thin one, Ames was often brought into the news in connection with military matters.

Though the NACA had always been noted as a government agency that did a lot with a small budget, money was a real problem until the advent of NASA. At times the money issue was taken up as a political refrain, such as in 1952 during the Korean conflict, when a congressional candidate used Ames as the focus of a patriotic campaign speech:

> In [this laboratory] may be found the solution to the problem which faces every mother and father within the sound of my voice who has a boy in Korea or one who may eventually land in Korea. Tyranny must be suppressed and all that we hold dear in life is at stake in our efforts to stem the rising tide of communism. . . . As I walked through those laboratories and saw those scientists at work on intricate model parts, I thought to myself, that man at that bench may be the one who will save my two older boys, now

approaching draft age, from the fate so many boys are meeting in Korea. If so, the $25,000,000 currently being spent for a new laboratory out there will be a small price to pay and I as a tax-payer will gladly meet that expense.[17]

The unitary-plan wind tunnels, to which the speaker referred, had greatly increased the capacity for testing at Ames. But Ames faced, in 1956–1958, another paralyzing problem. Manpower was lacking and had been ever since Ames had existed. By 1956 the laboratory was truly suffering from its inability to keep pace with industrial salaries, and it had lost a number of important research minds in the mid-1950s as a result.[18] The military suffered much less, for most of its aeronautical research was done by contracting with the private sector, and funds were available for contracting. In early 1956, Representative Charles Gubser brought up the problem on the floor of the House of Representatives. Though campaigning for funds for the entire NACA, he used Ames as an example, since the laboratory lay within his district. During his speech, he quoted extensively from a letter he had solicited from De France.[19]

De France focused on the government pay scale and how it affected both the obtaining and the retaining of high-quality professional personnel at Ames. At a time when scientific and engineering graduates were in short supply, industry was outbidding the government, "making it increasingly difficult for us to recruit college graduates and virtually impossible to recruit the outstanding graduates." In 1955 Ames had been able to recruit only 33 professional graduates, none of them in the upper portion of their classes. The reason, he held, was the disparity between the starting salaries that industry offered and the government pay scale. Ames could not even compete with the pay scales of state and local government.*

De France then took up the problem of retaining professionals. After citing specific offers from industry to Ames personnel in 1956, he observed that the offers had averaged a 50% increase. During the year Ames had lost 13 engineers to industry. Although losses had as yet been light, he thought they would increase. As De France saw it, the major advantage that the NACA had traditionally offered professionals had been the environment in which they worked. Not only were the NACA's research facilities unparalleled, but researchers had enjoyed colleagues of eminence and an easy association with nearby universities. In the case of Ames, Stanford's proximity had been a real factor in the laboratory's ability to retain its research complement in the face of more lucrative offers from industry.

---

*While the government offered $4,345 and a GS-5 grade to graduates with bachelor's degrees, industry was offering roughly $4,860. For outstanding graduates, competitive bidding among industrial firms pushed the starting salaries to $5,700.

79

The director of Ames foresaw a gloomy future, however, predicting that once the salary discrepancy became too wide to ignore, even the most loyal of his staff would resign. He urged that the crisis be "forcibly" brought to the attention of Congress, reminding members that the same conclusions had already been drawn by one of their own commissions.[20]

By 1957, Smith De France (seated) could well be proud of the laboratory he had built and shaped. In an almost jovial mood, he examines an award marking his 35 years with the NACA, while Associate Director Jack Parsons looks on. Meanwhile, Ames continued with high-speed aerodynamic research that eased America's entry into the space age.

Any picture of Ames in the immediate pre-NASA period contains contrasts. On the one hand, much research that was to be essential to the early space projects was being produced at the laboratory by a band of scientists and engineers who had obviously remained actively and enthusiastically involved in their work. On the other hand, some researchers had left the laboratory for greener pastures, and it was expected that more would go. For a 15-year-old institution, Ames was still relatively free from the bureaucratic arteriosclerosis that often appears after the first years of growth are over. Ames had, however, become considerably more complicated than in its

80

earlier years, and this had perhaps been an element in the resignations of some of the original Ames employees, men who remembered the first days of excitement and unstructured but effective management. Ames faced serious challenges in 1957, but also had many strengths, both in the quality and range of its research facilities and in its personnel.

THE NACA IN 1957

The NACA as a whole faced many of the problems that Ames had to deal with on a smaller scale. One was money. In his 1957 report to Congress, Chairman James H. Doolittle observed:

> Modest increases in appropriations for research have been largely offset by rising costs, so that the amount of research accomplished relative to that required has been diminishing when it should be increasing. In addition, the current pay structure, fixed by law, makes it more and more difficult to retain irreplaceable top rank research scientists and engineers. . . . The general level of the NACA research effort compared to that of the Soviets [has] lessened when it should be increasing. Thus, America's relative position in aeronautical science has been deteriorating. There is an urgent need at this time for a genuine increase in the level of research effort.[21]

The NACA had reason to complain. The preceding decade has seen major changes in the way aeronautical research was conducted. Before World War II, the NACA had been the major institution involved in basic research in the field. The war had temporarily deflected its research laboratories into specific problem-solving connected to wartime demands. After the war, the NACA intended to return to basic research, but the environment had changed. Industry and the military, especially the newly created Air Force, also began major research efforts. Where once only the NACA owned truly sophisticated facilities that could be used on a wide range of problems, now aircraft companies and military research establishments (particularly the Air Force's Tullahoma facility) could conduct research along the same lines as the NACA. Cooperation and collaboration certainly existed among the various groups on a practical level, but the NACA had become only one of several aeronautical research groups. All factions felt the urgent need to mount a national space effort and an equally urgent desire to be in the forefront of that effort. Competition naturally existed, especially between the NACA and the Air Force, each attempting, especially during

1956–1957, to achieve leadership in the race for speed and altitude. The Air Force's Dynasoar project and the Ames work on lifting bodies were different approaches to the problem.

In the period immediately preceding the launch of *Sputnik* in 1957, one of the NACA's strengths was its low-key reputation and its history of steady contributions to aeronautics. In the civilian arena, it had been pre-eminent for over 40 years. De France was a fitting representative of the agency — serious and professional, perhaps conservative, but undeniably effective.

The NACA had been planned as an "independent federal agency." The original members of the Committee (from the War Department, the Navy Department, the Smithsonian Institution, the Weather Bureau, the Bureau of Standards, and some from outside the government) were appointed by the President on the basis of their aeronautical interest or expertise. Unpaid and reporting directly to the President, the Committee elected its own chairman and appointed an executive committee, which managed day-to-day activities. Technical committees and subcommittees kept abreast of needs and developments in the various areas of aeronautics and advised where the NACA's modest budget might best be spent. Shortly after its formation, the Committee had appointed a paid director for research. As such, George Lewis had run the NACA almost singlehandedly over 20 years. He had been succeeded in 1947 by Hugh Dryden, who had attained scientific prominence at the Bureau of Standards. Lewis's style had been direct and effective. His hand always on the tiller of the smaller organization and operating in less complicated times, he had remained directly involved in all aspects of the NACA, from research to congressional lobbying. Hugh Dryden was very different, and the tone of the NACA changed when he became director. Teamed with Jerome Hunsaker, the chairman of the NACA until 1956, Dryden had sought to revitalize the organization in order to meet the many postwar challenges. Administratively, Dryden's assumption of command meant the regularization of many procedures that had been as highly irregular as those at Ames. Where Lewis had been singlehanded and forceful, Dryden was bureaucratic and methodical. His improvements were many, but his image was decidedly undynamic.[22]

The NACA had experienced other changes that eroded its prewar image of disinterested professionalism. By 1957 industry's influence on the technical committees and subcommittees had blurred the NACA's nonpartisan reputation, though in fact evidence of conflicts of interest were lacking. In 1957 the Army was admitted to the Main Committee of the NACA over stiff opposition by some members.[23] At the end industry and the military were filling nearly 70% of the technical committee and subcommittee memberships, a far cry from their minimal representation of earlier years.[24]

Though the NACA had been stressing the need, since the end of World War II, to return to basic research, this aim seems to have been impractical. As industry and the military exerted more influence over the NACA and undertook active research projects of their own, the NACA became involved in a series of investigations stemming from industrial and military sources. By the late 1950s over half its work was generated by specific military requests,[25] and industrial requests were not insignificant. Thus by 1957 the NACA was in many ways a service institution. Though its research contributions had been many, it was less independent than formerly — and perhaps less farsighted because of its lessened independence.

The statistics were impressive, however. With a budget of over $100 million and 8,000 employees, the NACA had, aside from its headquarters organization, five research installations. Besides Langley, Ames, and Lewis laboratories, it also maintained the High-Speed Flight Research Station at Edwards Air Force Base and the pilotless aircraft research station at Wallops Island, Virginia. The NACA would be a strong contender for a leading role in the national space program, even though its unique position was less clear-cut than it had been in its earlier years.

THE BEGINNINGS OF THE SPACE PROGRAM

The International Geophysical Year, a cooperative endeavor proclaimed for 1957–1958, demonstrated the competitive aspects of space-related research. As the IGY was being planned in 1954, Wernher von Braun, of the Army Ballistic Missile Agency, had proposed a satellite project. He argued convincingly that such a project was feasible, and a joint Army-Navy effort, Project Orbiter, was initiated. The Air Force too had developed a satellite proposal, and by the end of 1954 a three-way rivalry among Army, Navy, and Air Force was under way. The endorsement of a satellite by the international committee for IGY in late 1954 only reinforced the conviction, shared by both military and civilian scientists alike, that launching an artificial satellite was both possible and necessary.[26]

When the plans of the three military branches were reviewed, the Navy plan, which used a Viking rocket with two additional stages, was favored. The Air Force plan had been eliminated because it could interfere with ICBM development, an early example of the clash between science and military necessity in the U.S. space program. Over Army objections, the Navy plan was approved in September 1955 and Project Vanguard was authorized.

From the beginning Vanguard suffered from the Eisenhower administration's commitment to economy and the determination of the Department of Defense to give first priority to the development of military technology.

The Army, though it had lost support for the Project Orbiter plan, did not abandon its Redstone booster. By the summer of 1957, the Army Ballistic Missile Agency had used a Redstone-Jupiter C missile in a launch that clearly demonstrated the feasibility of orbiting a satellite. As the Navy's Vanguard continued to falter, the Army pressed for authorization to begin a crash satellite program of its own. The DOD, determined to consider the satellite purely scientific, refused to approve Army involvement, since it would be using military-mission hardware. Lt. Gen. James Gavin, the deputy chief of the Army Office of Research and Development, had his knuckles rapped several times for continuing the campaign.[27]

The administration continued to give the satellite program low priority and to maintain that the United States was not in a race with the Soviet Union for the first launch. As the summer progressed, there were numerous hints that a Soviet attempt was imminent. On 4 October 1957 *Sputnik* was successfully launched into orbit, and the administration began a months-long attempt to minimize its significance.

The reaction of the American public put the Republican administration in an awkward position. Public opinion saw *Sputnik* as a political and military victory for the U.S.S.R. and questioned why the United States had allowed itself to be beaten. The administration temporarily denied the military significance of *Sputnik* and repeated that the United States was not in a race. Eisenhower maintained that his national security apprehensions had not been raised "one iota."[28]

Though Eisenhower and his administration kept a calm front for some months, it was clear that a major effort in space had to be mounted. Ordering a stepped-up missile program, the administration consulted a number of advisers on the best course to take. As one scholar has observed, "*Sputnik* signaled the reappearance of the scientists as important members of the national political system, but with uncertain objectives."[29] Two competing approaches were available. One assumed that the importance of space lay in the military superiority it might give to those who could operate there. The other saw major scientific significance in space exploration, viewing the challenge as technological rather than military. Several organizations contended for management of the new space program.

Needless to say, the DOD considered itself the prime candidate for leadership, and in February 1958 the Office of the Secretary of Defense announced the formation of a new agency to direct and coordinate "certain advanced Research and Development projects"; the Advanced Research Projects Agency had the explicit mission of developing space projects.[30] ARPA was an interim arrangement to handle space projects until the administration had decided upon the final form the national space program would take. As might have been expected, the DOD continued to argue against the wisdom of a civilian agency's controlling the space program.

DOD was not, however, a monolithic institution. The services, retaining their distinctive interests on the issue of space exploration, presented three solutions to the question.[31] The Navy was embarrassed and discouraged about the Vanguard project, which had experienced two launch failures and numerous setbacks before a successful launch in March 1958. Not seeing space as either militarily essential or a naval preserve, the Navy seemed quite content to maintain a low interest in space research. The Project Vanguard director stressed the need for a centralized space effort, whether within DOD or not.

The Army favored a centralized military agency — ARPA. If space research were spread out among the services, the Army believed the Air Force would remain most influential, even though the Army's launch of *Explorer 1,* the first American satellite, gave the Army real standing in the contest.

Among the services, the Air Force had the strongest claim for leadership: space was only an extension of the Earth's atmosphere, its traditional domain. Also, the Air Force had been involved in space research for 20 years, though most of the work had been classified and was therefore not publicly known. With what seemed a clear prerogative in space, the Air Force was unwilling to surrender its interest to ARPA. From the beginning, therefore, ARPA was only one contender among many.

Meanwhile the administration had been bombarded with proposals by civilian groups. One of the major ones was submitted jointly by the American Rocket Society and the Rocket and Satellite Research Panel, a prestigious group of scientists and engineers from inside and outside the government. The panel, at the time headed by Dr. James Van Allen, had been involved in rocket research since the late 1940s.[32] The proposal supported a civilian National Space Establishment for research and exploration, separate from DOD but to be supported by all three services. DOD should have complete control of all military space matters. The assumption that the civilian and military aspects of space could be easily separated proved to be too optimistic.[33]

As might have been expected, the NACA had also been much involved in the question of the national space effort. Though the NACA's reputation had been made in aeronautics, and though the NACA retained a commitment to research in low-speed, low-altitude aeronautics, its involvement in space research, whether independently or as part of cooperative ventures with the military, had been growing steadily. If the NACA had no part in the emerging space program, it would lose importance; but leadership of the new program, which promised to be massive, would change the institution drastically. As a small, committee-run agency with a dubious organizational structure, the NACA was not administratively equipped to assume leadership of the space program. Dryden knew this and polled many of the younger

NACA personnel, soliciting advice concerning the NACA's future.[34] They were strongly in favor of the NACA pressing on for a strong role in the space program.

The result was a proposal of 14 January 1958, the "Dryden Plan" as it came to be called. The director of the NACA called for a cooperative space effort involving DOD, the National Academy of Science, the National Science Foundation, and a greatly expanded NACA. The NACA Main Committee, enlarging on Dryden's proposal, called for a doubling of the NACA staff over three years, as well as a doubling of its yearly budget.[35]

THE ESTABLISHMENT OF NASA

The NACA was supported in its proposal by two other groups. One was the President's Science Advisory Council, which had already decided that a civilian agency must control the space program, lest scientific objectives be subordinated. One of the members of the council, and undoubtedly influential in its recommendations, was James Doolittle, the NACA chairman. The Bureau of the Budget (BOB) saw enlarging an existing institution as cheaper than creating a new one to manage space activities. Another factor in BOB support was probably the NACA's reputation as a relatively low-budget, high-productivity organization.[36]

By March 1958 the administration was drafting legislation to create a civilian space agency based on the NACA as the nucleus. In April, as the legislation that would create NASA went before Congress, the NACA and DOD discussed the reassignment of some military space projects to the new civilian agency.[37] The projects under the sponsorship of the newly created ARPA were transferred to the civilian agency, including Project Vanguard, which had been wrested from the Navy, and various plans for lunar probes.

The National Aeronautics and Space Act passed both houses of Congress on 29 July 1958. As with most legislation, the end product was a compromise that attempted to answer objections voiced in both the House of Representatives and the Senate. The House had been skeptical about the NACA's ability to function as the base for the new agency, because of the NACA's conservative character and close involvement with past military projects. The Senate, on the other hand, feared that the new agency would usurp the military exploitation of space and wanted a clearly delineated distinction of authority.[38] Influential in the Senate position was Majority Leader Lyndon Johnson, who had led the Democratic attack on the Eisenhower administration for failure to anticipate *Sputnik* with a more dynamic space policy. In the end the Act contained clauses that asserted DOD supremacy in military space matters and provided for a National Aeronautics and Space Council to coordinate aeronautical and space activities among all agencies of the government. The council would contain government administrators, military advisers, and private citizens. Thus Congress hoped to provide for space activities in both civilian and military arenas, while reducing duplication of effort.

Before the Act went into effect on 1 October 1958, an administrator had to be chosen for NASA. Though many had assumed that Hugh Dryden as director of the NACA would automatically head the new agency, he evidently appeared too conservative for Congress.[39] The nomination went to T. Keith Glennan, at the time president of Case Institute of Technology. Dryden was named deputy administrator, a crucial position dependent on technical expertise. Both men were sworn in in mid-August. The appointment of the outsider Glennan was to be a factor in the transition of the NACA into NASA, and in the acceptance of the new regime by NACA personnel.[40]

On the face of things, the transition was smoothly accomplished. NASA acquired not only the ARPA projects, but lunar probes and satellite projects originally begun by the Army Ballistic Missile Agency (ABMA). The Jet Propulsion Laboratory at Cal Tech, part of the Army's missile development program, was transferred to NASA in late 1958, when NASA also gained access to ABMA's Development and Operations Division, von Braun's talented team, without prior Pentagon approval. With Project Vanguard, NASA also acquired the personnel from the Naval Research Laboratory who were attached to the project. By the end of 1958, NASA personnel numbered 8,420.[41]

At Ames the 1 October conversion was accomplished without fanfare. De France issued a typically restrained memorandum documenting the transition from NACA to NASA, from Ames Aeronautical Laboratory to Ames Research Center. When NASA's first organizational chart was issued in January 1959, Ames found itself, along with Langley, Lewis, and the High-Speed Flight Station, under the authority of the associate administrator for aeronautical and space research.

SOURCE NOTES

Chapter 4. The Formation of NASA, 1958

[1] This observation is based on conversations with a number of older employees.

[2] Russell G. Robinson interview, 30 Sept. 1981.

[3] The story was related by an Ames employee present at the time.

[4] See chap. 3. Alan E. Fayé interview, 1 Apr. 1981.

[5] Edwin P. Hartman, *Adventures in Research: A History of the Ames Research Center, 1940-1965*, NASA SP-4302 (Washington, 1970), pp. 186-187, 262-263.

[6] Ibid., pp. 195, 234-235.

[7] This observation has been made by many employed at Ames during the period.

[8] The description of the 1958 Ames inspection is drawn from the inspection program and booklet issued at the time. The booklet emphasizes the entire NACA much more than earlier editions, perhaps because the NACA at this time was fighting for all possible influence in the forming of the new space agency. Edith Watson Kuhr files, Ames Research Center.

[9] Alfred J. Eggers, Jr., H. Julian Allen, and Stanford E. Neice, *A Comparative Analysis of the Performance of Long-Range Hypervelocity Vehicles*, NACA TN 1382, 1958.

[10] Hartman, *Adventures in Research*, pp. 267-268.

[11] Clarence A. Syvertson interview by Walter Bonney, 25 Sept. 1974, NASA History Office, Washington.

[12] Ibid.

[13] Ibid.

[14] Ibid.

[15] Hartman, *Adventures in Research*, pp. 252-253.

[16] Robert L. Rosholt, *An Administrative History of NASA, 1958-1963*, NASA SP-4101 (Washington, 1966), p. 29.

[17] Speech by Arthur L. Johnson, candidate for Congress from the 10th District, on Radio KEEN, 7 May 1952. 63-A-224, box 6630, SBFRC.

[18] Hartman, *Adventures in Research*, p. 221.

[19] *Congressional Record*, 26 Jan. 1956, extension of remarks of Hon. Charles S. Gubser of California in the House of Representatives.

[20] De France was quoting a report of the Subcommittee on Research Activities, part of the Commission on Organization of the Executive Branch of the Government, made in Apr. 1955.

[21] James H. Doolittle, letter of submittal, 1 Oct. 1957, *43rd Annual Report of the NACA, 1957* (Washington, 1958).

[22] See Alex Roland, "Research by Committee" (unpublished manuscript, Apr. 1980), Chapter 10.

[23] Ibid., p. 415.

[24] Ibid., p. 417.

[25] Ibid., p. 417-418.

[26] Enid Curtis Bok Schoettle, "The Establishment of NASA," in Sanford A. Lakoff, *Knowledge and Power: Essays on Science and Government* (New York: The Free Press, 1966), pp. 164–173.

[27] Ibid., pp. 171–172.

[28] *New York Times,* 10 Oct. 1957, p. 1.

[29] Lakoff, *Knowledge and Power,* p. 181.

[30] Ibid., p. 197

[31] Ibid., pp. 199–213.

[32] See Homer E. Newell, *Beyond the Atmosphere: Early Years of Space Science,* NASA SP-4211 (Washington, 1980), pp. 34–36, for a brief history and description of the Rocket and Satellite Research Panel.

[33] Lakoff, *Knowledge and Power,* pp. 215–216.

[34] Rosholt, *An Administrative History of NASA,* pp. 34–35.

[35] Lakoff, *Knowledge and Power,* p. 234.

[36] Ibid., p. 238.

[37] Rosholt, *Administrative History of NASA,* p. 38.

[38] Lakoff, *Knowledge and Power,* pp. 247–249.

[39] See Rosholt, *Administrative History of NASA,* pp. 40–41, and Lakoff, *Knowledge and Power,* p. 247.

[40] See chap. 6.

[41] Rosholt, *Administrative History of NASA,* p. 48.

5

THE LIFE SCIENCES DIRECTORATE

The establishment of NASA ultimately transformed the character of Ames. Some of the changes came slowly and surreptitiously; only over a period of years would older NACA personnel realize how the laboratory had changed as they noted, for example, the differences between long-duration topical research and the new, mission-oriented projects. Project management — goal-oriented and time-limited — was a product of NASA's mission to assure American supremacy in the space race and, after 1961, to put a man on the moon before the end of the decade. Project work was also the result of the political constraints placed upon the agency. Not only did announced goals need to be met, but NASA had to justify itself as it proceeded toward them. The political overtones and the pressure to perform on a strict time schedule made project work quite different from the older kinds of research, which had been at least potentially open-ended and less constrained by hard and fast deadlines.

Other changes noticed at Ames resulted more directly from the higher budgets and larger physical size of the center, which were accompanied by several new complexities. NASA Headquarters originally did not differ much from the old NACA scheme of things. A few more personnel were interspersed in the line of command, perhaps, but since in the early months of NASA many old hands remained in still-recognizable positions, the transition began smoothly. But administrative and organizational changes in the early years soon redefined Ames's relationship with Headquarters, creating more labyrinthine routes to any final implementation of decisions. This was not so much a specific NASA problem as it was the problem of any new, large, and rich organization that was responsible to elected representatives of a reasonably sophisticated population. In short, it is hard to conceive how NASA could have embarked upon its gargantuan task without a great increase in bureaucratic complexity.

Ames was perhaps a passive recipient of some of the change that NASA bestowed. There was no way to avoid either increased administrative entanglements or task-oriented research. The research center adjusted to such changes gradually, in some cases with grace, in some cases awkwardly. But in other instances Ames management actively attempted to reshape the center according to the new demands and interests. In establishing the Life Sciences Directorate, it is very evident that top Ames management saw the addition as a potential transfusion, endowing Ames with another resource to bolster its faltering aeronautical investment. The Life Sciences Directorate represented a positive response on the part of De France to a changed environment, and though its grafting onto the existing institution was a difficult process, life sciences seems to have been a much-wanted addition to Ames, at least on the part of the Ames administration.*

LIFE SCIENCES COMES TO NASA

In July 1959 NASA Administrator Glennan appointed Dr. Clark Randt, a former colleague at Case Western Reserve University, as his adviser for life sciences. Space presented both a new medium for bioscientific research and a new set of physical demands on human trespassers. In the early stages of Project Mercury, the first U.S. manned space project, NASA cooperation with DOD left responsibility for human factors with the Air Force, but Glennan felt it was important to define NASA's own long-term interests in the life sciences.

Drawing further on the academic community, Glennan formed a Biosciences Advisory Committee, on which Randt sat as NASA's representative, to advise on NASA's life-science needs and possible ways to meet them within the framework of the agency. Over the next six months, under the chairmanship of Dr. Seymour Kety, the committee studied the existing relationship between NASA and DOD, evaluated the demands that space operations would place on NASA in the life sciences, and composed a report with very specific recommendations for a course of action.

The January 1960 Kety Committee report deserves examination, because many who were drawn into NASA's life-sciences efforts regarded it as a solid document for future planning, agreed with its basic assumptions, and believed that its recommendations needed to be acted upon. First, the committee identified three major areas in which work was needed:

*Although heads of the major research groups were called Assistant Directors, and had been since the early 1950s, the term "directorate" did not appear on organization charts until the mid-1960s. Whereas Harold Klein was originally called Assistant Director for Life Sciences, he later became, in the same job, Head of the Life Sciences Directorate. For simplicity, I use the term somewhat anachronistically.

1. Basic biologic effects of extraterrestrial environments . . .
and identification of complex organic or other molecules in
planetary atmospheres which might be precursors or evidence of
extraterrestrial life;

2. Medical and behavioral aspects of medicine and biology as
related to manned space flight; and

3. Medical and behavioral scientific problems concerned with
more fundamental investigation of metabolism, nutrition, etc.,
in space equivalent situations.

As is evident from the distinctions drawn in the report, the committee
believed NASA needed far more from life sciences than simply operational
support for manned spaceflight. The first category dealt with bioscientific
questions that were not necessarily human-related, and the third category,
though dealing with human responses to space, defined medical, phycho-
logical, and behavioral issues in a much more general manner. As the committee saw it, NASA had the opportunity to involve itself deeply in the
larger questions of life-science research in a space environment. In the same
vein, the committee urged the establishment of a central facility to guide and
carry out research in the three areas of inquiry. Both Goddard Space Flight
Center and the National Institutes of Health were named as possible sites for
such a facility.

Administratively the Kety Committee made equally specific recommendations. NASA was urged to establish a Life Sciences Programs Office reporting to NASA's head administrators and not subordinate to the existing
program offices (the Office of Launch Vehicle Programs, the Office of Space
Flight Programs, and the Office of Advanced Research Programs), which
were under the direct control of the associate administrator. The Kety Committee believed that as a program office itself, life sciences would contribute
to and coopcrate with the other three program offices as an equal partner.

The internal organization of the life-sciences program was to be
arranged according to the three areas of investigation that had been defined.
Interestingly, the Kety Committee specified intramural and extramural sections of the office, the extramural section being that concerned with outside
contract research. A clear distinction was thereby postulated between
in-house research and contract research, though as life sciences evolved, especially at Ames, this distinction would not hold. The program, as the committee saw it, would be weighted heavily toward in-house work. Advisory committees drawn from outside NASA would guide the intramural program, and
maximum integration with universities and academic colleagues would be
sought.

The Kety Committee's firm belief in a broad program with authority
and resources to deal with both present needs and future demands was

clearly stated even as it paid lip service to NASA's immediate space effort, Project Mercury. In concluding its comments concerning the intramural activities of the life-sciences program office, the committee stated: "The present research effort . . . within NASA appears to be concentrated upon a single specific goal, exemplified by Project Mercury, at the possible expense of broader, more remote, but fundamental aims. It is important that the bio-medical aspects of the Project be placed squarely under the jurisdiction of the Office of Life Sciences and that it be coordinated with other aspects of the Life Sciences Program."[1] The report concluded with budget estimations and the plea that NASA commit itself to holding its own against life-science activities in the armed forces, especially the Air Force, already linked with Project Mercury. Money could not be used skimpily; the initial effort must be undertaken with an eye to a sturdy foundation.

The Kety Committee made several truly wise observations. First, the three areas of recommended investigation paid due recognition to imme-diate, short-range needs, while clearly naming long-range necessities. Second, suggesting program status for life sciences, they sought to avoid the compe-tition for control of life sciences that later ensued among the original pro-gram offices, competition that created administrative chaos and weakened the program as a whole. Finally, by drawing a clear line between in-house and contract domains, the committee made it potentially easier to create a solid base of research that was the agency's own.

Administrator Glennan accepted the committee's report in late January 1960 and seemed to endorse the recommendations. As Congress was proving sticky in authorizing certain of NASA's funds for FY 1961, Glennan post-poned announcing the establishment of the Life Sciences Programs Office until after the House of Representatives had completed its hearings. Funding was diverted from research money already authorized, and with little con-gressional cross-examination, the new office was added to NASA's three existing program offices.[2] Not surprisingly, Clark Randt was named head of the office. As one Ames life scientist put it, "Life sciences was grafted onto NASA as a whole, almost as an afterthought."[3]

Almost from the beginning, the Office of Life Sciences Programs ran into difficulties. Randt found Glennan reluctant to commit the funding and staffing originally promised. Selecting the site for the life-sciences research facility involved endless wrangling. Perhaps even more maddening was the slow erosion of authority within his own office. When Randt sought involve-ment in Project Mercury's biomedical aspects, as the Kety Committee had recommended, he ran into firm opposition from top NASA administration and from the Office of Space Flight Programs, which controlled Project Mercury. Randt's campaign for biomedical responsibility in post-Mercury programs had a similar result. It was obvious that Randt and his office were regarded as trespassers in territory already claimed by other program offices.

Thwarted in his attempts to implement what he had considered a clear mandate from Glennan, knowing he was unsupported by Deputy Administrator Dryden, and unable to gain the ear of the new NASA administrator, James Webb, Randt resigned a year after he had become the head of the Life Sciences Programs Office. The office itself lasted only five months longer.

LIFE SCIENCES COMES TO AMES

During the first years of NASA's existence, all three former NACA laboratories attempted to revise their facilities, expertise, and — perhaps — images to better compete in the new environment. Though continual lip service was paid to NASA's being built on the foundations of the NACA, managers at the laboratories must have felt a bit overwhelmed by the dramatic changes to what had been a low-key operation. NASA in rapid succession acquired Vanguard,* the Jet Propulsion Laboratory at Pasadena, and von Braun's missile group at Huntsville. The new Goddard Space Flight Center grew like a mushroom. Even those among the old hands who wholeheartedly embraced the new circumstances must have been struck by the size and diversity of the new agency. Harry Goett, who left Ames in 1959 to become Goddard's first director, recalled, "That was one of the biggest changes I had to get used to, from [having] 150 guys working under me, [making deals that involved] $100,000 to [closing] a $10 million . . . deal in an afternoon . . . at Goddard. The difference was that Goddard had a $400 million budget, and Ames [under NACA] didn't."[4]

The centers responded in varying ways. Lewis Research Center entered space-age engine research immediately, making a relatively smooth transition from old demands to new.[5] Langley's Space Task Group, which had been formed under the NACA, quickly assumed a position of prominence as the developer of Project Mercury, NASA's first major effort. Though the Space Task Group was later transferred jurisdictionally to Goddard and then physically to Houston, its Langley origins aided that center's shift to space-related work.

At Ames, the old awareness of geographical separation from NASA Headquarters may have recurred. The period of adjustment is still remembered as awkward by those who had to make major career shifts or risk seeing their areas of expertise become, at least temporarily, backwaters. One Ames research engineer said that the transition

---

*Vanguard was transferred from the Navy to ARPA (DOD) in May 1958, a holding action pending the formation of NASA, which absorbed Vanguard at the outset in October 1958.

did bother some of us who weren't interested in getting into space work. As soon as the 1958 change was made, everybody was supposed to focus on space; people in the Flight Research Branch were asked to list ten items of space-research potential, and if you didn't, you were not well received. Some of us felt that although it was great to move into space, what about aeronautics? It shouldn't stop; there were still plenty of things to do, and we were still interested in doing aeronautics. That transition was hard for some of us. We were being pushed, by higher forces, to make space contributions.[6]

Harry Goett, who *had* gone from low-speed aeronautical research into early flight simulation work — which would become space-connected — was one of those who urged Ames management to get a piece of the space action. Years later he remembered sympathetically how the change had demoralized some aeronautical engineers who saw themselves upstaged by the heavily publicized space projects: "I used to tell them myself, 'Look, the fundamental boundary-layer stuff you've been working on, or this or that, is still just as important as it ever was, but you're not top dog anymore.' "[7]

Eventually aeronautics at Ames would reestablish itself successfully, partly through the continuing work done on V/STOL aircraft, partly through the questions raised in the late 1960s regarding the feasibility of the supersonic transport. In the early 1960s, however, flight research using simulators kept the Full-Scale and Flight Research Division from sinking into complete disfavor while providing a link between aeronautics and astronautics by focusing on the human factor in both. Flight simulation research, with increasingly sophisticated equipment and subtlety of investigation, was one Ames response to the new demands for space-oriented research.

Another area in which existing work helped ease Ames into space research was the automatic guidance and control of aircraft. As Ames researchers became more deeply involved in the electronics of automatic control, their research became increasingly applicable to the control of satellites. This expertise would help Ames acquire both the Biosatellite and Pioneer Projects. Familiarity with automatic control problems gave some Ames engineers greater flexibility in meeting the new research demands. It was probably a factor in the selection of Goett to be director of Goddard.[8]

Though the ability of the center to bend its ongoing research toward space applications helped its standing at Headquarters in the early NASA years, the overwhelming impression at Ames was that NASA was an eastern operation, with most of the exciting activity taking place in the East. Ames needed some singular element that might inject new vitality into the center and distinguish it from other NASA installations. De France was well aware that Ames needed to move with the times, and in early 1960 he began an active campaign to convince NASA Headquarters that his center was the best place for a new life-sciences research facility. In this, as Jack Boyd, later associate director of Ames, theorized, he was probably encouraged by Harvey Allen:

> Harvey knew we couldn't stay as narrow as we had been, and I think he wanted to give us a broader base, in whatever direction we could go, and I think he saw that life sciences was going to be important. . . . we had [already] gotten into simulation, and simulation became an important part of life sciences. If Allen hadn't supported it, I don't think it would have happened as fast.[9]

Far from being thrust upon Ames, life sciences was actively sought by De France, which should be remembered when considering the many problems life sciences subsequently created there.

De France lost no time in establishing his claim to the facility recommended by the Kety Committee. The week after Glennan established the Life Sciences Programs Office in March 1960, he traveled to the West Coast to meet with De France and tour Ames. The new life-sciences program crept into the conversation. De France immediately busied his staff, preparing an unsolicited report pointing out the "many advantages present in our area on which the program might draw."[10] On 11 March, he sent the finished report to Glennan.

The lengthy report makes very clear how badly De France wanted the research facility. While most of the correspondence out of Ames under De France's leadership was dry, to the point, even understated, this report was at times almost florid in praising the unique set of facilities and talents that might be useful to NASA's life-science needs. The report named researchers at local universities and laboratories who were working in areas of general interest to NASA. Institutions mentioned included Stanford University, the University of California at Berkeley, the Palo Alto Medical Center, San Jose State University, and the Lawrence Radiation Laboratory. While much of the research carried on under the auspices of these institutions would certainly dovetail well with NASA's needs, a retrospective reading of the Ames report leads one to question whether any area with several respected universities and some miscellaneous research facilities could not have produced a similar list.

In arguing the relevance of its own facilities and work, the Ames report made a much stronger case. Weightlessness experiments had begun. A series of preliminary studies on pilot behavior and restraint systems had been completed. Simulation studies on stress experienced during flight had been undertaken in cooperation with the Navy, and the report suggested that the simulators could also be used in time-cycle-change research. The Physics

Branch might help with radiation studies, and the Instrumentation Division would prove generally useful in life-sciences research. The concluding arguments stressed the economics of using available land and buildings at Ames, the lure of neighboring industry, and the lovely climate. A copy of the report found its way to Clark Randt's desk.

The arguments that Ames pressed were all perfectly valid reasons for locating a life-sciences facility at the center, but it seems clear that the report was composed hurriedly. While attempting an objective delineation of what was available at Ames and in the surrounding area, the report did "protest too much."

In April Russell Robinson discussed Ames's case with Clark Randt in Washington. Randt told Robinson that "only one NASA center will cover this area joining life sciences and the physical sciences, and that Ames is in the best position to acquire the responsibility." Calling Ames work in simulation and centrifuge studies *biotechnics,* Randt asked that proposals for a research program in biotechnics be sent to him. Robinson came away cautiously hopeful that Ames would be the choice for the facility.[11]

By summer 1960 the competition for the facility had narrowed to Ames and Goddard. Glennan was reputed to favor Ames, perhaps because of his earlier idea to turn Ames into the manned spaceflight center. There was a political hitch, however; the life-sciences laboratory was generally expected to be located close to the manned spaceflight center. That location had not yet been chosen, and there seemed to be strong congressional objections to placing it in California. This difficulty put the choice of Ames into jeopardy.[12] In addition, there was still the idea, mentioned by Randt to Robinson in the spring, that the main life-sciences research facility should be near Washington, to keep close ties with the Office of Life Sciences Programs.[13]

By fall Ames seemed to have been bypassed in favor of Goddard. De France could not have been happy when he received a copy of the proposed Life Sciences Ten Year Plan. Ames was not mentioned in it. Instead the plan urged construction of "a Life Sciences Research Facility for integrated life science activities within the Goddard Space Flight Center."[14] Headquarters seemed to have chosen the eastern option.

What occurred between September and November is unclear, but once again the tables turned. In early November, Clark Randt came to Ames and announced that the life-sciences research facility would be built there. It had been decided "not to await or depend on the final location of the manned spaceflight activity that will evolve from the present Space Task Group."[15]

With the good news, Randt also explained some intricacies that would haunt the new directorate. As a memorandum summarized the discussion:

Dr. Randt pictured the various phases of life science work as shown below, indicating overlapping areas, and by the dotted line, a natural boundary between research effort and development effort. As will be noted, research effort is to be carried out at Ames and the development effort at Space Task Group or its successors.[16]

As everyone concerned was to find out, where overlap began and ended was moot. In addition to the grey area which conceivably both Ames and the Space Task Group could claim, there was another potential difficulty. Obviously, the STG would be more immediately interested in directed research than in basic research. Would that create tension between the two groups? Other elements of the memorandum appeared problematic, and in a way they actually foreshadowed some of the major difficulties Ames would face in the next several years.

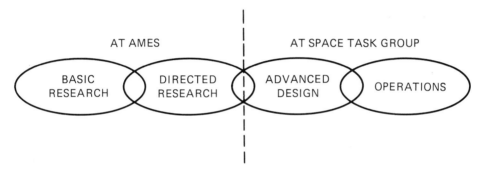

The relationship of the Ames life-sciences group to the rest of Ames and to NASA Headquarters was not to be straightforward. Headquarters cautioned that "no firm commitments on integration with Ames be made at this stage," but suggested that the head of the life-sciences group there be responsible to De France for operational matters and to the Office of Life Science Programs for direction and management of research programs. Thus from the beginning it was foreseeable that life sciences might not fit smoothly into the life of the center. One of the members of Randt's visiting group, stressing the "importance research biologists placed on an academic atmosphere," underlined the difference between "the superficial appearance of an academic atmosphere and the actual attainment of an atmosphere of considerable freedom."[17] Here was another indication that life sciences might become something very different from the older research organizations at Ames.

With this somewhat tentative and cautious beginning, the Ames Life Sciences Directorate came into being.

99

STUDYING THE PROBLEM TO DEATH

In early 1961 Congress approved funds for the life-sciences facility at Ames, and in July Dr. Webb Haymaker, a noted neuropathologist at the Armed Forces Institute of Pathology, was chosen to head the facility. Haymaker did not arrive at Ames until late 1961, and in the meantime the Office of Life Sciences Programs had been abolished. By the time Haymaker took charge at Ames, NASA's life sciences had been divided among the Office of Space Sciences (OSS), the Office of Advanced Research and Technology (OART), and the Office of Manned Space Flight (OMSF). The same November 1961 reorganization placed all the NASA centers under Associate Administrator Seamans.

NASA's problems in initiating an efficient life-sciences program stemmed from a number of factors — competition among the program offices for control of life sciences within their own spheres, the difficulty in convincing Congress that a major effort in basic life-sciences research was needed, the different outlooks on the issue by senior NASA officials, and the academic tone of the advice given by the Kety Committee and Randt. While that advice may have been sound, implementing it within the existing framework of NASA proved almost impossible. There was no obvious place to graft life sciences onto the existing NASA tree. Over the next few years, study groups and individual consultants would analyze the snags in the organization and attempt to develop real solutions to end the turmoil.

In March 1962 Bernard Maggin of the NASA Office of Programs chaired a life-sciences working group that produced a lengthy report on the ills of the program. The recommendation was to place life sciences "programming capability at the Headquarters level to make possible real coordination among the life science elements controlled by the three program offices." OART was named as a likely office to take responsibility for that coordination. The group also recommended that "reasonable technical capability in the field" was to be centered at Ames and NASA should proceed with the construction of the life-science laboratory, making it possible for Ames to double that staff, from 81 to 160, between 1962 and 1963.[18] Though NASA acted on some of the recommendations, it did not allow OART to coordinate work in other program offices, and lack of direction continued to plague the whole program.

In early 1963 Dr. R. W. Gerard, from the University of Michigan, was asked to evaluate the Ames life-science program. In the course of his evaluation (see below), he criticized the whole NASA life-sciences program, making many of the same points that his predecessors had. Later in the year Dr. Eugene Konecci, head of the Biotechnology and Human Research Division within OART, conducted yet another study of life sciences at Ames.

Understandably, Konecci was most concerned with what he saw as inadequate attention to applied research that would directly support manned spaceflight. The failures Konecci identified at Ames, however, reflected Washington's continued failure to provide clear directions in research, as well as the center's resistance to pressure from outside sources — including NASA Headquarters.[19]

Konecci's criticisms, while partially valid, reflected also the continuing struggle within Headquarters to define exactly what NASA required from life sciences, to decide who was to do what, and to set priorities. Just as Konecci was concerned with human factors, so managers of OSS might argue that NASA was not devoting enough effort to space biology and exobiology.[20] The next year, still another survey of the program produced the Life Sciences Directors Group, headed by the director of space medicine under OMSF, Dr. W. Randolph Lovelace. As had been true with past attempts at workable solutions, true coordination remained out of reach; competition continued to create confusion.

In 1969–1970, having received sets of similar recommendations for almost 10 years, NASA made yet another try. The most important measure was the appointment of a single life-sciences director, responsible for coordination of the entire program. Most life-science elements would be under his direction; those located under other NASA groups would be under his review for coordination within the entire program.[21] The change was intended to improve communications between life sciences and the NASA administration, as well as the outside scientific community.

The man picked for the director's position was Dr. Charles Berry, who had been in charge of the medical program for Gemini and Apollo. Highly successful in this position, he was well known in NASA's upper echelons. Although Berry would have his difficulties, his access to top officials would be helpful. Though his own interests were in the manned aspects of Apollo, at least some of the life scientists in the other areas believed his appointment was, on the whole, advantageous.[22]

Under OMSF in 1970, the life-sciences office was transferred to OSS in 1975. Although no change in program content was intended, it is not surprising that biomedical problems received a lower priority in OSS than they had enjoyed in OMSF.

EARLY PROBLEMS AT AMES

In the early 1960s, an observer might well have concluded that life sciences and Ames were not ready for each other. The difficulties were diffuse, some stemming from tangible problems of logistics, some much more subtle. The result was multiple tensions.

From the beginning, the problems that beset life sciences at Headquarters were reflected at Ames. One of these was lack of leadership. Webb Haymaker, though appointed in July 1961 to head the new life-sciences facility, did not arrive at Ames until near the end of the year. Therefore it was not until the beginning of 1962 that he was really familiar with the job. With a program barely defined and with vigorous competition among the interested parties in Headquarters, any director would have found the task formidable, but Haymaker proved an unlucky choice. A strong administrator was needed to shape the Ames program, build a strong relationship with De France and the rest of Ames, and bargain with Headquarters for an important place in the overall scheme of things. Haymaker was unsuited for the role.

The new director, a research-oriented academic, was determined to continue with his own work, studying the effects of cosmic rays on the brain. Flying primates on balloons, Haymaker was often absent from Ames retrieving his experiments or involved in the time-consuming work of brain-tissue analysis. In a situation that called for a leader with an overview of the whole directorate, Haymaker built a strong research team in the neurosciences, his own field, but left his subordinates to manage other areas. Strong-willed and determined to go his own way, he soon ran afoul of De France, equally strong-willed. As a colleague expressed it retrospectively, "De France was really intolerant of managers who didn't manage."[23] The absences of Haymaker and the more orthodox style of his immediate subordinate, Dale Smith, tended to create a dichotomy of administration that newly hired researchers found maddening. Less than two years after he was appointed, Haymaker stepped down from the directorship, though he remained at Ames as a research scientist. After a search of several months, Dr. Harold Klein, then head of the Exobiology Division, agreed to become the new director in January 1964.

Klein proved an effective head of the ailing program. Formerly head of the biology department at Brandeis University, he had originally joined the Ames staff while on sabbatical from his academic post. The challenge of building a smoothly running, well equipped, and productive organization from scratch was not new to him, since Brandeis itself was barely 14 years old. As department head, Klein had been heavily involved with planning facilities, recruiting staff, and raising funds. Realizing that new directorates, like new departments, do not run themselves, Klein attended to day-to-day responsibilities.

Another problem was the set of expectations with which many life scientists arrived at Ames. As originally envisioned by the Kety Committee, NASA's life sciences was to be strongly rooted in the academic community. The appointment of Haymaker, an academic, and the subsequent hiring of the Ames life-sciences staff produced a group of researchers largely drawn from universities. Haymaker and his staff believed that the atmosphere in the directorate would be much the same as at the universities they had left.

This was not true, and the differences manifested themselves in numerous frustrating ways. Freedom to select one's own research problems is a great attraction of academia, and the biologists, chemists, and physicists who arrived at Ames expecting to pursue their own interests exclusively soon found that NASA's needs did not necessarily correspond with their own interests; schedules sometimes forced them to curtail unfinished research and move on to other topics. The civil servant's time clock was an irritant. Academics are noted for irregular working habits and hours, but the research center began the day promptly at 8 and ended it at 5. De France, used to the regulated hours and work habits of a career civil servant, balked at keeping the new life-sciences library open on weekends. He disliked professional seminars during working hours for what he regarded as extracurricular self-improvement.

Another handicap was the lack of centralized facilities, important both for work and for constant interaction with colleagues. Universities routinely locate laboratories and offices close together. Ames management, remembering the laboratory built in the midst of a national emergency and the shoestring budgets on which it had long operated, regarded such niceties as less than essential. Harold Klein spoke of the early difficulties:

> One of the things I wanted to do first was to get my motley crew into one location — they were spread out all over the place. Eventually there was to be a central research laboratory, but I didn't want to wait. So we did a very unorthodox thing — we . . . rented a building on Charleston Road and built some beautiful laboratories. We were down there a couple of years. I had to argue with De France to do it. . . . Later, [after I became head of the directorate] we got our central building, [and] I wanted to have a library in it. De France was adamant — we weren't going to have a library because Ames already had one. Over the library I threatened to quit. De France finally gave in and we got the library.[24]

The newcomers encountered other obstacles to easy integration with Ames. The lack of direction in the life-sciences program left the boundaries of the original three divisions, exobiology, environmental biology, and biotechnology, unclear. Life-sciences funding came from two program offices in Headquarters; this caused a certain inflexibility in transferring money within the directorate, a handicap other Ames directorates did not have.[25] To add to the tension, the 1963 attempt by E. B. Konecci, as head of OART's Biotechnology and Human Research Division, to concentrate on applied research in support of space operations left the space scientists

1964. Dr. Harold P. Klein, Director of Life Sciences, explains a fine point to a visiting congressman. Klein, who headed the directorate for 20 years, built Life Sciences into one of Ames's strongest research areas.

feeling abandoned by Headquarters. In the early years interaction between life sciences and the astronautical and aeronautical directorates remained minimal, reinforcing both the life scientists' sense of isolation and the puzzlement of most everyone else as to what "they," in the white coats, were doing.

The 1963 Gerard report, which De France dismissed angrily as the product of Gerard's wounded feelings at being left out of Biosatellite discussions, appears to have been a sound analysis of the general malaise of the life-sciences program, both within NASA as a whole and specifically at Ames.[26] Proceeding from the general to the embarrassingly specific, the report probably did not reveal much that the life scientists did not already know firsthand.

Gerard's findings only underlined the larger unsolved questions within NASA Headquarters regarding life sciences. On the question of basic research versus applied research, Gerard urged, as had other academic critics, that NASA build an in-house capability that went beyond immediate needs. On the delicate balance between research "anarchy" and set-problem solving, he seemed to address De France: "The Life Sciences Directorate of Ames Research Center, presumably the entire Center, is not intended to be a

104

university-like mosaic of independent scholars and investigators, each pursuing his own intellectual interests; but neither is it intended to be an assembly-line problem-solving factory."[27]

Gerard differentiated between independent and task-oriented research, calling for more specific guidelines on who was to be detailed to what projects. He placed the blame for vagueness just as much on Washington as on Ames higher management. Reviewing project by project the research being supported at Ames, Gerard's general impression was that much of the work was either too imprecisely defined or was not immediately recognizable as sufficiently valuable to merit further support. The program was floundering, and the life scientists were frustrated.

Gerard's report, while it was the first analysis that dealt specifically with Ames, was not singular in its revelations. The problems it defined were those of newness, growth, lack of leadership and direction, and gaps between expectations and realities. Time solved some of the problems with Headquarters, but those of conflicting jurisdiction remained. Over the following years, Harold Klein bridged many of the early differences between Ames management and life-sciences personnel. As the new director of life sciences at Ames saw it, he helped to open the center to a more flexible mode of operation, as well as to make the work atmosphere less frustrating for his staff.

The latter half of the 1960s and early 1970s found life sciences progressing in a much more organized fashion. The organization, after its early traumas, steadily established its reputation as an important segment of NASA's research strength. During Apollo, Ames supported Houston in many of the biomedical areas and became heavily involved in the chemical and biological analysis of lunar samples. During Project Viking, Klein headed the biology team which planned experiments on Mars and analyzed the resulting data. As valuable research began to appear, the life-sciences directorate, by the end of 1965 housed in its own research facility, slowly came into its own part of the Ames community.

LIFE SCIENCES ACCEPTED – MORE OR LESS

For the young researchers who joined the life-sciences activity in the mid-1960s, many of the early problems were not particularly evident.[28] The new laboratory helped to strengthen feelings of integration within the directorate itself and to establish life sciences as a permanent and tangible entity at Ames. In the halcyon years of relatively plush funding, Klein gathered equipment and facilities with an eye to the future. By the 1970s, Ames had an impressive array of sophisticated research tools, including human and animal centrifuges, electron microscopes, mass spectrometers, a variety of well stocked laboratories, and a life-sciences library that could compete with those in academia. The equipment-buying policy, "loading us up wherever I could find a nickel," Director Klein recalled,[29] made it possible to continue to attract excellent staff, lured by research equipment better than that at most universities. The situation was similar to that of the prewar NACA, which had possessed the best assortment of aeronautical research tools in the country, and thereby attracted fine research talent. Dr. Harold Sandler of the Biomedical Research Division told a story familiar to Ames since its earliest years:

> I came from the University of Washington, trained in cardiovascular disease and physiology. I'd been drafted and sent to the Naval Air Development Center at Johnsville, Pennsylvania, which had the largest human centrifuge. I [used it to study] how the heart functions under gravitational loads. . . . After I went back to the University of Washington and research funding was hard to come by, I got a phone call from an [acquaintance] at Ames, who told me there were research opportunities here — there was a centrifuge here — would I be interested? I came down and took a look; they had all the elements I'd been working with at Johnsville.[30]

As the directorate built up its staff, it reorganized itself according to changing research needs and directions. Originally research had been organized along the three lines of inquiry defined by the Kety Committee. Hence the original divisions were biotechnology, environmental biology, and exobiology. Because life sciences was a small directorate — at its largest it held approximately 180 people — organization within divisions remained relatively simple, focused around areas of study rather than facilities, in contrast to the early Ames divisions, which had been organized around wind tunnels. Over the years, the divisions and branches were rearranged a number of times. Though in many ways the same basic structure continued to exist, the new names and relationships reflected changing focuses within both Ames and NASA.[31] During 1963–1976 the Life Sciences Directorate at Ames was under the authority, successively, of OART, OMSF, and OSS. The organizational changes at Ames reflect the differing interests and priorities of the three program offices. Though Ames learned to live with the somewhat tenuous organizational arrangements, the original problems present when the NASA life-sciences program was in its infancy in 1960–1962 remained factors in the life of the Ames directorate.

The arrival of life sciences at Ames was unfortunately timed. The old aeronautical laboratory was in the midst of other drastic changes — the shift to space research, the introduction of project work, the new presence of large numbers of contract workers, and the growing complexity brought on by increased budgets and the necessity of political rationale.[32] It is not surprising that white-coated biologists, chemists, and doctors caused tensions.

A continuing problem, especially difficult to deal with during the Apollo years, was the division of duties between Ames and the Manned Spacecraft Center at Houston. The conflict began in 1960 when Randt attempted, unsuccessfully, to wrest the biomedical work associated with Project Mercury away from the Space Task Group. The complex issue, seen retrospectively, was really three-sided. The first was simply that of authority: the Space Task Group considered that its responsibility — manned spaceflight — included all aspects of that job, including the biomedical ones. Life-sciences managers, both at the program office level and later under OART, contested this view. The problem was never really resolved over the years, despite the shifts in organization and attempts at bureaucratic solutions.

The second aspect of the conflict was philosophical. Life-science managers at Ames saw their efforts in terms of the original Kety Committee's plans for a strong in-house research facility. Though obviously life sciences would help solve problems related to humans in space, Ames researchers constituted a pool of talent involved in a variety of continuing quests relating to space and the life sciences. In this view, Ames's place under OART made sense. OMSF and Houston, however, tended to think of life sciences as a support team for Project Mercury or Apollo or whatever manned project demanded support. OMSF sometimes sponsored investigations in competition with OART. As Klein remembered, "During the years Ames life sciences was under OART, OMSF was doing life-sciences research work too, but they weren't calling it life sciences. They got into research OART was supposed to be doing, siphoned off research money from [other parts of their program] and did their own research."[33]

Eventually, a rough line was drawn and Ames concentrated mostly on animal research, leaving Houston the human research. Where Ames was also involved in human research, it was responsible for coordinating its efforts with Houston's. Here was the third element of the conflict in the Ames-Houston relationship. The two life-science groups were very different in tone. Ames research was geared to long-term goals and general scientific curiosity; Houston was dominated by the overwhelming operational demands and frantic activity surrounding manned spaceflight. Driven by political pressures to accomplish well publicized goals, Houston was bound by time limits that Ames did not feel. A sense of urgency made the Texas center impatient and unwilling to leave the development and finished products up to another center. Houston's insistence on doing much of the biomedical work was, from Ames's perspective, insulting.[34]

The organizational arrangement of life sciences at Headquarters was a continuing handicap to Ames. Klein thought it perhaps was the biggest problem his directorate faced over the years. Interested in supporting that aspect of Ames's work closest to their own fields, the program offices, as they took turns controlling Ames, kept the center struggling to offset what it perceived as an imbalance in research emphasis. Klein recalled,

> Working under OMSF, the problem was that they were interested in manned spaceflight. They would listen attentively to us when we talked about our work in manned-spaceflight research and would tend to turn a deaf ear when we talked about aeronautics or exobiology. Now we're in OSS. They don't do any manned spaceflight, so when they go to Congress [for funding], they aren't going to emphasize those problems.[35]

In spite of slow progress toward understanding and accommodation, the dealings of life sciences with the other two research groups at Ames remained in some ways as tenuous as its position within NASA as a whole. To this day there is a certain distance between the life sciences and aeronautical engineers. In many ways they go about their work differently. One example was publication. By training, aeronautical engineers did not publish technical reports until data had been checked and rechecked; life scientists, by contrast, published initial research results that might be rapidly outdated, adjusted, or even disproved.[36] It was the difference between a "finished product" attitude and a "work in progress" approach to publication.

For those engineers who had spent much or all of their careers working under the iron hand of De France, the life scientists must indeed have appeared to be a motley crew of revolutionaries. Perhaps the difference in tone between the engineers and life scientists was less a difference in their disciplines and more that between the university and the civil service. When the directorate was formed, the old NACA atmosphere fostered by De France was still very much present, and it is easy to imagine the mutually jarring effect the two groups had on each other. Under De France, for example, it had been forbidden for anyone under the rank of organizational director to sign an outgoing letter without approval.* Though De France was necessarily concerned with individuals making unapproved commitments or statements, the rule was ridiculous to the life scientists, many of them former members of university faculties. Klein claimed:

> We helped to make possible a more academic environment here. A lot of things we now take for granted at Ames we first punched

---

*A concession had been won by Pioneer Project Manager Charles Hall earlier. Hall had received permission to sign all Pioneer outgoing mail and to receive incoming mail directly, "unheard of at Ames in 1962." Hall interview, Dec. 1982.

through in life sciences, like ... signing your own letters, having in-house research seminars. .... We chipped away at a very closed, constrained organization.[37]

Life scientists and their different research methods, organizational needs, and procedural expectations undoubtedly furthered the process of change at Ames, and in this were aided by other new influences. The growth of contracting, with contractor personnel at the center continuously, was one. Also important was De France's retirement in 1965. Harvey Allen, the new director, had always been vigorously involved in research. Because his personal style was anything but bureaucratic, the new elements at the center found him approachable.

In some areas, however, life sciences would never be in quite the same category as the rest of the research center. Where aeronautics and astronautics overlapped in facilities and funding, life sciences remained largely apart. Physically, life sciences also remained both small and separate, comprising less than a tenth of the center's manpower and occupying only three buildings. Perhaps, as the head of the Biomedical Research Division remarked, life sciences at Ames would always be an island, having little to do with the rest

1962. Flight Research and Life Sciences combine efforts in experiments such as this one involving the 5-degrees-of-motion centrifuge, which studied pilot response to various motion patterns.

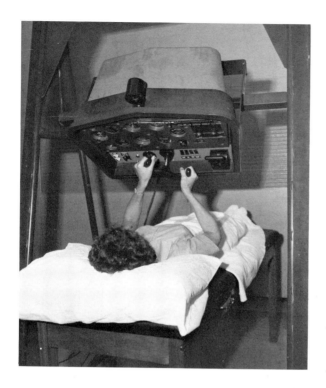

1978. In this bed-rest study conducted by Life Science researchers, the female subject is being tested on the effects of weightlessness and the ability to perform specified tasks in space.

of the center;[38] but if that is true, the directorate also came to be accepted by Ames as being a valuable component of its research strength.

As Ames gained its early reputation through crucial research, so did life sciences. Not only was the work proving essential to manned spaceflight, but aeronautical researchers also began to make use of the resident expertise to support aeronautical research. Interrelationships developed between life scientists and engineers involved in the human-factor aspect of aeronautics. Here, flight research questions and motion simulators dovetailed with the biotechnology division's interests, and cooperative projects were born. During the Viking mission to Mars and the later Pioneer mission to Venus, exobiologists and researchers in astronautics collaborated to plan and implement experiments. The growing involvement of life sciences with the aeronautical and astronautical segments of Ames was demonstrated in 1973 by the creation of the Flight Experiments Office within the life-sciences directorate.[39]

In the biomedical research areas, outside connections with contractors and university research teams brought Ames into prominence outside the immediate NASA framework. The Biomedical Research Division at Ames tended to follow research directions that had potentially far-flung applications. Because of this, the research reached a wider audience than the more specific, applied research connected to space projects. Devices for measuring intercranial pressures, microcatheter developmental research, and bed-rest studies brought Ames into interaction with a whole new segment of the scientific community.

The Aviation Safety Reporting System Office, within the Man-Vehicle Systems Research Division, proved to be another important avenue to the outside world. Heavily funded by the Federal Aviation Administration, the new office investigated reports of near-misses in flight. Attempting to identify crucial elements in pilot stress and examining physical factors of accidents and near-accidents statistically, the office has developed an extensive bank of information. Because any participant or witness can anonymously submit information, the office has become well known as a neutral consultant, a case of a highly visible and obviously pragmatic application of research to benefit the public.

The life sciences, especially biomedicine, touched more lives and excited more everyday interest than did aeronautics and astronautics. Some dramatic episodes — probably not representative of the directorate's real strengths — brought Ames and NASA fascinating and positive publicity. One such episode occurred in 1968, when a holdup victim was shot in the head. Surgery was impossible; by subjecting the patient to a 6-g force in the Ames centrifuge, however, a bullet fragment was shifted slightly, to a position where it would be less dangerous.[40] At least twice, physicians at the local hospitals borrowed pressure suits from Ames — suits similar to those worn by the astronauts — to bring persistent hemorrhaging under control.[41]

Such dramatic episodes, if ironic when viewed in the context of Ames's 40-year history, also confirmed the wisdom of seeking new research missions. Ames under De France, like the NACA under George Lewis and Hugh Dryden, had shunned publicity and had seen no need to seek approval or fame outside a narrow circle of professionals who were already convinced of Ames's importance. Yet by 1960 Ames management had recognized the need to reach a wider audience, if only to keep pace with the colorful space activities that brought NASA overwhelming support in the 1960s. Life sciences brought the center out of its narrower environment and helped to modernize its personality. But the institution paid a price that may not have been foreseen: De France's laboratory was radically transformed into a real research center.

The difficult birth of the life-sciences program at Ames is significant in another way. Many of the problems that beset the directorate within Ames also beset Ames in the larger NASA context. Just as life sciences saw itself an "in-house research facility," so Ames had enjoyed just that identification throughout the NACA years. Under NASA, both found themselves frequently cast in the role of problem-solvers for the space effort, a role that both resented. Basic research is a slow process of fits and starts, wrong turns, and much rethinking of problems. It seeks understanding, before solutions, and generally does not respond well to the pressure of fixed deadlines. For both the life-sciences academics and the aeronautical engineers used to the NACA's frugality, NASA's commitment to fast problem-solving with big budgets, though admittedly necessary in the new age, was close to sacrilege. For some the transition was easier than for others, but for all it was a major change, and one that was only gradually accomplished.

SOURCE NOTES

Chapter 5. The Life Sciences Directorate

[1] "Report of the NASA Bioscience Advisory Committee," 25 Jan. 1960, p. 15. Life Sciences Directorate, Historical Files of Dr. Harold Klein.

[2] See John Pitts, "The Human Factor: Biomedicine in the Manned Space Program" (unpublished manuscript, 1981), chap. 3, pp. 81–83, for details on the establishment of the Life Sciences Programs Office.

[3] Harold P. Klein interview, 24 Feb. 1982.

[4] Harry J. Goett interview, 3 Dec. 1981.

[5] See chapter 6, p. 120.

[6] Seth Anderson interview, 5 Feb. 1982.

[7] Goett interview.

[8] This is Goett's opinion, as he reviewed the shifts and changes in his own career.

[9] John W. Boyd interview, 23 July 1982.

[10] Smith J. De France to T. Keith Glennan, 11 Mar. 1960, 70-A-1261, V-4817, SBFRC.

[11] Russell G. Robinson to De France, 21 Apr. 1960, ibid.

[12] Pitts, "Human Factor," chap. 3, p. 97.

[13] Robinson to De France, 21 Apr. 1960.

[14] "Office of Life Science Programs Ten Year Plan," 15 Sept. 1960, p. 25, 70-A-1261, V-4817, SBFRC.

[15] Ames to NASA Hq., "Proposed Life Sciences Research Center," 10 Nov. 1960, p. 2. Life Sciences Directorate, Historical Files of Dr. Harold Klein.

[16] Ibid., p. 3.

[17] Ibid., p. 9.

[18] "Report of the NASA Working Group on Life Sciences," Mar. 1962, pp. 29 ff.

[19] See E. B. Konecci to De France, 3 May 1960, suggesting that Ames needed to align itself better with OART program objectives, and 1 June 1963, regarding the spring 1963 survey of life-sciences activities, NASA Hq. History Office.

[20] Homer E. Newell, *Beyond the Atmosphere: Early Years of Space Science*, NASA SP-4211 (Washington, 1980), chap. 16. Newell, at one time head of NASA's Office of Space Sciences, has written an excellent chapter on the difficulties that NASA's life-science program encountered.

[21] Ibid., p. 281.

[22] Klein interview.

[23] Ibid.

[24] Ibid.

[25] Edwin P. Hartman, *Adventures in Research: A History of Ames Research Center, 1940-1965*, NASA SP-4302 (Washington, 1970), p. 404.

[26] See R. W. Gerard to De France, 20, 21 Feb. 1963, and the accompanying letter from De France to Assoc. Admin. R. C. Seamans, Jr., 21 Mar. 1963. One of De France's obvious objections to the Gerard report was concern that its circulation would make the

113

task of replacing Haymaker more difficult. Life Sciences Directorate, Historical Files of Dr. Harold Klein.

[27] Gerard memorandum to De France, 21 Feb. 1963, pp. 3–4.

[28] Both Dr. Harold Sandler, head of the Biomedical Research Div., and Dr. Alan Chambers, head of the Man-Vehicle Systems Research Div., recalling their early years at Ames, remembered that though they were aware of difficulties, they felt unaffected by handicaps in their own work.

[29] Klein interview.

[30] Harold Sandler interview, 3 Feb. 1982.

[31] For the progression of organizational changes in the Life Sciences Directorate, see app. D.

[32] Edie Watson Kuhr interview, 27 Apr. 1981.

[33] Klein interview.

[34] This aspect of the Ames-Houston relationship was described by Melvin Sadoff of the Biomedical Research Division in an interview, 29 Jan. 1982.

[35] Klein interview.

[36] Walter Vincenti interview, 12 Dec. 1980.

[37] Klein interview.

[38] Sandler interview.

[39] Dir. Hans Mark to Ames organizational dirs., "the Flight Experiments Office," 5 Nov. 1973.

[40] Ames *Astrogram,* 18 Nov. 1968.

[41] The first incident took place in Sept. 1969 at the Stanford University Hospital; the second, related to the author by Dr. Alan Koslow, then resident surgeon at the local Veterans Administration Hospital, occurred in the spring of 1980.

6

AMES DURING NASA'S GOLDEN YEARS, 1958-1969

As we have seen, the addition of the Life Sciences Directorate at Ames was a direct result of the transformation of the NACA into NASA, and one that was traumatic for Ames in a number of ways. As life sciences personnel brought new expertise to the center, they also weakened the community of interests that had been a source of strength. And the new directorate was only one of the radical changes occurring at Ames during NASA's first decade.

That NASA would bring great changes to the old laboratories was perceived from the first, and the NACA, whatever its shortcomings, had inspired great institutional loyalty; many employees had spent their entire careers working for the NACA. They were convinced that its conservative and thrifty qualities, as well as its committee form of organization, were far preferable to a large agency, where politics might replace solid professionalism and feasibility studies might kill daring research schemes before they had a chance to be tried. Many NACA employees were leery of NASA at the beginning, even though they recognized that the NACA had been caught in an increasingly difficult situation, struggling between fixed appropriations and expanding requirements.

NACA veterans, reminiscing years later about the old organization, continued to stress the quality of the work done under its sponsorship and the quality of men hired. Clarence Syvertson, remembering his early years at Ames, recalled that Associate Director Parsons "looked over in detail every single man we hired in those days, so far as his record was concerned. I know if I proposed to hire someone he didn't think was quite up to snuff, he let me know it right away."[1] The character of the NACA was seen as exemplifying that of its leaders, from Ames to Dryden. Old employees felt strongly about the institution, stressing the "basic honesty and integrity and the efficiency."[2] As another veteran remembered, "Everything was honest and straightforward, or we didn't do it. We never would have thought of anything except the most straightforward honest approach to all the contracts and to all the relations with industry, and everything we did."[3]

115

That the NACA was honest, straightforward, and nonpartisan was firmly believed by many of its employees. Yet another conviction was that the very structure of the old NACA had been decisive in creating an organization in which there was no "hanky panky." Vannevar Bush, describing the evolution of the National Science Foundation, had praised the NACA form of organization, in which the director was responsible to the Main Committee:

> We had an excellent organization in the old National Advisory Committee for Aeronautics, a board made up of military officers and other government officials, plus citizens appointed by the President, which selected a director and reviewed his operations. When this was transformed into NASA it took the form [of a director appointed by and responsible to the President]. I think this was a mistake and said so at the time, for I have great sympathy for a director who stands alone before the public and Congress. But the men who organized it did not agree with me.[4]

The same sentiment was echoed by others, including James Doolittle, the last chairman of the NACA.[5] Manley Hood, who had been at the laboratory since 1940, spoke for his colleagues many years later:

> A lot of us feel [that NASA should have been set up as the NACA had been]. We had as a Board of Directors, for free, the best brains we could find, and we had in addition to those . . . the technical committees and technical subcommittees, and membership on those committees was sought after by a lot of different people. A lot of the members . . . were industry people, and they brought the industry viewpoint to those of us in the research job and a lot of them were military and there was a good angle there. . . . we had good friends all around. Industry was our good friend because we supported them with the research results they needed. . . . during those years we were not their best customer, as NASA became later. We weren't important as a customer, so the relationship was easy to maintain on a fair, honest, ethical level.[6]

IMMEDIATE CHANGES

Old NACA employees were immediately annoyed because Hugh Dryden had not been appointed head of the agency. Respect for Dryden was high, and his reputation as a scientist was renowned. He had never been a politicking promoter of the NACA, leaving that to Executive Secretary John

116

Victory, a master at the task. Dryden saw his job as directing research and development, and at that he had been highly efficient. His strongest supporters could not have called him an exciting leader, however; and Dryden had appeared stodgy to many of those planning the NASA organization. He had made only modest projections regarding what could be quickly accomplished in space. Even worse, he had referred to Wernher von Braun's proposal for a 250-kilometer manned space shot as akin to shooting a lady out of a cannon,[7] an unfortunate remark since von Braun's charisma had always found supporters on Capitol Hill. By personality and training incapable of promising more than he could deliver, Dryden was simply too low-key for the head NASA position. Dryden's final failing, however, was that he was a Democrat. Since NASA had been set up with the administrator reporting directly to the President, it naturally followed that the new post was a political appointment, changing with presidential administrations.

T. Keith Glennan, the new NASA administrator, was a staunch Republican. The political flavor of NASA was, from the beginning, a bitter pill for old NACA personnel, who had proudly believed that the NACA was above politics.[8] Many Ames employees saw the appointment of Glennan as a fair indication of the evils of political agencies, as opposed to nonpartisan committees. Before James Doolittle had become chairman of the NACA, academics had always headed the Committee; and Doolittle could claim a long and impressive association with aeronautics and an apprenticeship served on NACA committees. Glennan, a complete outsider, was sarcastically referred to by some as "that Hollywood man from the movies."[9] The epithet was only partially true, but Glennan had absolutely no experience or technical training in anything remotely resembling aeronautics.

With an undergraduate degree in electrical engineering, Glennan had indeed worked for the motion picture industry, specializing in sound systems. During World War II, he had headed the Navy's Underwater Sound Laboratories; after the war he had served on the Atomic Energy Commission. As president of Case Institute of Technology, he had an excellent reputation for management and had vastly improved the reputation of the school. His supporters hoped he could provide the energy needed to launch a vigorous agency. He was hardly only "the man from Hollywood," but to professionals whose careers had been molded by men like Ames, Lewis, and De France, he appeared suspect. For old-timers at Ames especially, far from Washington and not especially sympathetic to political realities, Glennan's appointment seemed ludicrous.[10]

Glennan's insistence on creating the post of associate administrator did nothing to dispel distrust at the laboratory. The new official would be a general manager for NASA, to coordinate programs and to relieve Deputy Administrator Dryden of some management pressure. The idea stemmed from Glennan's experience on the Atomic Energy Commission, and against almost unanimous opposition he succeeded in having the position established by early 1959, when NASA issued its first organization charts.[11]

To critics at Ames, the new post seemed an unnecessary complication. Management under the NACA had been simple. Laboratories merely reported to Gus Crowley, Dryden's subordinate. The decision-making process had been relatively straightforward; and the laboratories had been left a good deal of independence on many matters. This had been even more true of Ames than of the other laboratories, both because of the distance factor and because of the respect in which De France was held. The appearance of an associate administrator suggested that, in general, there would be much more management from Washington in the future.

And specifically, the new post removed the laboratory one step further from the NASA administrator.[12] Though Ames, Langley, and Lewis still reported directly to Crowley, now the director of aeronautical and space research, Crowley reported to the associate administrator. The laboratories no longer had as direct a line to the top as they once had, and bureaucracy took another step forward. Furthermore, the field installations that had been designated part of the space effort — Beltsville (later Goddard Space Flight Center), the Jet Propulsion Laboratory, von Braun's Huntsville group, Wallops Pilotless Flight Station, and Cape Canaveral — reported to the director of spaceflight development. This administrative arrangement split the laboratories, making communication among them more difficult. The old simplicity of organization was disappearing, and in the first months of NASA the prospect must have been disquieting at Ames.

Two more developments over the next decade would change Ames significantly. Under the NACA, the laboratories had functioned primarily as research institutions. Though the development phase of research often followed almost automatically as work progressed, emphasis was on the investigative process, whether the research was basic or applied. When Ames scientists and engineers had done specific problem-solving for industry or the military, the developmental stage of the project was usually left to the organization that had requested help. The NACA had been knowledge-oriented, not goal-oriented. NASA was different, being charged with developing, constructing, and operating space vehicles. NASA had the authority to contract out work to other government agencies, industry, or individuals.[13] The agency had a goal, exploitation of the space frontier. A new vocabulary emphasized the change in orientation: research centers had "projects," "project responsibilities," "missions"; new employees were welcomed "on board." The specificity of NASA's reason for existence immediately added a more urgent aspect to the developmental phase of research. As projects grew ever more sophisticated, the developmental aspects grew ever more complicated.

118

The second development was large-scale contracting. In the NACA, most work had been done in-house by civil servants. The goals of NASA made this impossible, because some tasks were one-time assignments not requiring permanent staff, and because NASA did not have within its organization the specific capabilities needed to get certain jobs done. By 1962, 90% of NASA's work was done under contract.[14] The same year, Ames awarded contracts totaling $14.4 million, only 2% of NASA's total contracting commitments but still an impressive amount.[15] Over the next decade, Ames found its administrative burden greatly increased by contracting. The financial management, monitoring, and coordination of contracts involved even the researchers in administrative duties from which they had largely been free in the past.[16]

The tendency toward more extensive contracting helped change the collective personality of Ames. In 1958, permanent employees numbered 1406. By 1968, there were 2084 employees,[17] along with a substantial increase in the number of contract employees working at Ames. By this process Ames was gradually divided between in-house and contractor employees, a split that mirrored the larger split Ames seems to have felt between itself and the headquarters organization full of new people. Those who were at Ames under contract could not feel the same sense of identification with the research center that its permanent staff did. At the same time, the old Ames employees felt a strong distinction between themselves and outside contractors. The appearance of contractor personnel at Ames, "outsiders" to the old NACA staff, is one of the frequently mentioned changes brought by NASA.[18] The feeling among Ames employees that they were part of a community with certain inbred standards of work and conduct had been inspired by De France and further nourished by uncomplicated lines of administration. Everyone knew everyone else and most of the staff seemed to have believed firmly in the excellence of the parent institution. This feeling of community began to be undermined as the presence of contract employees became impossible to ignore. Seen as temporary, even though their employer's contracts might be almost indefinite in length, contract employees were indeed aware that they were crashing uninvited into what had been a tightly knit organization. In the eyes of many of the older staff, the invasion of contractors effectively destroyed the personality of the old Ames.[19]

ORGANIZATIONAL CHANGES

The growing complexity of Ames and the need to regroup some projects for the sake of efficiency led to a major reorganization at the end of

1959. The changes reflected the tendency toward classification by goal rather than by related research areas. This was to be the first of several major reorganizations in the next few years, as the place of Ames in the NASA hierarchy unfolded and the center's major areas of commitment became clear. The 1959 changes, while extensive, were more a realigning than a major upheaval. A similar process was going on in all the old NACA laboratories. Two years after NASA's establishment, the changes were described and analyzed in one of the professional journals, using Lewis Research Center as an example.[20]

At Lewis, one of the major factors in the ability to convert from aeronautical concerns to space research was the flexibility of facilities. The changeover was accomplished in less than three years, with little extra spending. The old altitude wind tunnel, for example, was converted into a giant vacuum chamber and used for reentry studies on the Project Mercury capsule. Another factor was foresight in planning research programs that allowed for elasticity. A program in missile propulsion that had been begun in 1956 was easily converted to additional space work as rocket development advanced. In this same period, Lewis also shuffled and reshuffled its research teams to meet the new needs. Old teams were in some cases broken up, and new teams were constructed to create new combinations of expertise. Individuals were retrained. Rather quickly, the old NACA laboratory converted itself to new tasks. Flexibility in facilities, research capabilities, and staff expertise made the transition possible. In 1956, 60% of Lewis's work had been on airbreathing engines for manned aircraft; in 1960, the work was 73% space-related.[21]

A similar process was being accomplished at Ames. The 1959 reorganization was the beginning of a transition in administrative lines of command designed to accommodate future demands on the center. Specifically, the distinction between research that was primarily aeronautical and that which was space-related became sharper. This had been tacitly true previously, in the distinction between the Full-Scale and Flight Research Division and the High-Speed Research Division, but the new organizational tendencies underlined this.[22]

Since 1954 one assistant director, Russell Robinson, had been aided by two technical assistants. With the 1959 changes, Harvey Allen, who had been in charge of the High-Speed Research Division, was made an assistant director, and the two high-speed, space-oriented divisions were placed under his supervision. Thus the importance of space-related research was proclaimed and a greater distinction made between the disciplines.[23]

Allen's old High-Speed Research Division was recast as the Aero-Thermodynamics Division, with new branches organized more by task than by facility. The division included the supersonic free-flight wind tunnel branch, the heat transfer branch, the fluid mechanics branch with the 1- by

120

3-foot supersonic tunnels and the 2- by 2-foot transonic tunnel attached, and the trisonic aerodynamics branch with the 6- by 6-foot supersonic tunnel attached. Space-connected pieces of the old high-speed division were recast as part of the Vehicle Environment Division under Al Eggers. This division, which reported to Allen, was composed of a physics branch, an entry simulation branch, a structural dynamics branch, the 3.5-foot hypersonic wind tunnel branch, and the hypervelocity ballistic range branch. Two of the old high-speed tunnels — the 14-foot transonic tunnel and the 10- by 14-inch supersonic tunnel — were deactivated and their personnel reassigned.

Assistant Director Russell Robinson now had three divisions under his supervision. The Unitary Plan Wind Tunnel Division was unchanged, but the Full-Scale and Flight Research Division was renamed the Full-Scale and Systems Research Division, signifying another change in direction. The division had lost the heat-transfer branch to the Aero-Thermodynamics Division because of its space-related uses, but had gained a guidance and control branch. As regrouped, the division was composed of the following branches: 40- by 80-foot wind tunnel, flight and systems simulation and operations, dynamics analysis, and guidance and control. Harry Goett, who had long headed the full-scale division, had by 1959 become head of the Goddard Space Flight Center in Maryland. The new division chief was Charles Harper, who had worked under Goett.

Ames had suffered another loss in its low-speed division, reflected in the loss of "flight research" from the division's title. In 1959 NASA Headquarters had moved most of Ames's flight research to its Flight Research Center at Edwards Air Force Base. Ames retained the V/STOL research, because the 40- by 80-foot wind tunnel was necessary for the work. The decision was not happily received at Ames, where oldtimers saw their realms of research and reputation being blithely reassigned even as the center was being forced to embrace fields in which it had no previous experience. The loss of flight research must have been a particularly bitter pill, since the deicing work done in that branch had not only been Ames's very first work, but had also gone far to establish the reputation of the young research institution. Indeed, the transfer was a real handicap to Ames's continuing involvement in areas requiring flight research support, including high-speed flight dynamics, variable-stability aircraft, and man-machine integration.

The third division under Robinson, the Instrumentation Division, also reflected the growing need to coordinate and centralize activities to serve new research needs. Instrumentation had previously been organized separately from the research divisions, and had reported to either Parsons or De France. In the research divisions, a certain amount of instrumentation had been done ad hoc as the need arose. The organization of a separate instrumentation division was an attempt to coordinate this area of research more efficiently. Years later one of Robinson's technical assistants, Manley Hood, observed that the NACA had been

> slow in developing a group that could do real sophisticated instrument work.... We depended on the simple little instruments like I worked on in my first year down there. They served up to a point, but I think we were slow in getting to the real kind.... I think it was only when we got in NASA that we got real fine instrument groups.[24]

From the beginning, the Instrumentation Division was well differentiated, with branches concentrating in vehicle instrumentation research, facilities instrumentation research, electronic machine computing, and mechanical and electronic instruments, another illustration of the growing need to define much more closely the boundaries of research.

The administrative, technical services, and engineering services divisions still reported directly to the associate director or director, but this too would change over the next few years. As administration grew more complicated, the organization charts would reveal a greater differentiation among the nonresearch segments of the laboratory, a symptom of growing bureaucracy.

Though Glennan was NASA administrator only a little over two years, Ames's future was much affected during that time. The decision to place a life-sciences research group at Ames was made during his administration. In late 1958 a Manned Satellite Team was also appointed from among Ames personnel to consider design problems and propose a practical system for a satellite, at the same time recommending a suitable research program. The team was headed by Alfred Eggers, who had already been working on lifting bodies for some time. Glennan later revealed that he had wanted to convert Ames into a manned spaceflight laboratory,[25] and the manned satellite team, in all likelihood, was connected to the conversion. Nothing came of the scheme, but Eggers's team, and later the Ames Manned Lunar Mission Team under Alvin Seiff, were influential in planning the Apollo program.

Administrative flux was to continue at Ames for some time. The life-sciences group brought its own administrative problems as it attempted to build a solid research unit, and the established divisions of the laboratory were also rearranged over the next few years. The next important change came in August 1962, when a separate Space Sciences Division was established and placed under Harvey Allen. The new division had only one branch at first, theoretical studies. Staffing proceeded slowly, with much work continuing to be contracted out because of the lack of personnel.[26] The division was headed by Charles Sonett, who had been at NASA's Office of Space Sciences.

122

Sonett was the second major Ames appointment from "outside"; Webb Haymaker, appointed to head the Life Sciences Directorate, had been the first. As the laboratory expanded both in personnel and in research directions, the trend was to continue, further weakening the homogeneity of the old NACA staff. The development was unavoidable, given the complexities of administration and the expanding fields into which Ames was moving, but it further diluted the personality of the laboratory even as it lessened the isolation that Ames had experienced during the NACA years.

Dramatic organizational changes continued so that by January 1964 Ames's organization chart was barely recognizable when compared to one of the late NACA period. Three major developments are striking.

First, the tacit division between conventional aeronautics and space-related studies had been made explicit — Harvey Allen had been named assistant director for astronautics. The new title only underlined the change made by the establishment of the Space Sciences Division. Allen's colleague Russell Robinson, the assistant director for aeronautics and flight systems at the time, recalled that he had questioned the establishment of the Astronautics Directorate, feeling "it caused too much of a distinction to be made between the two aeronautical areas. Research areas are always overlapping; the creation of an Astronautics Directorate blurred this fact."[27]

Creation of the directorate was a logical progression of events that had begun a decade earlier with Allen's blunt-body concept for nose cones. High-speed aeronautics had involved space research for years, as witnessed by the 1956-1964 lifting-body work, the creation of the Vehicle Environment Division in 1959, and the simulation work begun in the late 1950s. Especially with the loss of a major portion of its flight research, Ames had to carve new research territories. Establishment of the life-sciences group and the formal differentiation between aeronautics and astronautics were conscious moves on the part of De France to maintain the position of the research center in a rapidly changing environment.[28] In the case of life sciences, the departure from Ames's past work was radical; the move into astronautics, while less drastic, indicated that Ames would be increasingly involved in development work.

The 1958 Manned Satellite Team and the 1960 Manned Lunar Mission Team were precursors of later project work, the second major development of the 1958-1965 period. Immediately following the formation of NASA, Ames had tried to obtain responsibility for the Orbiting Astronomical Observatory planned by Headquarters.[29] Top Ames leaders were split on the issue; De France and Allen had mixed feelings on the wisdom of getting involved in project work of any sort. Headquarters vetoed the proposal, but in 1960 Ames again moved toward project management. Alfred Eggers, who had been one of the major researchers in the earlier lifting-body work — and who by 1960 was head of the Vehicle-Environment Division under Allen — began investigating the possibility of an exploratory solar probe.

The collaboration of Eggers, his Assistant Division Chief Charles Hall, and a few others produced a 1961 proposal for a solar probe project to be managed by Ames. NASA Headquarters was still lukewarm to the thought of Ames taking on major projects because of their lack of experience in project work, but after a study by an outside contractor on a smaller, interplanetary probe, De France and Associate Director Jack Parsons took the proposal to Washington to make a case for the Ames project. In November 1962 Ames received permission to proceed with what became known as Pioneer, a series of interplanetary probes.

The Pioneer project, or series of projects, would reestablish Ames as a crucial part of NASA. Without considering here the technical history of the project (chap. 10), a few observations are worthwhile. First, De France's decision to campaign actively for the project in Washington marked a change from his earlier doubts about Ames as a manager of large space projects. He was probably responding to both outside pressure to make Ames more useful to NASA and inside pressure from younger staff members who recognized that the center must not only bend with events but actively seek new spheres of influence. It was a measure of De France's excellence as an administrator that, after an entire career devoted to aeronautics and the administration of an aeronautical laboratory, he could embrace the new proposal and lend it the weight of his reputation. The mere concept of Pioneer was an interplanetary distance removed from De France's 139th Aero Squadron of 1918.

Second, as originally conceived, Pioneer was a much more modest project than it eventually became. Not only was Headquarters seemingly reluctant to make a major commitment, but Ames itself still lacked the necessary manpower. The project was approved in 1962 with the stipulation that no more than 30 people be assigned to it, a measure of the limited commitment.[30] As time passed, Ames continued to promote the project in Washington, successfully urging additions to the original undertaking — another major change from earlier years. With less money at stake and few political overtones, the NACA had granted research authorizations with much less fanfare, and they could often be expanded with no further formalities.

Charles Hall, who had played a leading role in developing the proposals for Pioneer and became the project leader, was an example of the successful transition from aeronautics to astronautics made by many of the Ames staff. Employed at Ames since 1942, Hall's early career had been in low-speed aeronautics. He had worked on the P-38 dive problem and on P-51 stability and control tests, both accomplished in the busy 16-foot wind tunnel. In the late 1940s he had been involved in research on wing planforms and had tackled the problem of submerged inlet design. In the mid-1950s he had been responsible for the development of conical camber on wings to reduce

124

drag due to lift. In 1957 Hall was branch chief of the 6- by 6-foot supersonic wind tunnel, and with the 1959 organizational changes became the assistant division chief, under Eggers, of the Vehicle Environment Division.

Apart from his ability to move competently through a wide range of aeronautical research problems into what would become space research, Hall also displayed another talent that would be increasingly necessary to the research institution, that of planning and managing on a large scale. Over the 18 years of Pioneer, Hall proved to be a highly effective manager. The talents necessary were far removed from those needed in research and involved a whole new set of problems, ranging from the coordination of the many contract proposals connected to Pioneer to the management of huge sums of money and the dovetailing of various research teams.

Early in 1963 Ames also acquired a second major project, Biosatellite. The project grew out of a 1961–1962 study made at Ames, in which monkeys were to be tested for the effects of two weeks in orbit. As interest in biological experiments in space grew, a long-term project also grew around proposals submitted by a variety of research institutions and universities. When authorization was received, Carlton Bioletti was appointed project manager. More heavily funded than Pioneer, but beset from the start by conceptual and management problems, Biosatellite nevertheless was to perform many experiments for outside institutions over the years. Early in the project, Ames built a 50-foot-diameter centrifuge to aid in testing the monkey subjects, another piece of equipment that would in time be used for a variety of purposes.

The two projects acquired by Ames within such a short period necessitated yet another reorganization of the center in 1963. Involving facilities, management problems, and research groups that differed from those associated with Ames's existing research divisions, the new projects were placed under a new directorate, Development. To provide the new equipment needed, a Systems Engineering Division was organized under John Foster and attached to the Development Directorate. Forced to contract for much of its equipment and personnel, the directorate was from the beginning rather isolated from the research divisions. Because of the personnel shortage at Ames, there was a constant effort to keep civil servants out of project work and save them for the old research divisions; Biosatellite employed about 70 Ames personnel, Pioneer around 40. Though Robert Crane, the assistant director for development, hoped to create a symbiotic exchange of ideas and personnel between the research divisions and the Ames-managed projects, it would seem interdependence was less than it might have been. The result was another schism of the research center's staff.

Finally the 1964 organization chart revealed yet another contrast between the ways NASA and the NACA worked. Under the NACA, research was decided upon in a number of ways, but usually it was a natural progression stemming from ideas that promised to be exciting, like those of Harvey Allen, or from ongoing problems that needed solving, like those of transonic choking or heat transfer. NASA, however, had taken on the major task of putting a man on the Moon by the end of the decade, and this required not only large-scale centralized planning to accomplish the intermediate steps, but planning on the part of the research centers as well. Under NASA, advance planning became a conscious effort to generate research in specific directions that would fit into NASA's larger plans and make the most efficient use of Ames's facilities and personnel.

To this end another new directorate was formed, Research and Development Analysis and Planning under Alfred Eggers. Eggers had been in charge of the 1958 Manned Satellite Team and had also been responsible for organizing the early solar probe proposals that resulted in the eventual assignment of the Pioneer project to Ames. The new directorate was short-lived. When Eggers was transferred to Washington, the Headquarters-inspired Mission Analysis Division absorbed the directorate's functions. Under Clarence Syvertson, the new division undertook task analysis, while budgetary planning was handled by a Programs and Resources Office. Despite the 1963–1966 juggling of names and lines of authority, one thing was clear: the necessity for institutionalized planning and management represented further Ames involvement in the pre-research process, a distinct change from the years of low-budget, ad hoc feasibility studies, often with no paperwork at all.

In the same vein the administrative duties that Arthur Freeman had handled since 1940 now had grown to a directorate with four divisions. Freeman was still in charge, but the differentiation of duties underneath him bespoke the growth in bureaucratic complexity. The financial details of the laboratory, for example, which Ferril Nickle had once handled on a scratch pad, were now divided between the Planning and Resources Office and the Fiscal Division. The increasing need for standardized procedures and computerized record-keeping did not necessarily make for financial clarity. Alan Faye, a technical assistant to Assistant Director Russell Robinson at the time, recalled that although "every penny came to be justified with voluminous paperwork [no one] knew for sure what funding had been spent, what was still available, or where additional funds might be found."[31]

The new organizational relationships tied Ames to NASA Headquarters with transcontinental red tape. The changes were necessary, given the variety of research being undertaken, the center's supportive role in the space mission, and the vast increase in funding. Whether unfortunate by definition or only by implication, increasing complexity in administrative processes was an unavoidable part of growth and diversity. Adjustment to the new environment was not easy, however. For an institution that had operated successfully for decades with comparatively little complexity and bureaucracy, unhampered by the political handicaps suffered by so many government-funded institutions, the 1960s were a difficult period.

RESEARCH DIRECTIONS

A description of Ames prepared at NASA Headquarters in 1962 illustrated the new role the center was to play as a research institution. Ames was moving steadily into goal-oriented research, and NASA's primary goal was manned spaceflight and a lunar landing. Though aeronautics continued to hold its own with V/STOL studies and supersonic transport feasibility investigations, astronautics was much more visible as a research field during the

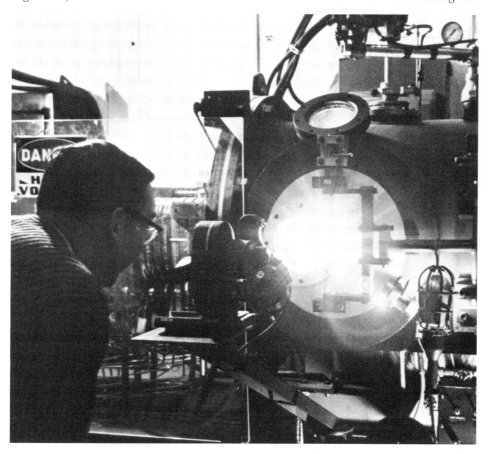

1961. One of the early reentry heating simulators. Ablation studies conducted here gave researchers new data on the behavior of various materials under reentry conditions.

1971. The gas dynamics laboratory during an experiment's run. Researchers check conditions of the experiment and data being produced.

period. The description illuminates the new alignment of research: "The principal mission ... is basic and applied research on aerodynamics of re-entry vehicles, flight control of space vehicles and aircraft, and space environment physics. Ames conducts flight research into vertical and short takeoff aircraft problems, and landing problems of the supersonic transport."[32] Estimates attributed 45% of Ames research to entry and environmental physics; 25% to aeronautics; 20% to guidance, control, and navigation; 8% to life sciences; and 2% to space sciences.[33] As the 1960s progressed, aeronautics would continue to play a secondary role in research, while space sciences would increase its toehold.

A fair measure of the changing directions at Ames can be seen in the frantic spurt of building in the early and mid-1960s. At NASA's inception in 1958, Ames was considered to be worth $80 million. By 1965 its research facilities were valued at $175 million.

Building of new facilities paralleled new research directions, and one need was for facilities that could simulate reentry speeds and temperatures. In the early 1960s a hypervelocity research laboratory and shock tunnel were built. In 1965 the 3.5-foot tunnel, whose pebble-bed heater had never worked well enough to operate the wind tunnel at the speeds for which it had been designed, was modified to operate using other gases, thereby simulating the Mars and Venus atmospheres. At the same time, a Mach 50 helium tunnel was completed, as was a hypervelocity free-flight facility that contained three separate testing devices. A new impact range was also built in the early 1960s, and in 1965 the speed of 11,300 m/sec was achieved in it. The impact range was used very successfully in meteoroid impact studies.

Out of the need to reproduce the extreme heat to which a space vehicle would be subjected came research into efficient arc-jets and their subsequent construction. The arc-jet tunnel uses a powerful electric arc to heat pressurized air which, when released, flows through a supersonic throat and test section en route to an evacuated receiving chamber. Refinement produced higher and higher temperatures. In 1962, because of the success in attaining temperatures high enough to be useful in reentry research, a gasdynamics laboratory was built. By the late 1960s nine arc-jet tunnels were operational at Ames.[34]

Flight simulators, which had captured the interest of Harry Goett in the late 1950s and were now to prove as useful in space research as they had been in flight research, were also advanced during the 1960s. From the rather crude pitch-roll chair, which simulated motion cues to the pilot about two of the axes of an airplane, Ames advanced to the "five-degrees-of-freedom" motion simulator. In addition to pitch, roll, and yaw, there was motion along vertical and horizontal axes, the simulator cab being on the arm of a centrifuge. The simulator was constructed cheaply, in the old NACA tradition, out of bits and pieces of equipment from other projects. The 1961 simulator was further improved two years later, becoming a "six-degrees-of-freedom" simulator. Another inexpensive flight simulator was the vertical testing machine that was to prove useful in V/STOL and helicopter research. Ingeniously, the vertical testing machine was installed on the outside of the 40- by 80-foot wind tunnel, making use of both its height and its supporting framework. The apparatus cost $170,000, a pittance in comparison to the amounts being spent on much of NASA's test equipment, and NACA veterans continued to be proud of being able to use their imagination to get the most out of their money.[35]

Flight simulation was further enhanced by use of visual simulation. Using computers to program takeoff and landing characteristics of various aircraft made it possible to present a pilot with a screen upon which cockpit views were shown. The pilot could thereby go through the motions of control using an instrument panel and the visual simulation picture, both connected to a computer.

It was a safe and inexpensive way to create realistic conditions on the ground. A landing approach simulator, built in 1962, was to be used extensively in flight training during supersonic transport research. In the early 1970s, when the Anglo-French Concorde was in its final test stages, the flight simulators were used in determining certification criteria. Ames pilots were exposed, via the simulators, to the Concorde's handling characteristics.

1965. Practicing landing approaches "flying" a double-delta-wing SST in a flight simulator. Such studies test the flight characteristics of aircraft still in the design stage and also monitor pilot performance while making landings.

When an Ames pilot was given control of the airplane during one of the early flights, he was able to land it routinely with one engine dead. Simulator training had so conditioned the pilot that a potential emergency became routine, even though he had never flown the aircraft before.[36]

Hypervelocity, arc-jet, and flight simulation facilities comprised the major portion of construction in the 1960s, but there were other important additions also. In 1965 a space environments research facility and a structural dynamics laboratory were built to simulate conditions in space and the forces acting on spacecraft. In 1965 the Life Sciences Directorate gained a major research laboratory, and in 1966 a spaceflight guidance laboratory was built. Physically, the research center became much denser, as new buildings were inserted wherever there was room.

The major problems connected to spaceflight focused on speed, the heat generated by speed, and control of the vehicle during flight. Ames's facilities lent themselves to research in these areas in a number of ways. Early in the 1960s, for example, models of the Mercury and Gemini capsules were tested in the hypervelocity free-flight facility, where airflow patterns were studied and stability experiments were performed. In 1962 flight simulators and Apollo capsule models were used to test spacesuit designs. Under flight conditions, astronauts tested the suits' mobility, efficiency, and comfort, as well as the ease with which the instrument panel was operated.

The center's changed position within the parent organization was well illustrated in the case of the Apollo guidance system, development of which began in 1962. Responsibility was apportioned in a manner foreign to the NACA scheme of things, but necessary in the complexities of a lunar landing mission. Massachusetts Institute of Technology had been awarded a NASA contract for the design and development of a prototype guidance system. In supporting MIT, Ames was given the task of working on midcourse and Earth-entry guidance. In particular, Ames computers were used to work out trajectories and correction factors for speed, angle of descent, and shape of the reentry body.

The problem of reentry heating of spacecraft presented a variety of related questions. An early realization was that the heating problem was two-fold: Not only would convective heating occur as the spacecraft reentered the Earth's atmosphere, there was also a problem of radiative heating caused by the high temperature rise in the air disturbed by the vehicle's shock wave. Radiative heat increased dramatically in the case of blunt bodies, which Allen had shown years before to be effective in controlling convective heating.[37] The research question lay in the trade-off between the two shapes to minimize undesirable effects, blunt body to control convective heat, missile-shaped to control radiative heat.

Crucially connected to the heating problem was ablation, the process by which heat is absorbed through melting, evaporation, and sublimation.

131

By coating a surface with an ablative material, much heat can be dissipated before the primary structure is affected. The arc-jet facilities proved most useful in the study of how ablation proceeds and what materials work best, especially because of the relatively long test times they made possible. As with his blunt-body work of the early 1950s, Harvey Allen and his colleagues went far toward solving the heating problem for high-speed reentry space-craft by adopting a cone shape.[38] Making the tip of the cone of a continually renewed ablation material solved much of the heat problem.

The study of ablation led Ames to meteoroid studies in the 1960s. By studying the materials of which meteors were composed and by calculating flights and landing patterns of meteors, researchers hoped to learn more not only about high-speed heating but about the composition of other planets and the space environment in which meteors are produced. Work on ablation was to lead Dean Chapman, later head of the Astronautics Directorate, to his long study of tektites, glass pellets that have been found at various places on the Earth's surface. Bringing aerodynamic theories to the study of tektites, Chapman developed a hypothesis on their origin based on study of the heat-ing patterns displayed by the pellets' shape and calculation of their flight speed. The origin of tektites, he suggested, was the Moon.[39] The tektite hypothesis provided a new perspective on the materials composing the Moon, and the forces that produced its craters. The tektite research became a prominent example of the thin line between applied and basic research and a happy reminder that a scientist can, with imagination, move back and forth between the two.

DEPARTURE OF DE FRANCE

In the fall of 1965 Smith De France, who had built, molded, and directed Ames with a firm hand since 1940, retired. Those who arranged his retirement dinner seemed to recognize that it marked the real passing of an era. Old NACA colleagues and associates from industry and the military were invited; the group represented De France's aeronautical connections of 45 years. The dinner was well attended, the testimonials respectful and restrained, and De France's remarks showed how touched he was by the efforts on his behalf.[40]

De France had enjoyed many advantages in his direction of Ames. He had started with a small group of engineers, many of whom he had known for years. The new employees were young, Ames was typically their first position, and De France was able to influence and mold them along with the laboratory. The times were on his side also, as World War II and the postwar rush into jet propulsion and supersonic flight created an atmosphere of urgency, even crisis, which kept morale and standards high. The tradition of NACA autonomy helped him maintain independence and keep bureaucracy to a minimum. By the mid-1950s, De France's imprint on Ames was so firmly established that increasing numbers, complexity in research and bureaucracy, even the eventual absorption into NASA, had left the laboratory with a personality that was distinctly his own. As an early Ames employee observed, "De France not only built Ames, he was Ames."[41]

De France's Ames had a sense of itself, its standards, and its ability to control its own affairs. Still largely staffed with former NACA employees, many of whom had been there for most of their careers, Ames remained in many ways a closed club of veterans attempting to retain their standards, independence, and sense of community against the press of the future. If De France had been conservative and straight-laced — and he was — he had a conscientious, tightly knit, and productive laboratory to show for it.

The time was past, however, when De France could move happily with the future. He had not been active in aeronautical research since the 1930s, and since that time aeronautics had become an entirely different field. Even more important, however, was the difference in atmosphere and tone that came with NASA. Ames had been slowly growing in personnel, facilities, and research activities from the beginning, but with NASA came a leap in all these areas in a very short time, bringing all the problems and intricacies of large-scale budgets and management. Project work, mission support, and contracting were radical changes, and it is to De France's credit that he actively campaigned for the Life Sciences Directorate and for project work like Pioneer. He left a laboratory that ran successfully for some years on momentum he created.

De France's successor was Harvey Allen, who was admittedly more happy as a researcher than as a center director. Where De France had been respected, Allen was loved. Where De France had been a rather stern figure, the bear-like Allen exuded good will, intellectual inspiration, a raucous sense of humor, and an unending interest in everything. He had been at Ames since 1940, owned a vintage Dusenberg, was a gourmet cook, a lover and player of classical music, a Perry Mason fan, and an amateur archaeologist. He was also a documented genius, without a doubt one of the reasons Ames had enjoyed such success both in its research and in its congenial atmosphere. Allen in the Dusenberg picked up a new secretary who had asked for a ride to work, not knowing he was the director of the center; Allen, with his endless circle of friends, called a dentist in Palo Alto searching for something to use as a special epoxy for one of his experiments; Allen could be found at home on weekends recoppering teakettles while conducting a Beethoven symphony on the record player.

Ames under Harvey Allen ran much as it had under De France, both because De France's personality had been strong and because devotion to

Allen kept morale intact. Many colleagues attested that Allen had not particularly wanted the job, but had taken it to keep the directorship from going to an "outsider," someone from NASA Headquarters who did not have a sense of the place.[42] There was evidently a strong feeling on the part of many that Ames needed a sympathetic member of the family at its head, someone who wouldn't introduce changes too traumatically and who would help preserve the character of the institution.

Allen did just that, and with a strong administrative staff, Ames almost ran itself under his directorship. He spent much of his time in research and took as little part in management as he could, always threatening to quit when the red tape became too entangling. His well-known distaste for the

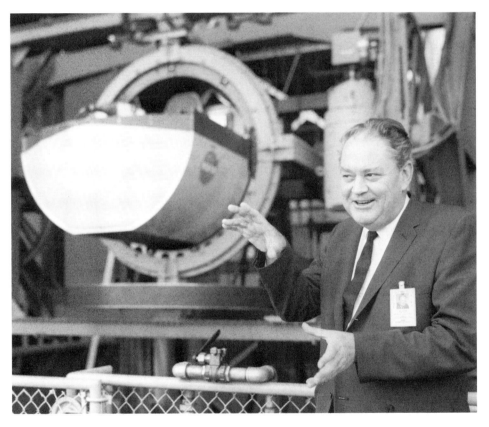

1966. Harvey Allen as Director of Ames explains the all-axis flight simulator. Wind tunnel testing, flight simulator tests, and actual aircraft flight tests complemented each other in providing various routes to needed research information. Eventually, computational fluid dynamics would simulate wind tunnel tests, reenforcing tunnel test results and providing another avenue of information.

134

necessities of administration and reluctance to interrupt research for trips to NASA Headquarters were very likely factors in the displeasure felt toward Ames by Washington.[43] He retired early in 1969, unwilling to tolerate increasingly complex management demands or to confront the unavoidable reduction-in-force choices everyone knew were approaching. The early deaths of three of his close friends at Ames — Bob Crane, Jackson Stalder, and Ralph Huntsberger — had also contributed to his unhappiness. Following his retirement, Ames's future was bleak for a time; there was even talk of closing the center, an idea that never got beyond sober speculation (see chap. 7). Some saw the possibility of the closing as a direct reaction by Headquarters to Allen's benign neglect of management. Whether this was true or not, both the rumor and the reaction to it at Ames underlined the rift between the center and NASA Headquarters. Like De France, Harvey Allen recognized that the new directions Ames needed to proceed were better followed under different talents. His retirement was a further severance with the past.

SOURCE NOTES

Chapter 6. Ames during NASA's Golden Years, 1958–1969

[1] Clarence Syvertson interview by Walter Bonney, 25 Sept. 1974, NASA History Office.

[2] Manley Hood interview by Bonney, 23 Sept. 1974, NASA History Office.

[3] Ibid.

[4] Vannevar Bush, *Pieces of the Action* (New York: William Morrow and Company, Inc., 1970), pp. 65–66.

[5] Walter Bonney, in interview of Hood.

[6] Hood interview.

[7] Enid Curtis Bok Schoettle, "The Establishment of NASA," in Sanford Lakoff, ed., *Knowledge and Power: Essays on Science and Government* (New York: The Free Press, 1966), p. 247.

[8] This reflection has been expressed by NACA veterans as one of the important differences between NACA and NASA.

[9] Many NACA employees who watched the transition from NACA to NASA still have little regard for Glennan.

[10] J. C. Hunsaker, former chairman of the NACA, criticized the new regime in a letter to Carl G. Holschuh of Sperry-Rand, 2 Nov. 1959. J. C. Hunsaker File, folder 1, series 3, record group 255, National Archives. In a 1965 speech before the Wings Club, Hunsaker continued to object to the form NASA had taken. J. C. Hunsaker Papers, NASA History Office Archives.

[11] Robert L. Rosholt, *An Administrative History of NASA, 1958–1963*, NASA SP-4101 (Washington, 1966), pp. 49–50.

[12] Ibid., p. 48.

[13] *NASA Act of 1958, As Amended, and Related Legislation* (NASA, Office of General Counsel, 1 July 1969), p. 7.

[14] Jane Van Nimmen and Leonard C. Bruno, *NASA Historical Data Book, 1958–1968*, vol. 1, *NASA Resources*, NASA SP-4012 (Washington, 1976), p. 5.

[15] Ibid., p. 257.

[16] This has been frequently mentioned as a continuing problem associated with a high level of contracting. The problem is still a complaint of both Ames management and researchers.

[17] Van Nimmen and Bruno, *NASA Historical Data Book*, 1: 11.

[18] This element, noted unenthusiastically, has been mentioned by all pre-1958 employees interviewed.

[19] This feeling has been mentioned frequently by both in-house staff and contractors.

[20] "How an Aircraft Laboratory Leaped into Space," *Business Week*, 4 June 1960, pp. 98–100.

[21] Ibid., p. 100.

[22] NASA release, 9 Nov. 1959; Director's Memorandum, 5 Nov. 1959.

[23] See Edwin P. Hartman, *Adventures in Research: A History of Ames Research Center, 1940-1965*, NASA SP-4302 (Washington, 1970), p. 318.

[24] Hood interview.

[25] Rosholt, *Administrative History*, p. 214; T. Keith Glennan interview, 18 Jan. 1964.

[26] Hartman, *Adventures in Research*, p. 326.

[27] Russell G. Robinson interview, 30 Sept. 1981.

[28] This has been mentioned by many of those involved in administration at the time.

[29] Hartman, *Adventures in Research*, p. 389.

[30] Ibid., p. 390.

[31] Alan Fayé interview, 1 Apr. 1981.

[32] *NASA Field Installations, 1962* (Washington, 1962), p. 24.

[33] "Ames Generates Basic, Applied Knowledge," *Aviation Week and Space Technology*, 2 July 1962, p. 100.

[34] Hartman, *Adventures in Research*, pp. 336–338, 422–424.

[35] The $170,000 price of the vertical testing machine is one of the most widely quoted figures around Ames and has become part of the center legend.

[36] The story is another oft-told Ames anecdote, related to the author by many employees.

[37] For a detailed description of the problem, see Hartman, *Adventures in Research*, pp. 366–378.

[38] H. Julian Allen, Alvin Seiff, and Warren Winowich, *Aerodynamic Heating of Conical Entry Vehicles at Speeds in Excess of Earth Parabolic Speed*, NASA TR R-185, 1963.

[39] Hartman, *Adventures in Research*, pp. 381–385, 469–472.

[40] See "De France Retirement" folder, in 75-A-1324, 21896, box 5, SBFRC.

[41] Walter Vincenti interview, 8 Aug. 1980.

[42] Many colleagues of Allen's have mentioned this fact.

[43] This opinion is widely held among Allen's contemporaries.

7

AMES AFTER APOLLO, 1969-1976

Harvey Allen was director of Ames barely three years. During that brief period, the demands placed upon the center had continued to grow. Though *Apollo 11* would not land on the Moon until July 1969 — the climax of the Apollo program — NASA's in-house personnel had peaked in 1967. Since then civil servants had been encouraged to retire early, and programs had been cut back as budgets were trimmed. Ames personnel had peaked at 2,310 in 1966. By mid-1968, the number was 2,197 and the downward trend showed every sign of continuing. Similarly, though the Ames budget for 1968 was a comforting $103.53 million, there was no reason to be particularly optimistic on that score either. Further examination of budget figures reveals that though the 1968 program plan at Ames had been allotted $3.2 million, none of that money had been immediately committed for FY 1968.[1] The years of easy funding obviously were over, and the entire agency was involved not only in fiscal retrenching, but also in redefining its missions. Ames had not been in the forefront among NASA installations during the Apollo years; the waning of that program might offer the center a new opportunity to improve its position in NASA's total scheme of things.

Retrenchment after a period of rapid expansion brought a second set of dramatic changes to the research center in a decade. In mid-1958 Ames had employed 1,413 people. By mid-1966 that number had increased by over 60%. Even more dramatic was the operating budget, which had increased from the FY 1959 figure of $20.05 million to the FY 1968 peak of $103.53.[2] The growth, both in personnel and in money, had changed the character of the institution, and the change was the more dramatic because of the former personality of the center.

Under the NACA, Ames had grown slowly. New personnel had been absorbed easily. The Ames family was grounded in shared college experiences, in-house marriages, and closely related fields of expertise. With aeronautics the principal — almost sole — activity at the laboratory, professional research interests were clustered in a narrow range. Intercommunication had been easy. There had been only the distinction between low-speed and high-speed aeronautics. Though the two fields indeed presented different research problems, the same aerodynamic principles applied in both areas. It was symbolic that Harvey Allen, the wizard of high-speed aerodynamics, had helped to design the 40- by 80-foot wind tunnel, the classic monument to low-speed wind-tunnel research.

DIVERSE ACTIVITIES

Under NASA, with life sciences, space probes, and manned spaceflight, aeronautical research quickly became only one activity among many. By 1968 only 17% of Ames personnel worked in aircraft technology; 45% were involved in space research and technology.[3] The impersonal atmosphere, blamed by many veterans on the increasing numbers of contract personnel, was also a result of the increasing diversity of research.

Another major change for Ames had been the tangible and psychological effects of geometrically increased budgets. At first glance larger budgets might appear to be an unqualified blessing, but they brought with them much more paperwork. The NACA, with its small budgets and low profile, had received yearly appropriations from Congress with a minimum of fuss. Though in many years the NACA felt underfunded, the process by which funds were obtained and allotted was at least relatively simple. Under NASA, competition for funding took much more time and demanded a lengthy bureaucratic process. This change turned many researchers into administrative money-managers and program salesmen.[4]

Psychologically, the effect of big budgets had been equally dramatic. The NACA, and Ames under De France, had been scrimpers and savers. They did so partly from principle. (NACA officials had been proud to return money to the Treasury, something that is considered a mark of poor management today.) They also saved because in the days of minimal bureaucracy laboratory directors could easily transfer funds from one area to another. It was possible to save enough, for example, to append another relatively inexpensive test section to the 12-foot pressure wind tunnel.[5] For those in charge during the NACA period, people like George Lewis, Hugh Dryden, and Smith De France, conservative funding and relative freedom in managing money once it had been appropriated were highly suited to their own management styles.

De France had especially enjoyed administrative freedom with a minimum of Washington interference. That freedom, however, disappeared as research projects became more complicated, as contracting increased, and as NASA, very much in the public eye, met congressional demands to account

140

for its huge budgets. The Ames budget in 1940 had been approximately $5 million; in 1950, $7.5 million. In 1958 it was $26.5 million, and when De France retired in 1965, it was $91.7 million.[6]

In many respects De France and Allen, his successor, had coped with change quite successfully. De France had taken an active role in obtaining the Biosatellite and Pioneer projects for Ames. He had increased the Center's involvement in flight research using motion simulators, which proved important in Ames's institutional future. He had obtained the life-sciences research facility, and he had bent with the times as the new directorate began to change the character of Ames. In the last five years of his career, De France had made decisions that perhaps seemed revolutionary in light of his managerial conservatism, but he had accomplished what every founder of an institution hopes to — he had ensured that the laboratory he built had a viable future, even if that future entailed major change. Al Eggers, whose constant stream of new ideas helped to push Ames into new areas of research, retrospectively saw De France's ability to recognize the necessity for change and his determination to leave Ames as strong as possible as the explanation behind his 1957–1965 decisions. In addition, De France had had the support of Harry Goett, a strong proponent of space research, and of Jack Parsons, who in the early 1960s became convinced that Ames needed to develop project-management skills to meet the new era.[7]

Allen, younger and more open to new ways of doing things than De France, had nevertheless been unwilling to modernize center administration, although much of its mode of operation was outdated. Procurement methods were inefficient, research organization was sometimes too loose, and some staff changes needed to be made.[8] Allen, committed to his own research and perhaps myopic from long involvement with Ames, left much of the daily administrative details to his staff. Not as enthusiastic about project work as some, Allen was less inclined to push for new directions in project areas and remained more interested in things that intrigued him from a research angle, rather than responding to a need for long-term planning. In a time when increasing cooperation and communication between the center and Headquarters, and among centers involved in combined projects, was necessary, Allen's unwillingness to spend all his time on administration hurt Ames in Washington. At the center, however, he was a genial and approachable director, with an inspiring professional reputation and the unfailing ability to excite others to imaginative research. "Harvey had a fabulously creative mind; he just understood air," as Eggers put it.[9] If, as Ames director, Allen wore the cloak of management reluctantly, he served as an actively involved mentor for many young engineers, while at the same time he must have been a reassuring link with the past for the older employees.

Allen resigned in 1968, having reached the point where the burden of administrative responsibilities was more than he chose to accept. As his administrative assistant recalled years later, Allen had recognized the need for new approaches in the administration of Ames and felt a new director could better accomplish those changes.[10] During the search for a new director, Jack Parsons stepped in briefly as acting director.

The choice was a natural one, as Parsons had been both De France's and Allen's associate director since 1952. One of the first Langley people at Ames, Parsons had been De France's liaison at Ames while De France was still at Langley and his construction director afterward. Quiet and perhaps somewhat eclipsed by the stronger personalities around him, Parsons had been crucial to both De France and Allen as a source of information regarding the center, and at times as a mediator. Parsons's ill health, however, forced his retirement almost immediately. He died barely five months later, leaving a large gap in the Ames administrative hierarchy. Allen returned briefly as acting director. In February 1969 NASA announced a new director at Ames: Dr. Hans Mark, professor of nuclear engineering at the University of California at Berkeley and head of Berkeley's research reactor at Livermore.

The research center that Hans Mark inherited had an array of enviable facilities being used for many research and development projects. Spread over 366 acres, Ames in 1969 operated 18 wind tunnels, 2 sets of ballistic ranges, and 10 flight simulators. There were 11 arc-jet facilities in operation and 8 laboratories. Major buildings numbered 55, soon to be increased by the completion of the Flight Simulator for Advanced Aircraft (FSAA) built for testing the characteristics of jumbo jets and supersonic transports. Costing $2.6 million and six stories high, the huge simulator capped the range of research tools available at Ames in the flight-simulation field. John Dusterberry, the engineer responsible for much of the development of the FSAA, described its advantages:

> The unique things about the simulators at Ames are the motion systems associated with them. As far as computers and visual systems, the outfitting of the cockpit and so on, every major aircraft manufacturer does the same thing. The motion system moves [the pilot] around in space so that he gets the motion cues, whether he's leading forward or backward, . . . all the motion cues he'd feel if he were in the aircraft. . . . The motion systems that move the cockpit around with a great amount of travel define the time you can sustain the acceleration cue. The longer the travel in the fore and aft direction, the longer you can sustain that cue. The FSAA has [30 meters] of lateral travel so you can put side force cues on and leave them on for a long time. This requirement really came from [supersonic transport] work. Work could be done on the SST most completely [at Ames]. Now the FSAA is being used for some shuttle landing work.[11]

142

In January 1969, just before Mark was appointed director, Ames also announced the beginning of construction on a Space Sciences Research Laboratory; it was to include a vertical gun for impact-cratering studies and a large vacuum chamber with an ion beam for plasma-instrumentation work.[12] As had been true of the life-science groups, until the new laboratory was ready, the staff of the Space Sciences Division was housed in nooks and crannies around the center. In addition to the earthbound facilities at Ames, the center also boasted a growing contingent of research aircraft, among them a twin-engine Learjet, a Convair 990 research laboratory, a Convair 340 flying laboratory, and also a de Havilland C-8A Buffalo, soon to be converted into an augmentor-wing jet STOL aircraft.

The transfer of the Ames flight-research aircraft to the Flight Research Center at Edwards Air Force Base in 1959 had been a psychological blow to Ames, but over the next decade the center slowly regained its aircraft, especially those involved in V/STOL research. As one flight research engineer recalled, "Centering all activities [like flight research] in one place looks good on paper, but it doesn't necessarily turn out to be the most expeditious way to do research." As was soon discovered, the climate of the Mojave Desert — hot temperatures, high winds, and high altitude — were "all the things you don't want for doing flight testing" on V/STOL.[13] Not only was the low altitude and denser air of the Bay Area exactly what was wanted, but for flight *research,* as opposed to flight *testing,* Ames really was unique in its facilities, with the 40- by 80-foot tunnel and the flight simulators providing a variety of ways to obtain, check, and expand V/STOL data. FRC, having no wind tunnels and only limited simulation capability, could not compete. In the next few years, research aircraft would become more and more essential to Ames's activities.

Another source of strength for Ames in the late 1960s was its relationship with the Army Aeronautical Research Laboratory, which had been established at Ames. The product of a February 1965 agreement between NASA and the Army that recognized the agencies' mutual interests in aviation technology, the collaboration sought to "achieve tangible economies and promote efficiency with respect to continuing research and development of aeronautical vehicles."[14] The Army had agreed to staff and operate certain Ames facilities, while Ames supplied technical and personnel support. The immediate result was that the Army refurbished and modernized one of the two old 7- by 10-foot wind tunnels, the "war horses" of low-speed wind-tunnel research of World War II, and assigned 45 people to help in research. Ames could therefore continue to use the tunnel at little cost. Joint research projects were soon under way in that tunnel, as well as in other facilities in the flight research branch. The association was to become even more important in the following years under Mark's sponsorship.

The list of 1968 achievements that Ames found noteworthy shows both the range of activities at the center and the public image that Ames sought to display.[15] *Pioneer 8,* which had been launched in August 1966, continued to transmit useful data from the outer solar system, as had each of the previous Pioneer flights. In June, NASA announced that *Pioneer 8's* data suggested that the Earth's magnetic tail might be *shorter,* by millions of kilometers, than had previously been calculated. The steady production of data by the probe kept both the project and Ames in the news. Later in the year, *Pioneer 9* was launched. The Biosatellite Project, acquired in October 1962, was engaged in preflight testing of primate behavior in the capsule that would carry a monkey on a month-long spaceflight in 1969. Typical of project management work, the testing involved not only Ames, but experimenters at the University of California at Los Angeles (UCLA) and the General Electric Company.

In astronautics, sounding rockets launched from the White Sands Missile Range carried Ames payloads. Test flights designed both to check the rocket's control system and to map the magnetic field of the flightpath were successful. In cooperation with the Air Force, the X-24 lifting body had undergone full-scale wind-tunnel testing at Ames. Perhaps most newsworthy, with the Apollo mission still uppermost on NASA's activity schedule, Ames scientists developed a method of calculating lunar soil depths using measurements taken from Lunar Orbiter and Surveyor photos. A few months later, a group of scientists conferring at Ames announced that they had selected a combination of electromagnetic systems to gather data on the Moon's interior.

In life sciences, exobiology was at the forefront of publicized Ames activity as Dr. Cyril Ponnamperuma, one of the center's most active researchers, announced two fascinating hypotheses — that Jupiter's giant red spot might be red organic dye, millions of kilometers wide, and that the original sequence of chlorophyll syntheses on Earth had possibly been recreated in the laboratory.

On slightly more familiar levels, in 1967–1968 Ames developed blood-pressure sensors small enough to pass through a canine artery into the heart itself. The device would be developed as a human diagnostic monitoring device over the next few years. The research behind the sensors provides a fascinating example of the way interaction between research areas develops, sometimes in unlikely ways. The designer of the sensor, Grant Coon, far from being a member of the biomedical research division, as one might expect, was an engineer in the electro-mechanical research branch. The sensor was an elaboration on a pressure cell that he had previously designed for use in wind-tunnel tests where small size, high sensitivity, and high frequency were required. The reduced size of the new sensor made possible much more accurate measurement of blood flow. But the story is even more

144

complicated, for the sensor development had originally been requested by researchers in the environmental biology division who were not directly interested in blood pressure, but in investigating the transmission of artificial and heart-pulse waves through blood vessels. The research came full circle as the aeronautical researchers also discovered that they could make use of the tiny sensor in their work.[16]

Finally, in aeronautical research, two future strengths of Ames research were evident in 1968. One was the developing Convair 990 program of flying aeronautical laboratories. Operated as a national facility for scientists, the first 990 was about to be equipped for a variety of research tasks, among them infrared photography, meteorological testing, and fire spotting. Second, a new V/STOL aircraft, the Ryan Vertifan, underwent flight tests before delivery to Ames. The aircraft was equipped with counterrotating propellers submerged in the wings and driven by jet exhaust. These provided lift for vertical takeoff, hovering, and vertical landing. Last, but in many ways more directly connected to day-to-day aeronautics, Ames, Langley, and the short-lived Electronics Research Center in Cambridge, Massachusetts, became involved in a five-year program to improve light-aircraft technology and devise a workable collision-avoidance system. The three NASA installations each had $500,000 to spend on different aspects of the program. Ames's role was to flight-test six or more general-aviation aircraft, as well as to perform a series of wind-tunnel tests on its Learjet.

The variety of important research being conducted at Ames in the late 1960s is evident from the highlights above. One of the problems Ames faced, however, was that in the NASA family of research installations, Ames did a little bit of almost everything, which made it easy for NASA Headquarters to question, as it faced continued budget cuts, whether Ames was essential to the rest of NASA operations. Ames had excellent, even unique, facilities; but could not most of the work being done there potentially be done elsewhere?

The need for a new outlook, or at least a new image, was evident at the time to many. Some of the Ames staff felt that the center had been passed by in the excitement of the space program. The old feeling of geographical separation was still present, despite the shrinking of distances through faster travel. This was often expressed as a suspicion that Langley would use its proximity to Headquarters to advance its own interests (a suspicion that was perfectly correct): "Langley always had a little advantage in . . . certain areas because they were so close to Headquarters. They were continuously up there — could shuttle up in an hour or so — to get the upper hand in any program that was coming along. We were isolated."[17]

Another aspect to Ames's isolation is important to mention for this period, if only in contrast to what was to come. Since its beginning, Ames had had institutional and personal ties with academia, industry, and the military. Ties with industry and the military were formalized in traditional ways.

With academia, the ties existed on a more personal level of collaboration among colleagues in similar fields. In the local community, Ames had few real ties at a working level. Local officials were invited to annual inspections, but Ames as a working research center took little part in local life, and when it did, it did so quietly. Public relations, in the contemporary sense of the term, did not exist under De France, who felt that quality work would produce all the recognition that was needed without calculated flagwaving. The low-profile, nose-to-the-grindstone approach, admirable in many ways, was suitable in its day, but it too created a certain isolation among researchers, as felt by the newcomers from academia who comprised the life-sciences group. Perhaps even more detrimental, the policy of understatement created a public image Ames could no longer afford in the late 1960s. What was needed was a clear-headed assessment of Ames's strengths and weaknesses, and a practical program for eliminating weaknesses and ensuring recognition of Ames's strengths by NASA Headquarters.

THE NEW APPROACH

Hans Mark came to Ames at a turning point in its history. His credentials were impressive. His family had fled Hitler's Germany in 1940, when Mark was 11. He was educated at Berkeley and MIT; his 15-year teaching career was a steady stream of accomplishments. He had held administrative positions in academia, carried taxing teaching loads, and served in various capacities as a consultant to the Army, Air Force, National Science Foundation, and Institute for Defense Analysis. His published articles made an imposing bibliography in nuclear engineering. As a scientist who had maintained a research career while also holding high administrative positions, Mark promised to take a much more active role in the details of administration than Allen had. Also completely committed to continuing his own work in nuclear-engineering research, however, Mark could be expected to have empathy with the problems of researchers and understanding of the research process, a quality that De France probably had partially lost.

In strong contrast to his predecessors, Mark was new to Ames and NASA. He would view the institution with the perspective of a stranger. While a disadvantage in certain respects, his lack of old ties and habits would make it easier for him to see the need for changes — and to implement them.

Mark was also an academic, not a civil servant, and he brought with him a set of work habits and associations that differed from those of De France and Allen. These differences, combined with Mark's professional record and energetic personality, meant that the center, which a veteran manager would later characterize as having become "stodgy," was destined to change, whether gradually or forcibly.

With his strong views on solutions to Ames's problems, Mark perhaps managed the center, both internally and externally, less diplomatically than an insider would have. As an aggressive leader, he chose directions for Ames to which some objected. However one evaluates the wisdom and effectiveness of his management, the atmosphere certainly changed under his direction. Some viewed the differences as a transfusion, bringing fresh air into the old institution.[18] Others criticized both his goals and his methods, accusing him, at least privately, of destroying the last vestiges of the old pre-NASA intimacy. Decisiveness is always controversial, because almost by definition it steps on toes. The end question is, were drastic measures imperative to keep the center viable in a changing environment of shifting research needs and less generous funding? Evidence suggests that they were.

Hans Mark, Director of Ames 1969–1977. Mark brought to the Center an outsider's view of Ames's strengths and weaknesses, and an energetic management approach that created an effective variety of research options for the Center.

In 1969–1970 the question of Ames's continued existence as a NASA installation was a topic of conversation at Headquarters. Though the threat of closure never came close to reality, the possibility was rumored around the center. NASA Deputy Administrator George Low discussed it with both Mark and Deputy Director Clarence Syvertson, former head of the Astronautics Directorate.[19] He and Mark felt at the time that the possibility of closing was "fairly valid."[20] Had NASA pulled out, the center probably would have been put to use by another federal agency, very likely the Air Force. At the time, the Ames administrators convinced Low that they needed time to make changes and improvements. Though the center still faced reduced manpower, budgets, and programs, closure possibilities went no further than those conversations with Low. In a way, however, the circulating rumors aided Mark, who had to decide where reductions should be made. "We really took advantage of the fact that Ames closure stories were going around. It made our job much easier, because people listened to you. . . ."[21]

The new director changed the working atmosphere almost immediately. Creating an aura of urgency through his own work habits, Mark involved himself in every aspect of running Ames. Often working 12-hour days and expecting his staff to do the same, he quickly became noted for his production of "Hans-o-grams," detailed memos that were fired from his office with alarming rapidity. They struck at every level and quickly alerted all personnel to the fact that they had a director who missed little in the way of detail. His monthly correspondence file was often 3 cm thick. Staff, both administrative and research, were likely to be summoned for weekend meetings and brainstorming sessions, a logical practice for someone with a seven-day work week, but an unpopular intrusion to many of those involved.[22] The Strategy and Tactics Committee, a floating group of Ames personnel, was instituted by Mark as a way of involving key researchers in institutional planning for the center. "We'd ask them to put together various game plans," Mark recalled, "and then we'd modify them. A lot of people got involved in the management of the center."[23] According to one of the members, the committee meetings often featured fierce debates, during which various future projects and facilities were hashed out.[24]

Another practice Mark instituted, both to remain abreast of current research and to sort out the Ames talent, was the research review. Every section head with an active research project was called upon to give an account of his work before the director and the entire chain of command in the section-head's directorate. If sometimes traumatic for those making the presentations, the practice institutionalized a periodic self-examination by the researchers themselves.[25] Under De France and Allen, a researcher had had to use his own initiative to get a hearing with top management. Though this had always been possible, it had probably occurred only sporadically.

In April 1972 Mark also began frequent project reviews at Ames, both to aid in preparing the Ames reviews for Headquarters and to keep the center staff alert to potential problems. As Mark once observed, "the project management task is of major importance, [and] much of the future of the center depends on how well our projects are managed."[26] Identified by Mark for periodic review were current and future projects — Venus Pioneer, Tilt-Rotor, Pioneer F and G, Illiac, and the 91.5-cm airborne infrared telescope.

Mark continued Allen's practice of using technical research assistants. Whereas Jack Boyd had freed Allen from management details, Mark relied on Boyd and the succeeding technical assistants for technical expertise as well as management assistance. These long-term Ames employees, experts in their fields, greatly eased Mark's adjustment period by educating him on aeronautical technology. Eventually the research assistantships were also seen as training positions for younger persons who might someday be in management positions, giving them a broader view of the whole center. Similarly, staff-assistant positions were created for the deputy director on the same principle. The arrangement provided the director with firsthand ties to the research activities of the center and gave valuable management perspective to the technical assistants. A division chief later remembered his three years as a research assistant as a practical education that someone moving up from research into management by normal advancement (researcher to section head to branch chief, etc.) would have missed.[27]

Other changes followed. During the next few years, Mark made new appointments in the administrative staff, shifting personnel into new positions where greater effectiveness might be obtained. Some organizational procedures were changed. One example was the procurement system, which previously had served the whole center without differentiation by research area. The new director of administration, Louis Brennwald, who had a background in industrial management gained from years with the Northrop aircraft company, reorganized the system by creating separate procurement branches for each major research area. In this way responsibility was clearly apportioned and procurement procedures became more responsive and efficient.

Mark's first year saw the creation of a new directorate, that of research support. Headed by Loren Bright, it contained computer operations, research facilities and equipment, and technical-services divisions. Eventually it would also contain the Institute for Advanced Computation, built around the Illiac IV computer that Ames acquired a few years later.

Though the visible shifts Mark had made in the way the center operated seemed dramatic enough, he created even more stir as the major Ames emissary to Headquarters and other agencies. Where Washington had seldom seen De France and had had to summon a reluctant Allen when needed, Mark descended on Washington both frequently and persuasively. In an early

1970s OMB-NASA meeting, where the question of closing a research center was to be discussed, Mark appeared uninvited and presented such a favorable picture of Ames that OMB was noticeably impressed.[28]

It was not uncommon for the Ames director to make two trips to Washington in a week, promoting center projects and establishing ties that would lessen the transcontinental isolation from which the center still suffered. Riding the late-night "red-eye special" to be in Washington early in the morning, Mark planned tightly scheduled itineraries and announced his presence by dawn deliveries of San Francisco's sourdough bread left on many NASA desks. After a day of meetings, he would return to Ames on the late flight, to be at his desk the next morning.

In addition to changing the Headquarters image of Ames, Mark also embarked on what became a three-part plan to make the center indispensable to NASA. First, he sought to obtain even more unique facilities for Ames, facilities that would draw to them important research projects, much as the 40- by 80-foot wind tunnel had drawn the V/STOL work. Astronautics Director Dean Chapman described Mark's attitude: "[He] had a fundamental sense of property . . . that many Europeans have. . . . He has always been more willing than many to consider the possibility of collapse. The whole thing may collapse, . . . so you get as much steel and concrete set in dirt as you can."[29] Second, he fostered as many outside associations and joint research projects as possible, both to increase Ames's value outside NASA and to make it more difficult for NASA Headquarters to control and cut back the center's work.[30]

The third aspect of the plan, and the last to appear chronologically, was to introduce the concept, first at Ames itself and then at Headquarters, of very specific areas of expertise for each center. By gradually carving out a research niche for Ames that would be unique, the center's existence could not then be challenged with the argument that other centers could duplicate its work. Fascinated with the implications of technological interrelationships,[31] Mark planned to expand the range of facilities and then to ensure that those facilities were used by a much wider variety of research groups, who would then become added justification for continued support by NASA. Years later, Mark described the train of thought involved in his planning:

> In the NASA system, Ames competes with Langley. Langley is somewhat bigger than Ames; it's older, better established, closer to Washington. We recognized early that we could not compete with Langley across the board, that we had to establish strong areas and put all our marbles on those, and then become the best. . . . Ames was the first to make projections for the future about long-term trends. By 1973 we knew we were on the right track; if we simply

did our own thing, established ourselves as being excellent in the areas we had chosen, the agency would have no choice but to give us those areas.[32]

NEW FACILITIES

A major resource at Ames was its assortment of motion simulators. Though approved back in 1965, the Flight Simulator for Advanced Aircraft was not put into operation until Mark's first year. The event was made much of both at the center and outside it. The facility guaranteed that important flight testing of the supersonic transport and the space shuttle would take place at Ames. The simulator was to form an important part of Mark's argument that Ames had, as was indeed true, the best flight simulators in the world. The Vertical Motion Simulator, planned during the early 1970s, was submitted as part of the projected facilities building program for 1974. It was eventually approved in 1975, a result of steady efforts on the part of Ames to convince Headquarters that it was essential for both VTOL and helicopter research.

Simulator workloads reflected their changing role at Ames. Originally simulators had been used mostly in support of NASA's own in-house research. Simulation studies had validated wind-tunnel work and airborne research. Eventually, however, both industry and the armed services came to recognize the simulators as essential tools for testing specific models while still in the prototype stage. Outside users like the military often used the simulators instead of the wind tunnels for testing, providing strong support for continued expansion of simulation facilities.

Another facility acquired in the early 1970s greatly strengthened Ames for work in theoretical fluid mechanics, as well as concentrating superior computer strength at the center (see chap. 8). In 1971 Ames entered into an agreement with the Advanced Research Projects Agency (ARPA), part of DOD, to house and manage the Illiac IV computer complex, which would be the largest and most sophisticated in the world. Obtaining Illiac IV was a coup for the center, and though some time was needed for the problems in the system to be ironed out, by early 1973 it was in use. The association with ARPA was a step toward the entangling alliances that Mark desired. In 1974 the High Reynolds Number Channel was brought into operation, a facility built to evaluate computer codes for the numerical simulation of viscous turbulent flows. In combination with the computer system, the High Reynolds Number Channel, using real airflow, gave Ames further means to check and expand acquired data.

The 40- by 80-foot wind tunnel, which had been in continual use since its June 1944 dedication, continued to be one of Ames's most important facilities. As low-speed V/STOL work gained in importance, the huge tunnel was operated round the clock to accommodate the many demands on it. In 1973 it was refurbished, and a few years later an extension would be added to create a second test section, an 80- by 120-foot offshoot attached to the original tunnel. Increasing the versatility of the tunnel, the addition would greatly strengthen the unique facilities argument.

Research aircraft, while not facilities in the usual definition, play a similar role in the life of a research institution. In 1969–1976 Ames acquired several aircraft or the programs that would in turn bring such aircraft to the center. In 1970 the C-141 that was to be fitted with the 91.5-centimeter telescope was acquired, becoming operational in 1974. In the same year Ames, in cooperation with the Canadian government, began plans for a jet-powered, augmentor-wing STOL research aircraft. A converted C-8A de Havilland Buffalo was delivered to Ames in the summer of 1972, the first of a new line of experimental short-haul research aircraft. That same year, in cooperation with the Army, a tilt-rotor research vehicle was planned, another example of major V/STOL work that involved a NASA commitment to an "outside" customer.

The Convair 990 *Galileo* had become one of the major programs at Ames, proving invaluable in a variety of cooperative research ventures with other agencies. A medium-altitude research airplane, *Galileo* had undertaken a number of weather and resources surveys. Tragically, in April 1973 it collided over Moffett Field with a Navy P-3 while both were making landing approaches. The loss of the entire crew of *Galileo* was a real blow for Ames, but plans were immediately laid to acquire another Convair 990, which was delivered near the end of the year. In 1974 *Galileo II* resumed the work of its predecessor.

Another major addition to Ames was to be the Quiet Short-Haul Research Aircraft, for which design plans were completed in 1974. When operational, the graceful aircraft was to prove an exciting research tool, its remarkably short touchdowns approaching avian competence.

NEW ASSOCIATIONS

Mark's firm belief that Ames stood to benefit from ties that extended beyond NASA was pursued through a series of short- and long-term collaborations. Not only did Ames benefit from pooling research efforts and funding, but the new ties gave the center much greater visibility than it had previously enjoyed, a necessity in the most competitive post-Apollo years.

1976. Mid-altitude Convair 990 research aircraft over Lake Tahoe. The aircraft has under-taken research projects ranging from studying wildlife migration patterns and ice-floe movements to making archaeological surveys of Mayan ruins and studying monsoon behavior in the Indian Ocean area. The Convair 990 represents another direction in Ames's aeronautical research, that of using an aircraft itself as a research tool.

As already observed (see chap. 5), the Life Sciences Directorate had formed a variety of associations with other groups and institutions. These projects had made new professional contacts for Ames, with noticeable results in the world of public relations. Similar efforts in aeronautical projects produced much the same kind of public exposure in the 1970s. In 1973 a joint NASA-Soviet study undertook to analyze ice flow, meteorological data, and wildlife migration patterns in the Bering Sea; for this study Ames provided the Convair 990. Also in 1973 Ames earth-resources survey aircraft, two high-altitude U-2s, cooperated with the Department of the Interior and the State of Arizona to produce the first accurate land-usage maps for the whole state. The next year the same aircraft assisted Oregon and Washington in surveying tussock-moth damage and also measured flood damage along the Mississippi and in California's Sacramento and Feather River basins. In 1976

153

One of the new directions for Ames resulted in a NASA-Army partnership on rotorcraft research, which produced in 1977 the XV-15 Tilt Rotor. The aircraft, with an engine-prop rotor assembly, has the properties of helicopter flight when its rotors are shifted to a horizontal position and conventional flight when its rotors are oriented forward. It represents one of the more exciting varieties of V/STOL aircraft.

the U-2s supported several state agencies by following uncontrolled forest fires in northern California.

Even more useful to Ames, however, was the development of long-term cooperative projects with other powerful government agencies. The Ames-ARPA Illiac IV project has already been noted, but in three other areas, Ames committed itself to associations that proved valuable both for immediate research and, over the longer term, in strengthening Ames as an institution.

Cooperation with the Army for joint research in VTOL studies, dating from 1965 (p. 143), was greatly expanded in 1969. Army personnel at Ames doubled. In 1970 the Army consolidated its flight research and development as the Army Air Mobility Research and Development Laboratory, with headquarters at Ames. Cooperative work in VTOL and V/STOL studies led into additional exploratory and advanced research, with the Tilt-Rotor Research

154

Aircraft and the Rotor System Research Aircraft programs coming out of the first joint successes.[33] Eventually the Army's endorsement of Ames would help the center gain the lead role in NASA's helicopter research.

In 1973 a similar agreement for jointly developing new experimental aircraft was reached with the Air Force. In February both agencies agreed to cooperate on the development of both the Air Force's Advanced Medium STOL Transport Prototype and the NASA Quiet Propulsive Lift Flight Research program. Later in the year, an Air Force office was established at Ames to administer joint programs, with Air Force personnel permanently assigned. Thus another link was established to the armed services.[34]

Ames also concluded a valuable agreement with the Federal Aviation Administration and the Department of Transportation in September 1971. The agreement made Ames simulators available for qualifying checks on new commercial aircraft. By 1976 cooperation with the FAA had expanded to include joint research using the Augmentor Wing C-8A Buffalo and establishment of the Air Safety Reporting Systems Office, which sought to conduct continuing analyses of air-safety factors.

NEW PHILOSOPHIES

Not by chance did the Army, Air Force, and Federal Aviation Administration start cooperative work with Ames on V/STOL aircraft and helicopters. A new perspective on the center's place within the NASA network was slowly emerging, taking advantage of changing national priorities and consciously guided by Hans Mark.

In late 1968 the Senate Committee on Aeronautical and Space Sciences had announced that a new commitment was to be made in federally supported aeronautical research.[35] Clearly this would affect Ames, since its research strengths within NASA had always tended toward aeronautics rather than toward space. Indeed, Mark's annual report to the center in 1970 mentioned the strong possibility that Ames would play a leading role in future short-haul aeronautical research, including V/STOL aircraft.[36] Two years later he was able to announce that the national budget for research and development in aeronautics had increased from a little over $100 million in 1969 to $161 million.[37] Meanwhile, Mark campaigned to establish wide public recognition of Ames's strengths in short-haul and V/STOL research. Speaking to the House Subcommittee on Advanced Research and Technology in 1971, he underlined his center's capability by "illustrating how our organization works in aeronautical research" as he discussed both STOL and simulator research.[38]

In 1972 and 1973 Mark began to develop and publicize the concept of areas of aeronautical emphasis for Ames. In developing presentations for OMB, the Ames staff constructed budgets and research programs that emphasized research tools unique to Ames: low-speed, short-haul aviation research tools like the 40- by 80-foot wind tunnel and the flight simulators. Ames was already involved in just such research; future planning built on a solid framework.

Early in 1973 NASA's Office of Advanced Space Technology (OAST) appointed Clarence Syvertson to prepare an institutional planning document, forecasting future research undertakings at the OAST centers. When asked to comment, Mark emphasized the developing philosophical trend at Ames: concentration in areas where Ames already had clear research talents and facilities to support future programs.[39] At the end of the year, the OAST institutional plan produced a list of areas of focus for Ames that were defined along the lines Mark had verbalized earlier.

Six areas of emphasis were listed: short-haul aircraft research, flight simulation, theoretical fluid mechanics, planetary atmospheres, airborne sciences and applications, and life sciences. In recent years Ames had undertaken highly visible activity in each of these areas. Further, there was relatively little overlap between Ames and other centers; Ames already had most of NASA's competence in all of them. Though there was some reluctance at Headquarters to adopt the concept of areas of emphasis,[40] within a year NASA had officially accepted it, including the list of specialties Ames was to monopolize.[41]

The emphasis on short-haul aircraft research forms a fitting climax to the present history of the research center. When Ames became the center for short-haul aircraft research, it appeared logical to go even further in the same direction. Consequently, after a campaign waged by Mark on his frequent trips to Washington, NASA Headquarters transferred the helicopter research being done at Langley to Ames. The result was clearly defined control by Ames of all NASA's short-haul areas, both V/STOL and rotorcraft programs, and the equally visible support of that role by the Army, Air Force, and the Federal Aviation Administration. Mark's comments on the transfer underlined the claims Ames was able to make for its case:

> By the time we got the Langley helicopter research, we'd made the first modification to the 40- by 80-foot tunnel, had the second one approved, built the vertical-motion simulator. We had all the facilities for helicopter work, and most important, we had persuaded the Army to put its rotor-craft research laboratory at Ames. So we had the Army in our corner. So with all those things, the rationale for moving it here was absolutely unanswerable. All Langley had on its side was tradition.[42]

The decision to transfer helicopter research from Langley has remained, at least in some quarters, controversial. At Ames, some researchers felt they "were being sold something that didn't originate here, and Langley was already doing it. It was a whole new field, and we had to reeducate a lot of people."[43] Langley had been involved in helicopter research since the 1930s, and supporters of that center were understandably upset at losing that element of its research. Resentment focused both on Mark for perpetrating the transfer by his "area of emphasis" concept, and upon Ames in general for "stealing" Langley's research program, some of their personnel, and their research rotor aircraft. For Leonard Roberts, Ames director of aeronautics and flight systems, the subject was particularly delicate. Roberts was responsible for arranging the details of the transfer, and as a former Langley researcher, he was faced with an awkward task.[44] After the decision was announced, NASA Administrator James Fletcher, seeking to sweeten Langley's bitter pill, pointed out that the transfer was logical in terms of Ames's short-haul center designation, and in view of the relationship that

1976. Three directors of Ames gather. Hans Mark, left, and Harvey Allen, right, congratulate Smith De France on his 80th birthday. The three men represent facets of aeronautical/astronautical research and its management stretching from World War I into the space age.

157

Ames had established with the Army Air Mobility Research and Development Laboratory.[45] The helicopter research provided tangible proof of the significance of the alliances Ames had built and the ability of the center's management to use them for Ames's benefit.

The 1976 shuffle was not all to Ames's benefit, however; the Pioneer project and future planetary missions went to the Jet Propulsion Laboratory at Pasadena. The loss of Pioneer, managed from the outset by Ames, was a blow for which the expansion of research strength in short-haul aircraft might compensate. Thus Ames once more faced major changes that would test its managers' ability to realign priorities and to establish a new sense of mission within NASA. As we have seen, Ames's fortunate history, flexible leaders, depth and breadth of facilities and personnel — all these strengths augered well for the future.

The remaining chapters will investigate more closely three aspects of Ames during recent years: the working of a research directorate, the center's changing role in the community, and an assessment of changes in the institution over its first 38 years.

SOURCE NOTES

Chapter 7. Ames after Apollo, 1969-1976

[1] Jane Van Nimmen and Leonard C. Bruno, *NASA Historical Data Book, 1958-1969*, vol. 1, *NASA Resources*, NASA SP-4012 (Washington, 1976), pp. 255-257.

[2] Ibid., pp. 255-256.

[3] Ibid., p. 256.

[4] This factor in the changing Ames personality was mentioned by virtually all interviewees who had been employed at the center before 1958.

[5] De France was particularly good at doing more with allotted funds than originally planned, and several small additions to the center's facilities resulted from leftover funding.

[6] See app. B for yearly Ames budgets.

[7] Alfred J. Eggers interview, 6 Oct. 1982.

[8] These opinions were expressed by a number of interviewees commenting on the first decade under NASA.

[9] Eggers interview.

[10] Edie Watson Kuhr interview, 27 Apr. 1981.

[11] John C. Dusterberry interview, 21 Apr. 1981.

[12] Ames *Astrogram*, 16 Jan. 1969, p. 1.

[13] Seth Anderson interview, 8 Feb. 1982.

[14] Summary of AARL-Ames agreement of 1965, in statement issued by the Army Air Mobility Research and Development Laboratory Office, June 1978.

[15] See *Astronautics and Aeronautics, 1968: Chronology on Science, Technology, and Policy*, NASA SP-4010 (Washington, 1969), *passim*.

[16] Ames *Astrogram*, 25 May 1967, p. 3.

[17] Anderson interview, 8 Feb. 1982.

[18] Harry J. Goett interview, 3 Dec. 1981.

[19] Hans Mark interview, 20 May 1982, and Clarence Syvertson interview, 31 Aug. 1982. Both recounted the conversation with Low, which took place during the first year of Mark's directorship.

[20] Mark interview, 20 May 1982.

[21] Ibid.

[22] The weekend meetings, often mentioned by interviewees as one of Mark's radical innovations, were almost universally unpopular among the older Ames staff.

[23] Mark interview.

[24] Howard K. Larson interview, 23 June 1982.

[25] Mark's research reviews were described by Edie Watson Kuhr, 27 Apr. 1981. A researcher's perspective was added by Dell P. Williams III, 27 May 1982.

[26] Mark to deputy director and organizational directors, 24 Apr. 1972, 74-A-1624, box 163100, SBFRC.

[27] Alan B. Chambers interview, 24 Feb. 1982.

[28] Ibid.

[29] Dean Chapman interview, 28 Apr. 1982.

[30] Chambers interview.

[31] See Edward Teller, Hans Mark, and John S. Foster, Jr., *Power and Security: Critical Choices for Americans*, vol. 4 (Lexington, 1976).

[32] Mark interview.

[33] *NASA-Army Agreement — Joint Development and Operation of Tilt-Rotor Proof-of-Concept Research Vehicles at Ames Research Center*, NASA Management Instruction 1052. 154, 1 Nov. 1971.

[34] *NASA-USAF Memorandum of Understanding — Coordination of USAF AMST and NASA Quiet Propulsive-Lift Flight Research Programs*, NMI 1052.163A, 7 Feb. 1973.

[35] U.S. Senate, *Aeronautical Research and Development Policy*, report 957, Jan. 1968. Sponsored by the Committee on Aeronautical and Space Sciences.

[36] "Director's Annual Report to the Center," 20 Mar. 1970, *Astrogram*, 26 Mar. 1970, p. 2.

[37] "Director's Annual Report to the Center," 18 Feb. 1972, *Astrogram*, 2 Mar. 1972, p. 2.

[38] Speech to House Subcommittee on Advanced Research and Technology, 24 Mar. 1971, in 255-77-0020, 1/60, box 081780, SBFRC.

[39] Mark to Clarence Syvertson, 3 Jan. 1973, ibid.

[40] Chambers interview, 24 Feb. 1982. Chambers thought that NASA management opposed the division-of-research concept because it lessened their own management options.

[41] "Director's Annual Report to the Center," *Astrogram*, 10 Apr. 1975.

[42] Mark interview.

[43] Anderson interview, 8 Feb. 1982.

[44] Leonard Roberts interview, 8 Sept. 1982.

[45] *Sunnyvale Valley Journal*, 11 June 1976.

8

HOW A RESEARCH DIRECTORATE WORKS

Over the years the organization of a research institution continually evolves; identifiable, perhaps even dominant, organizational entities change shape and may even disappear. The directions of research also change; some investigations are completed satisfactorily, some are abandoned, others are modified. It is relatively easy to trace the organizational changes from published charts and changes in research activities by statements about projects and their progress, but understanding the motivation behind those changes is much more difficult. Yet it is in precisely this area that one may grasp the essence of the research and development process — what that process is and what factors can be identified as crucial. Anyone who has been a part of a research institution will recognize some common factors in the story, but others may find some interesting surprises.

Perhaps most surprising is the role of fortuitous circumstance. Chance seems an odd ingredient in research and development; one assumes that scientists and engineers know where they're going, or at least where they intend to go. However, though external needs and researchers' areas of interest define general trends in research, chance often provides an opportunity calling for an institutional response. That response may result in a new set of opportunities requiring further decisions. The process, we learn, is more a series of responses to evolving influences, rather than a predefined plan to which research adheres over long periods of time. Broad master plans may well exist, but they are themselves subject to the whims of circumstance, personality, and unforeseen developments. The research process, in other words, defies generalization and remains stubbornly recalcitrant when we try to pin it down to pat analytical formulas. For each research story, successful or unsuccessful, different factors combine, and often success rides on serendipity as well as intelligent planning and diligent research.[1]

Each research directorate at Ames has experienced evolutionary changes in both structure and areas of research. We have seen examples in the evolution of the Life Sciences Directorate. This chapter will examine more closely the Astronautics Directorate, seeking to answer such questions as: How did the directorate change over a period of years? What were the reasons for those changes? What were the factors in some of its research decisions? How did those factors interact to affect the directorate and, eventually, Ames as a whole? The directorate changed substantially from 1969 to 1976. From that period we will examine three areas of research evolution. The details behind the origin and progression of research in each area underline the singularity of each research story. That, perhaps, is the crucial point to be made as we try to understand Ames as a working research organization: there are no general models for research success, but there are fortuitous combinations of forces and events that have led to success. Not all research progresses as successfully as the examples chosen, but all research has its own interesting life story — different origins, rhythm of progress, and different factors and personalities affecting its success or failure.

ORGANIZATIONAL CHANGES IN THE
ASTRONAUTICS DIRECTORATE

The Astronautics Directorate of 1969 (fig. 1) would be strikingly different by 1976 (fig. 2). The modifications over the seven-year period illustrate a number of forces that are typical of those affecting any research organization governed by changing research demands, finances, and opportunities for changing research priorities.

In 1969 the directorate had consisted of three research divisions and an office that reported directly to the director. The most dramatic of the changes that occurred by 1976 were the addition of the Pioneer project and a support division for space projects, which was charged with advanced planning for future space projects and their developmental needs. In addition, significant alterations had occurred below the division level. Some branches no longer existed; some had been renamed; and some had been shuffled, more or less intact, to other locations. What combinations of factors had produced these changes?

In very general terms, the changes made in the organization of the Astronautics Directorate revealed the major influences affecting Ames in the years after Apollo.

During 1969–1971, Ames faced the threat of closure. Beginning his tenure as director under this cloud, Hans Mark made a point of emphasizing areas in which research activity was both visibly healthy and obviously salable. Activities that were not so easily justified were either redefined or dropped. Though some of the amputations seem drastic on paper, often what was involved was redefinition of major research directions, relocation of key research teams to different organizational elements where they could continue their work, or reassignment of individuals to new tasks as their previous jobs ceased to exist.

While faced with the threat of possible closure, Ames also faced the reality of reductions in force ordered by Headquarters. The result of beleaguered budgets and changing government priorities, RIFs theoretically affect positions and not personnel; but the connection between a condemned position and its incumbent is undeniably real. Therefore, a standard reaction to RIFs or expected RIFs is to find new positions for the potential victims before the RIFs occur, or to redefine the positions so that RIFs are less likely to affect them. Some of the changes in the Astronautics Directorate represented management response to continuing RIFs that threatened research positions. The most dramatic of these was the abolition of the Vehicle-Environment Division, which Mark believed to be vulnerable. In 1971 he abolished a branch and a section of the division, and the next year he abolished the division altogether, relocating its personnel to other positions. The addition of Project Pioneer and the Space Projects Division resulted from less threatening factors. Originally located under the separate Development Directorate, both Project Pioneer and Project Biosatellite had

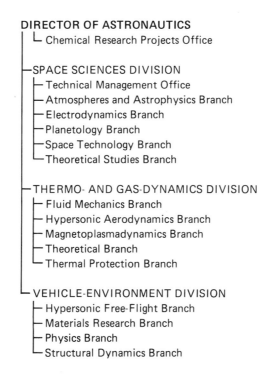

DIRECTOR OF ASTRONAUTICS
└ Chemical Research Projects Office

├ **SPACE SCIENCES DIVISION**
  ├ Technical Management Office
  ├ Atmospheres and Astrophysics Branch
  ├ Electrodynamics Branch
  ├ Planetology Branch
  ├ Space Technology Branch
  └ Theoretical Studies Branch

├ **THERMO- AND GAS-DYNAMICS DIVISION**
  ├ Fluid Mechanics Branch
  ├ Hypersonic Aerodynamics Branch
  ├ Magnetoplasmadynamics Branch
  ├ Theoretical Branch
  └ Thermal Protection Branch

└ **VEHICLE-ENVIRONMENT DIVISION**
  ├ Hypersonic Free-Flight Branch
  ├ Materials Research Branch
  ├ Physics Branch
  └ Structural Dynamics Branch

Figure 1.— Astronautics Directorate in 1969. From Ames Organization Chart, July 1969.

163

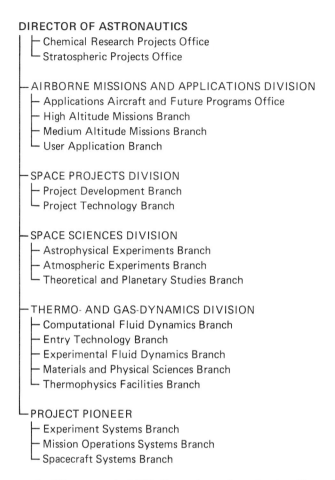

DIRECTOR OF ASTRONAUTICS
- Chemical Research Projects Office
- Stratospheric Projects Office

AIRBORNE MISSIONS AND APPLICATIONS DIVISION
- Applications Aircraft and Future Programs Office
- High Altitude Missions Branch
- Medium Altitude Missions Branch
- User Application Branch

SPACE PROJECTS DIVISION
- Project Development Branch
- Project Technology Branch

SPACE SCIENCES DIVISION
- Astrophysical Experiments Branch
- Atmospheric Experiments Branch
- Theoretical and Planetary Studies Branch

THERMO- AND GAS-DYNAMICS DIVISION
- Computational Fluid Dynamics Branch
- Entry Technology Branch
- Experimental Fluid Dynamics Branch
- Materials and Physical Sciences Branch
- Thermophysics Facilities Branch

PROJECT PIONEER
- Experiment Systems Branch
- Mission Operations Systems Branch
- Spacecraft Systems Branch

Figure 2.— Astronautics Directorate in 1976. From Ames Organization Chart, Sept. 1976.

been managed as separate entities, unattached to existing research divisions. By 1975 Biosatellite was completed and Pioneer had completed the most difficult stages of its mission. When the director retired in 1975, the Development Directorate was abolished. The Systems Engineering Division, which supported both projects, was absorbed into the Space Projects Division. The Astronautics Directorate was the logical place for both Pioneer and the Space Projects Division, although the problems of the research divisions and the problems of project management, being quite different, would complicate the job of the astronautics director.

New research directions and capabilities in the form of new facilities were responsible for some of the organizational changes, the most dramatic of which was creation of the Airborne Missions and Applications Division. While this change can now be seen as recognition that airborne science had become of major significance to the center, at the time it seemed merely the culmination of a series of organizational shifts that gradually grouped the C-141 Starlifter, the Convair 990, the Learjets, and the U-2s under one programmatic umbrella. As the aircraft were acquired and their research programs grew more extended, the need for a separate division became apparent. The C-141 and the Convair 990 were organized into the Medium Altitude Missions Branch and the U-2s were assigned to the High Altitude Missions Branch. (Branches in the Space Sciences Division were responsible for experimental planning to take advantage of the unique capabilities of the C-141 and the two U-2s.) The User Application Branch provided liaison between the developing technology and potential users of satellite and aircraft data. The importance of Ames's role in expanding uses for Earth-observation aircraft was underlined in 1972, when an Ames proposal to become the lead center was accepted by NASA Headquarters. With the later establishment of the Applications Aircraft and Future Programs Office, Ames assumed the coordination of not only its own Earth-observation aircraft, but also those at Johnson Space Center. This inter-center coup illustrates the effectiveness of Mark's plan to establish clear areas of excellence at Ames.

On the branch level, shifts within the three 1969 research divisions of the Astronautics Directorate illustrate how organizational changes accommodated the declining NASA budget, lower personnel ceilings, and the new research requirements of the post-Apollo period. Research areas that had been crucial to Apollo were not necessarily rendered superfluous, but priorities shifted. As old research tasks reached their maximum exploitation, they often exposed new problems and opportunities, thereby creating a new focus of investigation which in turn led to organizational changes. This process, common in any field of research, was especially striking in astronautics in the post-Apollo period.

The Space Sciences Division was transformed during 1969–1976 by two major forces: completion of the Apollo mission ended major activity in some of the division's areas, but acquisition of new research facilities opened opportunities in other fields. By 1976 the Electrodynamics Branch, the Planetology Branch, and the Space Technology Branch had been abolished, largely because of Apollo's running down. Researchers in electrodynamics and space technology were absorbed into other research groups, whereas the Planetology Branch was combined with the Theoretical Studies Branch. Planetologists had been concerned with hypervelocity impact phenomena, the origins of craters, and the study of meteoritic materials. With the culmination of their work in the lunar landing and the extensive data returned by the later Apollo missions, emphasis on planetology studies decreased, and many researchers left Ames. The rest were absorbed by the creation of a new branch, Theoretical and Planetary Studies.

In contrast, the acquisition of two new and unique research tools led to the expansion of the Atmospheres and Astrophysics Branch. In the early 1970s Ames researcher Michel Bader and his colleagues developed the idea of mounting a large telescope in a flying laboratory and using it for astrophysical and astronomical research. The idea found support; in 1972 a Lockheed C-141 Starlifter arrived at Ames. When a 0.97-meter telescope was fitted, a new field of infrared astronomy was opened. So much work was generated around the C-141 that the Atmospheres and Astrophysics Branch was split into two branches; the new Astrophysical Experiments Branch used the C-141.

Likewise, the field of infrared photography from high altitudes grew from the acquisition of two Air Force U-2s, which will be discussed later in this chapter. As possibilities for using the U-2s expanded, the Atmospheric Experiments Branch was created. In both cases, initial research proposals had resulted in unique facilities that in turn inspired the expansion of the original research areas. By 1976, therefore, the Space Sciences Division had changed substantially. From Apollo-support work, the division had shifted to an emphasis on infrared research, and indeed had proposed to NASA and the IRAS Telescope Project, an infrared astronomical satellite to carry the work of the C-141 a step further into space.

In the Thermo- and Gas-Dynamics Division, similar forces had produced changes in organization. In 1969 the Theoretical Branch was dealing with a variety of research subjects, some of which had declined in importance after Apollo. Information concerning high-temperature radiation characteristics had been crucial to the lunar-landing mission; thereafter, that field had faded. In 1970 Division Chief Dean Chapman restructured the Theoretical Branch into the Computational Fluid Dynamics Branch, dedicating it to purely numerical work and redirecting its research into new fields. The Magnetoplasmadynamics Branch, which studied the behavior of high-temperature gases in magnetic fields, was gradually abolished. Because it was a difficult area of study and an arcane one, Ames Director Hans Mark believed it was vulnerable to potential RIFs. In 1971 Chapman diverted all researchers in the branch into work on the newly approved large arc-jet facilities. By renaming the branch the High-Enthalpy Research Branch and restructuring its research, Ames responded both to the threat of reduced manpower and to the challenge of organizing an efficient work force to develop the additional arc-jet facility. When the new arc-jets were finished a year later, the branch was disbanded and its members reassigned to the Thermal Protection Branch, which used the new facilities. By this time, as Chapman recalled, the Thermal Protection Branch — renamed the Entry Technology Branch in 1976 — had become RIF-proof, since its research was connected with the Shuttle.[2] In much the same manner, the Fluid Mechanics Branch was converted into the Physical and Gas Dynamics Lasers Branch, eventually combining with the Materials Science Branch to become the Materials and Physical Sciences Branch.

The Hypersonic Aerodynamics Branch was also hardy, since its 3.5-foot hypersonic wind tunnel was NASA's largest such facility and much of its work in the 1970s was Shuttle-connected. To balance the new Computational Fluid Dynamics Branch, however, it was renamed the Experimental Fluid Dynamics Branch. The two branches represented the old and the new in aerodynamic research. While experimental wind-tunnel work sought data through actual tests on models, the computational approach attempted to duplicate wind-tunnel conditions numerically without actually running tests to acquire data. Finally, in 1976, the Thermophysics Facilities Branch was created to develop and operate division facilities.

The Thermo- and Gas-Dynamics Division had undergone radical changes during the 1969–1976 period because it had been so closely connected to Apollo during the 1960s. Apollo had also been the main concern of the Vehicle Environment Division, but it was perhaps less amenable to transformation than was Chapman's division. In 1972 Mark abolished the Vehicle Environment Division, moving Materials Research into the Materials and Physical Sciences Branch of the Thermo- and Gas-Dynamics Division. In contrast, the Structural Dynamics Branch was abolished, because Langley had always been strong in structural research, while Ames had had only a foothold in that specialty. Many members of the Physics Branch moved to Computational Fluid Dynamics, a field that Chapman was continuing to build, but the Hypersonic Free-Flight Branch was abolished and its personnel relocated. Some were assigned to the Development Directorate, at the time planning the Pioneer-Venus project; others were divided among the Research Support Directorate, the Aeronautics and Flight Systems Directorate, and the Airborne Sciences Office.[3] Somewhat atypically, the division chief of the Vehicle Environments Division, Alvin Seiff, returned to active research after being in management for some years, a move most scientists find difficult to make.

Generally, the organizational changes within the Astronautics Directorate during 1969–1976 were caused by conditions that were new to Ames. In earlier years the occasional organizational alterations had resulted from more or less straight-line growth, such as larger facilities and increased bureaucratic complexity. In the post-Apollo period, however, organizational change reflected changed research directions and, sometimes, retrenchment. Strengths were consolidated, vulnerable areas abandoned or redirected. In most instances, management was anticipating problem areas and attempting to present alternatives to RIFs, as well as to establish visibly unique areas to ensure the center's future. Rather than a simple organizational shuffling to provide better management, the changes represented varying methods of dealing with shifting circumstances.

The restructuring of the directorate was sound strategy. It was perhaps equally sound, tactically, to present an active and aggressive stance, initiated within Ames to deal with the future on its own terms. As Smith De France had changed Ames by adding a new research area in life sciences and a new project-management role with Pioneer, the Astronautics Directorate provides a good example of change within an existing research unit to provide for the future. As individual researchers shifted their careers to meet new research needs, the center's organization mirrored those changes on a larger scale.

Within a research organization, the routes by which research evolves vary just as widely as do the motivations behind organizational change. In an institution with the history, personnel strengths, and facilities of Ames, the means by which ideas grow into major undertakings differ dramatically. Such work is sometimes generated at the branch level and pursued for a time with a good deal of freedom from superiors. In some cases the decision to press ahead in a new research direction spurs the acquisition of new facilities that, in turn, influence the choice of future research projects. Lucky circumstances can have much to do with the selection of profitable research. The balance of this chapter will investigate three major research endeavors that originated in different ways.

REUSABLE SURFACE INSULATION – BRANCH-LEVEL INITIATIVE

A major problem facing the designer of a high-speed, high-altitude vehicle is the heating caused by reentry into the atmosphere. Harvey Allen's studies of missile nose cones and manned spacecraft ablation in the early 1950s had led to further exploration of the phenomenon. One field of study that grew out of interest in the ablation process was investigation of the surface of tektites — curious, button-like pieces of dark glass found in various places around the world. By reproducing the ablation process on synthetic tektites in a hypervelocity wind tunnel, not only was the process itself better understood, but the terrestrial origin of tektites was called into question. In the early 1960s, Dean Chapman and Howard Larson used the ablation patterns on natural tektites to calculate their trajectories. The researchers deduced that tektites were of lunar origin.[4] In 1963 Larson was named chief of the Hypersonic Aerodynamics Branch and became involved in the ablation patterns of ICBMs and how ablation affected their flight behavior. In 1968, as chief of the Thermal Protection Branch, he continued his work on missiles and returned to the field of ceramic materials, a natural extension of the tektite work he had undertaken with Chapman.

During the late 1960s the initial planning that eventually led to the Shuttle prototype was also taking place. Obviously one important issue was the reentry heating problem on a vehicle that was expected to be reusable. Unless an ablation shield was replaceable, the ablation process could not be used. An alternative presented itself in the idea of a heat shield that would not ablate, but would instead reradiate heat and insulate the vehicle.[5]

The idea was not new; similar plans had been a part of the Dynasoar project of the mid-1950s, though the shield envisioned for that spacecraft would have been metallic. In the late 1950s a beryllium heat-sink heat shield had been proposed for the Project Mercury capsule. Difficulties in producing acceptably pure beryllium in adequate quantity, as well as concern over the safety of a heat-sink heat shield on a manned spacecraft, resulted in the ablation shield being chosen instead.[6] In the mid-1960s the Lockheed Missiles and Space Company began working on reusable surface insulation, eventually convincing Max Faget, the principal engineer and spacecraft designer at Johnson Space Center, that a reusable insulation system was preferable to a replaceable ablation system. The reusable system would be more economical in the long term and would reduce turnaround time between Shuttle flights. By the late 1960s the concept of reusable surface insulation was being pursued by a number of contractors besides Lockheed, among them General Electric, McDonnell-Douglas, Martin, and Grumman.

While Larson had become involved in the field originally by studying the ablation of meteorites, tektites, missiles, and laser targets, Howard Goldstein had spent much of his career working on heat shields for missiles and spacecraft. By 1968 he was working for a small contractor doing materials testing at Ames. A year later he became an Ames employee and was assigned to Howard Larson's branch. Thus two of the principal researchers who were to investigate possible reusable insulation materials began working together.

By 1970 Ames was conducting tests for the various NASA contractors who were developing possible insulation materials. Two things had become clear. First, facilities were inadequate for accurate testing at high temperatures using a large enough test section. The available arc-jets at Ames, while producing the necessary temperatures, were inadequately powered for sustained high temperatures in a test section sized to accommodate large samples of the heat-shield materials that needed to be tested. Second, Larson's branch realized that the results of tests could not be analyzed satisfactorily. Apparently not enough was known about the properties of the materials being tested. Both discoveries were crucial to later developments.

In 1970, as Thermal Protection Branch personnel were wrestling with these questions, the viability of the Shuttle was by no means universally accepted. It was known throughout the center that Director Hans Mark had personal doubts about the concept. The testing of insulation materials that the branch was undertaking in support of industrial contractors was, therefore, of relatively low priority at the center. But Larson — an accomplished researcher and effective branch chief — enjoyed the support of the astronautics director and ran the branch with little interference from Ames management. Larson's team needed larger facilities for testing and more work by Ames researchers so they could understand the heating phenomenon they were dealing with.

Facilities acquisition was, as we have seen, one of Mark's major goals for Ames, so two proposals for new testing facilities won his support in 1971. One plan, developed by Larson, called for a gas-combustion facility using carbon or methane as fuel to produce a hot airstream that could be directed through a nozzle into a test section. The other proposal, put forth by Dean Chapman, was for an arc-jet facility with a 60-megawatt power source, three times as powerful as existing facilities. A combustion facility was less expensive, but Ames had the largest DC power source in NASA, which made a good argument for a large arc-jet. If larger arc-jets were needed, Ames was the logical place to build them. Both facilities were given preliminary approval by OAST in mid-1971.

Competition between Langley and Ames became highly visible over the following months. Ames was attempting to consolidate its position as a lead center for reentry materials testing, as well as to improve its general status by acquiring new and potentially important facilities. Langley management objected to the Ames proposals. On the grounds that any gas-combustion facility was really a structures facility and that Langley was the research center for structures work, Langley Director Edgar Cortwright argued that the gas-combustion facility should be built at his center. In due course the gas-combustion proposal was transferred to Langley. Ames was given approval to build arc-jet pilot facilities and, eventually, the 60-megawatt arc-jet.

With better testing equipment assured, Ames became more heavily involved in developing, as well as testing, new materials for the Shuttle's reusable surface insulation. What had been a sideline pursued without fanfare and without top management support expanded steadily. By 1972 Ames research in thermal protection materials had progressed to the point where in-house investigations were aiding the contractors in their work. As Larson's division chief, Dean Chapman, later observed,

> The contractors can't admit that the technology [knowledge] isn't there. They have to [maintain that it's] just a question of developing the system. But the research workers often realized that there were going to be problems with the existing design, and with their technical understanding they started to develop solutions before [Johnson Space Center] said they had problems to the budgeting people.[7]

1976. Space Shuttle tile being tested in the 60-megawatt interaction heating facility.

A year later, when Lockheed had become the principal contractor for the surface insulation tiles on the Shuttle, Ames was able to use its accumulated knowledge to aid their development. By then the material that had proved most satisfactory was made of silica fibers, and Lockheed had subcontracted with another firm for their production. Those fibers had not worked well, and Lockheed was considering buying more expensive fibers abroad. Ames research showed that the American-made fibers could be made usable, and the Shuttle project was saved sizable amounts of money. By March 1975 the 60-megawatt arc-jet facility was operational, and Ames had become heavily and visibly involved in Shuttle tile research.

Subsequently, new and better thermal protection materials were developed for the orbiter. In 1975 the branch developed a reaction-cured glass coating for the high-temperature tiles, which increased stability and resistance to cracking. Another Ames contribution was a second generation of basic tile material — the LI-2200 tile — which was to replace much of the original LI-900 tile developed by Lockheed. Over the next few years, Ames contributions substantially changed the whole thermal protection system for

REACTION-CURED GLASS COATING
- Improved emittance, stability, crack resistance
- Used for all high-temperature reusable surface insulation tile and for 70% of reusable surface insulation tile
- Developed in 1974, adopted in 1976

LI-2200 TILE
- Higher strength and temperature capability than LI-900, the tile developed earlier by Lockheed
- Used in over 10% of reusable surface insulation
- Developed in 1974-1975, adopted in 1977

GAP FILLER MATERIAL
- Protected structure from plasma flow in gaps between tiles
- Over 4,000 used on STS-1 (*Columbia*'s first operational flight), 4,700 on STS-2 (*Columbia*'s second flight)
- Developed and adopted in 1978

ADVANCED, FLEXIBLE REUSABLE SURFACE INSULATION
- Improved toughness, lower cost, and lighter weight
- Replaced 2 square meters of earlier flexible insulation in elevon cove for STS-2 to solve overtemperature problem
- Developed in 1975-1976, adopted in 1978

Source: Entry Technology Branch, Jan. 1982

Figure 3.— Ames Materials adopted for Orbiter 102 (*Columbia*).

the Shuttle orbiter, and what had been a branch-inspired research task evolved into a major contribution of the center (see fig. 3, p. 172). It was a unique situation: the branch manufactured, tested, and evaluated the new materials, a complete process of research and development, which is not typical of a research laboratory.[8] Equally important, the research project had evolved from a sideline based on curiosity into a major effort, a result of the happy combination of interested researchers, specialized facilities, and the freedom that allowed Larson and Goldstein to pursue their work over a long period of time.[9]

COMPUTATIONAL FLUID DYNAMICS – MANAGEMENT DECISIONS

The process by which Ames developed competence in the field of computerized aerodynamic research provides an interesting contrast to the Thermal Protection Branch's entrance into orbiter insulation. In 1969, when Hans Mark became director and Dean Chapman became chief of the Thermo- and Gas-Dynamics Division, Ames had the poorest computer facilities within NASA, an IBM 7094 machine that had been built in 1960. Despite that handicap, however, Harvard Lomax in the Theoretical Branch had been calculating supersonic flow over blunt-nosed bodies for some years. In the Hypersonic Free-Flight Branch, located within the Vehicle-Environment Division, Robert MacCormack was doing much the same type of computational work on viscous flow. Though tackling different problems, Lomax and MacCormack were working in the same new field that used equations of fluid motion to calculate the effects of high-speed airflow over various bodies under varying conditions. Their analytical approach contrasted sharply to the traditional use of wind tunnels to derive similar information.

Both Mark and Chapman were anxious for Ames to enter the new research field. As Chapman recalled,

> I'd been out of fluid mechanics for eight or nine years when I took over the division in 1969. When I reviewed the field and saw what computers were doing even then, it became clear to me that they could do a lot of things that I as an experimentalist never dreamed about, so I decided to press into that area. Mark was a vigorous enthusiast of the same thing, for a different reason. As head of the experimental branch at Livermore, he [had seen] the computer take over. We both had the same idea as to what should be done.

In 1970, after chairing a committee to define the future computer needs at Ames, Chapman created the Computational Fluid Dynamics Branch, using as a core the old Theoretical Branch. Harvard Lomax became chief, assisted by Robert MacCormack. Those two, plus two graduate students, had been the only researchers who could claim to be involved in computational fluid dynamics. Chapman's immediate task was to enlarge this cadre. "What we did," Chapman later recalled, "was to convert everybody in the branch whom we judged to be convertible to numerical work on the computer. It was also clear to me that since Hans was religiously enthusiastic about it . . . it would be a good haven for any bright employee who was willing to change his career around."[10] He had to find other niches for Theoretical Branch personnel whom he judged could not make the transition.

As Chapman was gathering personnel for the new branch, Ames management was also investigating various computers and how they might be procured. Upgrading the computational facilities was crucial, and Mark — not to mention the new branch's researchers — meant to replace the old IBM machine as quickly as possible.

Mark once admitted that he had "sticky fingers for airplanes," losing no opportunity to acquire research aircraft for Ames. He might have said the same thing about computers. As he later remembered, "Government regulations for computer procurement would have taken forever, so we very early decided on avoiding normal channels in getting them." The first opportunity came when Mark learned that an IBM 360-67 system was about to be declared surplus. It belonged to the Air Force's Manned Orbiting Laboratory program and was almost literally next door, in Sunnyvale. Seeing opportunity and responding in a typically decisive manner, Mark moved quickly: "The day the MOL program shut down, we had our people over there with a truck, moving that computer out. I knew it would be declared surplus and moved into the [General Service's Administration] system, so I thought we'd better get it and install it fast."[11]

Acquisition of the 360-67 opened the door for an aggressive research program by the new Computational Fluid Dynamics Branch. At the same time, it taught Ames management an effective method for improving their computer facilities. The early 1970s saw the retrenchment of many programs throughout the government, and Ames managers remained alert for other computer facilities that might be orphaned. They intended to "be there with a truck and lift them," as Mark put it, before the computers became officially caught up in government bureaucracy.[12] The next Ames computer, an IBM 7600, was also from the Air Force, obtained by Director of Research Support Loren Bright, who found out that it was about to be declared surplus. The 7600 became the main Ames computer until 1976, when the Illiac IV became reliably operational.

174

Ames acquired the Illiac IV under different circumstances. During its prime the Illiac was the largest computer in any aeronautical establishment and one of the most sophisticated in the United States. Three hundred times faster than the old 7094, its presence at Ames gained the center recognized preeminence in the field of computational fluid dynamics and practically guaranteed that when NASA bought better computer facilities, they would be placed at Ames.[13] Even if the Illiac had never performed successfully, both Mark and Chapman saw its acquisition as the deciding factor in establishing Ames as *the* center for computational fluid dynamics.[14]

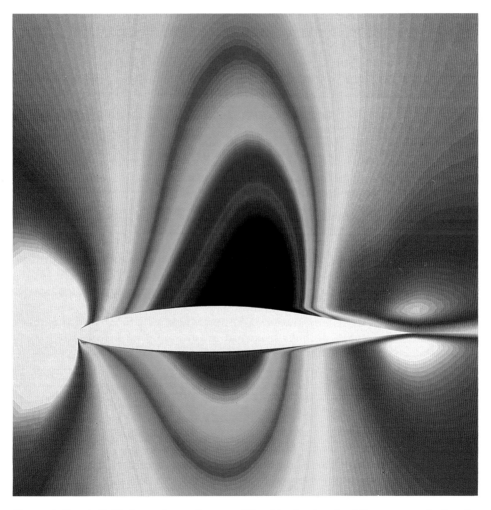

Computational fluid dynamics makes possible this simulated schlieren, reproducing the same type of information resulting from wind tunnel tests.

The Illiac's arrival was the culmination of a series of lucky coincidences. Dr. Edward Teller, Mark's longtime friend and colleague, knew he wanted to improve computer facilities at Ames. In 1970 Teller alerted Mark to a developing situation that involved the Advanced Research Projects Agency (ARPA), the University of Illinois, and the Illiac, at that time in the conceptual stage. Planned as an ARPA research facility, the Illiac was being designed by the University of Illinois and would be located there and operated under contract with ARPA. As student unrest grew during the late 1960s, ARPA became increasingly nervous about the Illiac at the university.

Mark was happy to promise adequate protection for the Illiac if ARPA would place it at Ames. Again, Mark's widespread circle of acquaintances proved useful: "I'd gone to high school with Dan Slotkin, the Illiac's developer," recalled Mark.[15] After a period of negotiations, ARPA agreed to place the Illiac at Ames, and in December 1970 NASA Deputy Administrator George Low approved the plan. Formal announcement of acquisition of the Illiac was made in January 1971.[16]

The Illiac arrived in the summer of 1972, and though initially troublesome, it eventually became one of Ames's great research strengths. By 1975 computational fluid dynamics had made such impressive strides that Mark, Chapman, and Melvin Pirtle, head of the Illiac program, argued in an *Astronautics and Aeronautics* article that the relationship between wind-tunnel testing and computational fluid dynamics was shifting. While wind-tunnel research would always be necessary, the three authors believed that computational fluid dynamics would play an increasingly important role in the future.[17] Expectedly, the article produced some howls of indignation from the experimentalists, who accused the authors of endangering the future of the wind tunnel. Though the alarmists had misread the article, the furor it caused was indicative of the influence computational fluid dynamics was beginning to have.

Creation of the Computational Fluid Dynamics Branch and the unconventional procurement policies followed in obtaining improved facilities for computational research illustrate another variation of the research evolution story. In this case, upper management at Ames had clearly grasped the potential of a new field for the center and had moved aggressively in that direction. New and better facilities being essential, they were procured. This differed from Mark's motives in supporting the proposal for gas-combustion and arc-jet facilities. These had been procured in line with his general principle of acquiring as many unique research tools as possible. While Ames grew into its role in NASA-wide thermal protection research through branch-level decisions, in computational fluid dynamics, higher management made a clear decision to proceed in a new direction and organized a strategy to support that decision. Facility acquisition followed a research decision, and both facilities and research grew together through mutual support.

176

U-2 RESEARCH – FACILITIES LEAD TO NEW RESEARCH

High-altitude photography and remote sensing for Earth-resources investigations were not, originally, research directions that Ames had clearly defined. In 1970, however, the Air Force announced to other federal agencies that it was ready to make available two of its high-altitude U-2 reconnaissance aircraft for research purposes.[18] Agencies, and even private industry, were invited to submit proposals for the use of the aircraft.

NASA was in the final planning stages of the Earth Resources Technology Satellite (ERTS) program, with the first launch planned for 1972.[19] Researchers were becoming concerned that they would have trouble analyzing the data, since all available high-altitude visual-spectral-band and infrared photography came from altitudes where atmospheric distortion was minimal. The ERTS satellites would be recording radiation that had passed through the entire atmosphere, and distortion would certainly be greater. The possibility that NASA might acquire the U-2s as research aircraft added inspiration to a developing idea.

If photographs from above the densest part of the Earth's atmosphere could be obtained, the data should be similar to the data ERTS would produce. With U-2 photography, analysts should be able to prepare themselves to analyze the data the satellite would later produce. With this use for the high-flying U-2s in mind, NASA asked the Air Force to transfer the aircraft to them. Using infrared cameras, the aircraft, like the satellite, could measure the chlorophyll content of vegetation — a major feature of ERTS data. In infrared, the reddest portions of a photograph indicate high chlorophyll levels.

Anyone seeing a Lockheed U-2 might have immediately understood why an agency devoted to aeronautical research would have wanted one. Sleek and fragile looking despite its size, the single-seat aircraft had extraordinarily long, narrow wings attached to an equally streamlined fuselage. Even to the untutored eye it was the epitome of refined grace, a plane one might imagine would require a subtle touch. Designed by De France's old Lockheed colleague Clarence L. ("Kelly") Johnson in the mid-1950s, the U-2 remained, despite its age, a thoroughbred among aircraft, capable of reaching 21,000 meters in altitude.

The U-2, however, required almost a separate education in flying and maintenance. Carelessly flown, it would "crumple into a ball of aluminum foil."[20] Carelessly maintained, it would quickly become a hazard to fly. The Air Force, though impressed by NASA's proposed use of the aircraft, was convinced that NASA was completely naive about the complexity and sensitivity of the U-2s and was therefore reluctant to decide in NASA's favor until it was certain that the aircraft would be suitably provided for with both expert flight personnel and careful maintenance.

After prolonged discussion between NASA and the Air Force, Martin Knutson, one of the first U-2 test pilots, was dispatched to NASA to tutor the agency on the intricacies of the U-2. With his help, the Office of Space Science and Applications devised a utilization plan that was acceptable to the Air Force, including strict requirements for flight crew selection and maintenance provided by crews from the Lockheed division that had developed and manufactured the U-2s.

While negotiations were progressing, NASA deliberated on where the aircraft should be based. Ames made a strong case for acquiring them. Long-lived rumors at Ames have it that Johnson Space Center, already operating high-altitude B-57Fs, maintained that the U-2s were too dangerous for routine work and should not be accepted. Whatever the JSC position, the result was that NASA Headquarters decided to place the aircraft at Ames. Knutson, ready to retire from the USAF, reconsidered a NASA offer and agreed to take charge of the U-2 project at Ames.[21]

In June 1971 the U-2s arrived at Ames, with a minimal maintenance crew and one other test pilot besides Knutson. The sensor system for the aircraft was still under development. A short two months later, however, a U-2 flew its first satellite simulation flight. Knutson's operation, under the Airborne Sciences Office, became the Earth Resources Aircraft Project (ERAP). At that time the plan for the U-2s went no further than ERTS simulation, with the expectation that once ERTS-A was in orbit, simulation flights would no longer be needed.

As circumstance would have it, the future of the U-2 project at Ames became assured through bad luck in another NASA quarter. ERTS-A was due to be launched in spring 1972; but developmental problems arose, threatening postponement of the launch date. In the case of ERTS-A, this delay was catastrophic, since the satellite was to be short-lived and had been earmarked for a crop survey during the spring growing season. Those data were to delineate the benchmark against which later observations would be compared. Goddard Space Flight Center, managing the ERTS project, called Ames.

The ERAP staff, after hurried consideration, produced a plan that answered Goddard's dilemma. The Pre-ERTS Investigator Support program took the planned satellite survey and restructured it for the two U-2s. The data could subsequently be compared with information obtained by the tardily launched satellite. With a great deal of midnight oil and a certain amount of luck, over a three-month period the two U-2s made hundreds of flights and accomplished the mission originally assigned to ERTS-A. "After that," Knutson recalled, "research branched like a many-limbed tree in every different direction."[22] Not only did the U-2s continue to support satellite

1980. A U-2 image of Mt. St. Helens after its eruption helps researchers understand aerosol particle behavior and ash dispersal. The picture is cropped closely for detail.

data for ERTS and later Landsat and Skylab, they also provided information in other resource surveys and were used extensively in disaster assessment. Using U-2s, NASA, cooperating with other federal agencies, provided, at a surprisingly low cost, information sometimes unobtainable by any other method.

179

In 1974, for example, a U-2 surveyed the Dudaim melon infestation in the Imperial Valley at a fraction of what a ground survey would have cost. The melon, an alarmingly vigorous weed, was smothering the California asparagus crop. The melon was not only difficult to detect, but ground surveying was made even worse by dreadful heat, the rough vegetation, and rattlesnakes. By the time the Ames aircraft were employed, the melon had been indicted in federal court! The survey was not only successful in locating infestations, but it also cost little more than $3,000, where a ground-based investigation had been estimated at $64,000.[23]

The U-2s provide another variety of research pattern: their uses became apparent after they had been acquired. Contrary to the acquisition approach of the large arc-jets and the series of increasingly powerful computers, Ames obtained the U-2s in an opportunity that presented itself. There was no existing program in high-altitude work and no plan to form one. Hans Mark indeed had sticky fingers for airplanes; but in this case he only responded to a set of fortuitous circumstances, to the definite benefit of the center.

This consideration of some activities in the history of the Astronautics Directorate has provided some insight into the workings of a research institution. Structural organization, as we have seen, reflects the ebb and flow both of larger agency goals and of the center's own research priorities. Economics and directives from Headquarters play an important role in the restructuring of research units. The examples of thermal protection materials, computational fluid dynamics, and the U-2s reveal the variation of research patterns and the different levels at which crucial decisions are made. Just as research decisions can originate at a higher management level, so they can also begin at a branch or section level. As often as conscious plans are developed, luck can provide a research route without a plan. The secret, then, seems to lie in meeting opportunity head-on.

SOURCE NOTES

Chapter 8. How a Research Directorate Works

[1] I am grateful to Dr. Dean R. Chapman, director of astronautics at Ames Research Center (1974-1980), now professor of aeronautics and astronautics, Stanford University, for much of this chapter. He was very generous with his time and invaluable in helping me to understand the research process.

[2] Dean R. Chapman interview, 17 June 1982.

[3] Ibid. Personnel moves were also traced through the Ames telephone directories for 1972-1974.

[4] Dean R. Chapman and Howard K. Larson, "On the Lunar Origin of Tektites," *Journal of Geophysical Research* 68 (15 July 1963) pp. 4305-4358. NASA TN-1556 is an earlier version of this article.

[5] I am grateful to Howard K. Larson and Howard E. Goldstein for much information regarding the development of reusable surface insulation in the Thermal Protection Branch. Both men played crucial roles in the research.

[6] Loyd S. Swenson, Jr., James M. Grimwood, and Charles C. Alexander, *This New Ocean: A History of Project Mercury*, NASA SP-4201 (Washington, 1966), pp. 138-142.

[7] Chapman interview, 29 June 1982.

[8] Chapman interview, 17 June 1982.

[9] For a complete description of the Ames work on the Shuttle orbiter thermal protection system, see Howard K. Larson and Howard E. Goldstein, "Space Shuttle Orbiter Thermal Protection Material Development and Testing," in *Proceedings of the 4th Aerospace Testing Seminar*, Los Angeles, 2-3 Mar. 1978, pp. 1-5.

[10] Chapman interview, 29 June 1982.

[11] Hans M. Mark interview, 20 May 1982.

[12] Ibid.

[13] Chapman interview, 29 June 1982.

[14] Mark interview, 20 May, and Chapman interview, 29 June 1982.

[15] Mark interview, 20 May 1982.

[16] *Astronautics and Aeronautics, 1971: Chronology on Science, Technology and Policy*, NASA TP-4016 (Washington, 1972), p. 23.

[17] Dean R. Chapman, Hans Mark, and Melvin W. Pirtle, "Computers vs. Wind Tunnels for Aerodynamic Flow Simulations," *Astronautics and Aeronautics* 13 (Apr. 1975): 22-35.

[18] I am grateful to Martin A. Knutson, former chief of the Air Missions and Applications Div., for information regarding the acquisition of the U-2s.

[19] See Pamela E. Mack, "The Politics of Technological Change: A History of Landsat," Ph.D. dissertation, University of Pennsylvania, 1983.

[20] John Joss, "U-2: The Original Bear in the Air," *Flying*, no. 100 (May 1977), p. 36.

[21] Ames's locale was the deciding factor in Knutson's decision, as it seems to have been with many Ames personnel.

[22] Martin A. Knutson interview, 29 June 1982.

[23] NASA release 74-22, 10 June 1974.

9

AMES IN A LARGER CONTEXT

Although NASA was built upon the foundations of the NACA, absorbing its personnel and facilities, the new agency soon differed radically from the old in many ways — and nowhere more than in the practice of public relations. The NACA had been a quiet agency in a very specialized line of work. To those connected with aeronautics, it had been highly respected and well known; but to the general public, it was one of the less familiar government agencies. In the early years of Ames, its managers made little effort to conduct a public relations program, which was considered neither desirable nor necessary.

Not that Ames lacked ties with the local community, especially the academic community; but those ties were very conservative and usually ad hoc. There were professional ties among colleagues in the same fields; there were arrangements whereby Ames personnel could study or teach at Stanford, or graduate students could work part-time at Ames; there were the important ties resulting from Professor Durand's eminence in the NACA. But there was little institutionalized joint research, little formalized, continuing collaboration. The results of Ames research did not reach beyond the aeronautic community because of the nature of the NACA's work. What would later be called *spinoff technology* did not exist.

These three areas of public involvement — public relations, academic ties, and technological spinoff — changed greatly after 1958. NASA started with a completely different outlook on life, owing its very existence to public awareness of the implications of Sputnik. The need for an immediate, major financial commitment dictated a new approach to the public. The range of research increased dramatically as NASA became involved in space technology and life support, while continuing the aeronautical research that had gained the NACA its reputation. The increased scope of investigation changed NASA's relationship with academia and created technology that could be adapted to subsidiary uses. This chapter considers changes in these areas at Ames in the late 1960s and early 1970s.

COMMUNITY TIES

As one Ames veteran remarked,

> In the old days, we did very little in public relations. Every three years, we invited congressmen and local mayors to what was mostly a technical open house. We didn't feel it necessary to make a big effort to improve public relations, though. Now, public relations activities are more important, in part, because of the increased emphasis on space research.[1]

NASA brought a whole new approach to public relations. Under De France, public relations were restrained in tone and limited to infrequent gestures on a local basis. Undoubtedly, De France felt that public salesmanship was inappropriate. Gestures that would have been considered routine public relations by any business he saw as potential conflicts of interest, and he discouraged Ames personnel from placing themselves in public situations that could be seen to have the remotest connection with their position at Ames.[2] The public, therefore, was not encouraged to much interaction with Ames. The triennial open house, where congressmen, representatives of industry, and local dignitaries were given a tour of the laboratory and informed of research accomplishments, was not open to the public. It was left to the Washington office to keep up political contacts and to create a respected image for the NACA; as Ames managers perceived things, the task of the laboratories was research, not diplomacy.

NASA, dependent on public support for its large appropriations and born in the full glare of political limelight, took an active approach to public relations from the very beginning. The research centers followed suit, and after 1958 the local newspapers seemed to carry more publicity about Ames. It also seems that De France was still reluctant to plunge into such outside activities.[3] By the late 1960s, however, Ames was taking an active role in community affairs, in decided contrast to its first two decades of existence. Evidence of the change is widespread.[4]

On a community level, much of the new public exposure was the result of efforts to act as a mentor for both students and teachers. The 1963–1968 period saw increased participation in activities sponsored by the National Science Teachers Association; Ames hosted prize-winning high-school students and served as an audience for the presentation of their research projects. In 1965 Ames began to take part in President Johnson's Youth Opportunity Campaign, designed to offset high unemployment among teenagers by creating new jobs in federal agencies. The first year Ames hired 25 young people aged 16–21 for summer employment.[5] The numbers grew each summer. The practice not only benefited the students by providing them with work; it also served as another means of integrating the center into the surrounding community in a very practical manner. During the same period, Ames became involved in teacher education with an annual lecture series for science teachers of Santa Clara County.

In the mid-1960s Ames began to place exhibits at county fairs, and both NASA as a whole and Ames in particular received a good deal of publicity through this exposure. In 1966 Idaho sponsored an Aerospace Week, and Ames provided the major exhibits and educational programs. That same year Ames staff members taught a course in atomic energy to a local boy-scout troop.

Some of the publicity that Ames enjoyed during NASA's first decade resulted from the public's fascination with space rather than any effort made by the center. In the mid 1960s news of Ames was featured on some prestigious television programs, emphasizing the range of research done at the center. In 1963 a documentary depicted the center's work on the supersonic transport. The next year Ames test pilots involved with the X-14A were interviewed, and the following year two members of the Ames life-science staff discussed the effects of space on the human body. While perhaps minor exposure on a national level, the growing mention of Ames in the media served to remind the local public that interesting things were taking place there and, indeed, had been for years. When Smith De France retired in September 1965, the *Palo Alto Times* devoted an editorial to a finely worded appreciation of the man and the institution he had been so influential in molding.[6]

The trend toward major efforts in public relations throughout the agency was emphasized in 1966 when NASA instituted a "communications improvement" campaign. Public information officers were charged with maximizing their center's positive image in the local community.[7] The timing suggests that the first flush of enthusiasm for space inspired by the formation of the agency and the Mercury and Gemini projects had faded and needed bolstering by a conscious effort at salesmanship. Another element in Ames's growing involvement in outside activities undoubtedly stemmed from gregarious Harvey Allen's influence as the new director. He was irrepressibly eclectic in his interests and acquaintances. Under Allen, the Ames bias toward isolationism began to fade; the director's natural sociability was matched by his commitment as a researcher to a less limited field of professional and public dialogue.

Over the next few years, the scope of the Ames public affairs office increased as the center became ever more involved with the public. Tours of the research center, unlike the highly formalized affairs of the NACA period, grew into routine offerings to an assortment of groups, from elementary school classes to visiting scientists from other countries. Ames activities were mentioned with increasing frequency in the local papers. In 1970, when NASA closed its Western Operations Office at Pasadena, Ames assumed the duties of conducting NASA's public affairs in the 11 western states. This widened the Ames public affairs office's duties to include distribution of educational films and publications, management of NASA exhibits, and response to public and press inquiries.[8]

In 1971 Hans Mark reassigned Arthur Freeman, who had been the director of administration since 1940, to a new role. As Freeman put it later, his job was "to explain as carefully and as thoroughly as possible what we are doing and why we are doing it — not only what we are achieving from a scientific standpoint, but also how it impacts on and contributes to both the local economy and the future of mankind." His task was over and above that of the public affairs office. Freeman was to stay in "contact with appropriate representatives of state and local governments, local businesses, labor organizations, and business and professional associations, the purpose being to determine how we, as a Government research activity, can materially increase our contributions to and improve our relations with our 'area of responsibility.' "[9]

Freeman's summary, prepared for Headquarters, gives a good indication of how widely Ames had extended itself into the public sphere since 1958. For example, by 1971 the center had a "small-business specialist" whose task was to educate small firms on how to do business with Ames or other federal agencies. He specifically sought out small local businesses to supply some of Ames's needs, and with a reasonable amount of success: of 109 research and development contracts issued in a two-year period, 32 went to small businesses.[10] In a similar manner, the Contracts Compliance Office was instrumental in implementing a Small Business Minority Entrepreneur program, under which service contracts were negotiated with minority-owned small businesses. The hope was that the experience would increase their success in gaining other contracts.

Cooperation with the Neighborhood Youth Corps of Santa Clara County, which began in 1967 with summer employment opportunities for local students, grew by 1971 into a program by which Ames employed over 50 high-school dropouts, with the purpose of teaching job skills that would enable them to gain jobs within the community. By 1971 almost 400 had participated in the program.

On the high-school and college level, Ames's cooperation had progressed past occasional interaction to a number of continuing relationships. From one high-school district, 40 students were bused to Ames five afternoons a week as part of a credited work-study program. The same was true for Foothill and De Anza Community Colleges; Ames provided part-time employment for nearly 20 students annually, as part of the colleges' financial aid programs. In 1970 a separate special training program was begun

186

with the Foothill Community College District. Students received classroom instruction on campus and practical work experience in the Ames shops and facilities.

As a source of employment and job training Ames was becoming more of a force in the local community; but in addition to that, the center was beginning to stretch its facilities and personnel resources outward into the community. Besides organizing and staffing teacher workshops for college-credit coursework, Ames began offering more specialized programs. In 1970 an Ames craftsman gave a three-day forum for high-school shop teachers interested in developing courses in plastics. Various one-day institutes for college classes were given some 10 times a year, and a teacher resource center was developed. This provided local teachers with the chance to preview audio and visual aids for classroom use, to reproduce visual material, and to use the Ames library. In addition, local colleges were invited to participate in the seminars that Ames conducted for its own staff, a tradition that had begun to develop under Allen's directorship.

By 1971 Ames had also become involved in mutual research projects with students, high-school teachers, and university professors. During the school year, between 20 and 30 high-school students studied with an Ames researcher one day a week, working on a research project of mutual interest. As part of the program, members of the life-sciences staff taught a course in space biology; at the year's end, Ames awarded fellowships to the most promising students for the continuation of their research. For high-school teachers, similar opportunities were present; the National Science Foundation sponsored 30 summer fellowships for teachers interested in research-oriented courses. Like the students, they were given the chance to pursue a summer research project with an Ames staff member.

One of the most interesting programs in which Ames became involved was the Faculty Fellowship Program jointly sponsored by NASA and the American Society for Engineering Education. Begun in 1964, the 10-week summer program was constructed to give experience in space research and engineering systems design to college faculty who were outstanding in related fields. In the cooperative study and research program, Stanford shared with Ames the combination of research and coursework responsibilities; 50–60 professors worked with the Ames senior staff and attended classes and seminars at Stanford. The program was a two-year one; most researchers returned for a second summer to continue their projects. In 1968, for example, 20 of the participants produced a system design of a manned lunar scientific observatory. NASA received the benefits of a useful study, and the researchers gained experience in designing multidisciplinary engineering systems.[11]

As an aid to those earlier along in their careers, Ames also took part in the National Research Council's Resident Research Associateship program.

The Fellows were funded by money allocated to the Council by NASA Headquarters and chosen by a panel appointed by the President of the National Academy of Sciences. The researchers could work in any fields that were of interest to Ames; the Fellows were often renewed to continue their work over several years. The program began in 1961 with one post-doctoral associate and grew steadily; by the end of 1976, participants numbered 38, half new appointments and half renewals.[12]

On a less technical level than the NASA-ASEE program, Ames had also developed educational ties in ways that increased the center's visibility and rapport with the community and bridged the gap between highly specialized technology and the Bayshore Freeway commuter who occasionally looked at the collection of wind tunnels and idly wondered what happened there.

In the adult community, the center had begun participating in local adult education programs, offering instructors for courses on aeronautics and space sciences. In addition, members of the staff served on high-school and college curriculum councils, evaluating course offerings and recommending alternatives. In cooperation with local industry, a number of center personnel were members of a science and mathematics council, which also included local high schools and colleges, that attempted to coordinate educational needs with local resources.[13]

By the late 1960s Ames had developed a conscientious program of classroom visits to local elementary and high schools. By Freeman's estimate, center personnel visited over 300 elementary schools over a five-year period. Over 10,000 students visited Ames, with the staff providing both tours and classroom lectures.[14] Two Explorer Scout posts in aeronautics and astronautics were sponsored at Ames, to provide experience in various research fields and to aid career planning.

RESEARCH TIES WITH ACADEMIA

NASA, and Ames, needed the resources of the academic community in a way that the NACA had not. Not only did the increased scope of research demand outside assistance, but the sheer volume of that research necessitated, in many instances, combining efforts. Collaboration was attractive to the universities, for NASA was a welcome source of funding and had many facilities that the universities could not match. Throughout the agency, offices were established to administer the various relationships between academia and NASA. At Ames, the University Affairs Office was established in 1965; 1967 saw the beginning of a separate and innovative Ames-university understanding. All NASA centers had university affairs offices, but the office at Ames was run somewhat differently from those at the other centers. The variety and number of relationships between Ames and academic institutions probably exceeded that of any other NASA installation.[15]

The University Affairs Office evolved slowly. In 1965 a Grants and Research Contracts Officer was named within the Programs and Resources Office to process academic proposals and administer grants to universities. Grants, through which NASA financed research in hopes of productive results, went through the Procurement Division for processing, after having been approved by Headquarters. In 1971 Headquarters began to decentralize control of activities dealing with academia. The move was one of several steps taken to cut costs in the face of shrinking resources. As Hans Mark retrospectively observed, Ames, because of the various methods it had already established for dealing with academia, was in a position to benefit from the decision because it already had the machinery to perform the task.[16] Headquarters transferred to Ames the responsibility for awarding grants as well as administering them. At that time, however, the Procurement Division was still responsible for grants; the Ames University Affairs Office was made a part of that division a year later to expedite processing.

In 1976 Mark made the University Affairs Office a separate entity, reporting to the Administration Directorate. In addition, the office obtained authority to administer the financial details of grants, without having to go through the Procurement Division. Most individuals who dealt with the universities were thereby freed from the time-consuming procurement regulations. Contracts, by which Ames purchased specified products, remained with the Procurement Division, but contracts accounted for only a small part of the Ames-university relationships.

By 1976 Ames had a budget of $8.2 million a year for awarding grants.[17] It had entered into twice as many university agreements as any other NASA center. Knapp A. Tomberlin, who took over the University Affairs Office in 1976, saw two factors that contributed to the success of the office: management support for working with universities was strong, and the administrative process utilized by the University Affairs Office bypassed both NASA Headquarters and the procurement process. That simplification, in Tomberlin's opinion, existed only at Ames.[18]

After 1967 Ames increased its ties with academia dramatically by means of another unique innovation. Growing from an arrangement with the University of Santa Clara Law School, the NASA-Ames University Consortium provided a relatively simple means of establishing collaborative relationships with universities without going through procurement processes. The idea that eventually resulted in the consortium grew out of frustration. Jack Glazer came to Ames as chief counsel in 1966. At that time, space law was a new and exotic field, and extensive legal research was badly needed. Indeed, the unplowed area provided such research opportunities as every law student dreams about. Glazer, without colleagues, quickly found himself overwhelmed with both awareness of the research need and excitement over research opportunities.

Shortly after Glazer's arrival, he fell into conversation with Cyril Ponnamperuma of the Life Sciences Directorate, who told a sorry tale of his attempt to obtain the research talents of a visiting colleague at Stanford University. By the time the necessary paperwork had been processed, only a month or so had been left for research, and the visiting professor had shortly thereafter returned to his home university in Europe. Unfortunately, because the relationship *had* been formalized, he was still responsible, even after leaving Stanford, for his share of the task. A simple desire for professional collaboration had turned into a nightmare for both researchers, and Ponnamperuma, needless to say, was loath to enter any more such arrangements.

Glazer needed research assistance. The logical place to find that assistance was any of the nearby law schools, where students needed research experience. Wondering how to bring the solution and the problem together, the Ames lawyer perused the National Aeronautics and Space Act of 1958, which had founded NASA. Glazer discovered that Congress, "in a sunburst of enthusiasm . . . had given the agency certain powers."[19] Besides contracts and grants, NASA also had the authority to enter into less formal arrangements that were exempted from the procurement process. Sec. 203c(5) authorized the agency to enter into "contracts, leases, cooperative agreements, and other transactions"; (6) permitted NASA "to use, with their consent, the services, equipment, personnel, and facilities of Federal and other agencies with or without reimbursement, and on a similar basis to cooperate with other public and private agencies." These provisions gave NASA surprising latitude in pursuing joint ventures. The only limitation was that the type of business relationship envisioned must differ from those associated with the formal procurement or grant process. Since Glazer was contemplating a partnership with a law school, a collaboration to which each party contributed, this requirement was met, as neither grants nor contracts established partnerships.

Ames thereupon entered into a joint venture with the University of Santa Clara Law School in 1967 to produce basic research in space law. Two years later the first results were published, the beginning of a continuing stream of space-law research. Santa Clara's students gained valuable experience and were paid modestly for their services; for $5,000 Ames had the benefit of the students as researchers and gained another academic friend in the local community. In contrast to a grant agreement, the university had shared substantially in the cost of the research, and Ames had also remained very much a part of the research process. In contrast to an R&D contract, where research is bought for NASA's benefit, the partnership was mutually beneficial; Santa Clara's students gained apprenticeship experience as they contributed to a NASA need. Moreover, Ames's services, rather than money

190

alone, were of value to the university. In another agreement Glazer taught space law at the university as part of NASA's share of the partnership, while the university in return did research in the life sciences. The arrangement worked; the cost was probably 25% of what it would have been under a formal grant or an R&D contract.[20]

Other managers at Ames were quick to notice what Glazer had accomplished. He had, under the special authority of the Space Act, acquired assistants while at the same time establishing a research relationship with a local law school. In 1968 and 1969 Ames entered agreements with the University of Iowa and the University of New Mexico. In 1969 a standard consortium agreement was drafted to provide for the reciprocal use of services, personnel, facilities, and equipment. Thereafter negotiation with an individual school had to cover only specific activities.

The consortium was unusual in two ways. The partnership between Ames and the universities was designed to be a real, working relationship, whereby Ames added tangibly to the joint venture, providing professional expertise, facilities, teaching time — not just funding. Further, when reimbursement was involved, only direct costs were considered. This meant that Ames's financial contributions were kept low. The limit to a consortium agreement was $30,000 per year, not to exceed two years. But that money, as Glazer observed, was "manna from heaven" to some less prosperous colleges and universities, which were seldom chosen for the larger grants.[21] This result, as Glazer saw it, was only good; it spread money to additional institutions, where unexpected excellence was often discovered. It also extended Ames's ties with the academic community much further than they had spread under contracts and grants. Mark's "octopus principle"[22] was at work again: the more tentacles an institution spreads, the harder it is to dislodge it.

The appeal of the consortium is evident in the statistics. In 1971, 13 universities were part of the arrangement; five years later the consortium had 70 members and awards totaled over $1 million.[23] The larger universities had also seen the advantages of the partnership with Ames, and by 1976 the membership list contained several of the more prestigious schools. With grant money becoming less available, consortium agreements gained in favor.

In 1971, four years after the first agreement with the Santa Clara Law School, the Ames-University Consortium held a plenary conference to assess the program. Glazer underlined clauses in the consortium agreement that permitted flexible relationships. Ames, for example, undertook to put at the university's disposal any requested personnel for meetings or consultations. Facilities of the center, including libraries and laboratories, were available without users' fees; the center was also able to utilize the talents of qualified students without regard to civil-service laws. In addition, Ames employees could audit courses within assenting universities at no charge.

191

That the consortium was welcomed by Ames was also evident by the presence of two of the research directorate heads, Glen Goodwin of the Astronautics Directorate and Harold Klein of the Life Sciences Directorate. Klein, in his down-to-earth manner, described what the consortium agreements had meant to his directorate:

> In 1967, we in the life sciences at Ames were very, very new . . . and most of our people . . . had not come from space-related institutions [but] from universities. [We] saw in this opportunity a way of continuing to do research more or less [as we] had been accustomed to. . . . We saw that these agreements could bring a certain measurement of this university style into our own laboratories. So we quickly climbed on the bandwagon.

By Klein's count, 17 faculty members, 14 graduate students, and 35 undergraduates had already worked at Ames and 17 papers had been published at a cost of less than $8,000 apiece.[24] As Klein saw it, his directorate had certainly gotten its money's worth.

The consortium agreements, as they increased in number over the years, also tended to act as screening devices for potential grants. During a two-year consortium agreement for a specific research purpose, Ames could evaluate what could be expected from a larger, longer investment. Often, one result of a consortium agreement was a later grant for a larger amount, after the university had successfully demonstrated its potential. Thus, both as an end in itself and as a step toward a larger undertaking, the consortium played an important role in extending Ames as a national resource beyond the bounds of the local community. The ease with which agreements could be reached made informal collaboration more feasible. A method of formal procurement "avoidance, not evasion," as Glazer insisted,[25] the consortium made it possible to conclude a short-term, small-budget research agreement quickly, often within three weeks. Normal procurement procedures, especially in 1967 when the consortium was conceived, often took many months. The consortium was a happy example of a creative way in which bureaucracy can be conquered and horizons widened.

SPINOFF TECHNOLOGY

Public relations attempted to advertise Ames and its achievements. Academic ties also accomplished this, while benefiting both parties. Spinoff technology, which transferred research accomplishments into the public sector, often performed a public relations task as well.

Much Ames research contributed to spinoff technology, and as a result of a NASA-wide effort to identify civic needs that might be satisfied with federal research, more and more NASA research reached the public. In the early 1970s six NASA regional dissemination centers throughout the country began to provide industry with information concerning possible spinoff technology, using a computerized data base. Easy access to technological answers helped to widen NASA's technology audience.

In 1972 Daniel J. Harnett, head of NASA's Office of Industry Affairs and Technology Utilization, testifying before the Senate Committee on Aeronautical and Space Sciences, mentioned a recent study by the Denver Research Institute that had investigated NASA contributions to industrial technology.[26] The study, which became an annual review, identified examples of successful technology transfer throughout NASA. In many instances, Ames research was cited as the basis for the advances. The center's contributions ranged from the exotic to the mundane, but the very assortment underlines the wealth of applications Ames research embraced.

In the early 1970s, for example, Ames research on spacecraft insulation led to development of fire-retardant insulation foam. What made the foam unique were just those fire-retardant aspects so necessary in spacecraft, for most commercial foams at the time were highly flammable. Used as core material in furniture and wall panels, fire-retardant foam had obvious advantages.

The Department of Housing and Urban Development (HUD) became interested in the problem of flammable foam in housing. A data search by one of the NASA Technology Application Teams led to the discovery of the Ames work on foams, and HUD arranged for the spacecraft insulation to be tested for both fire retardation and ease of manufacture. Even while the foam was in the testing stage, the Port of New York Authority expressed interest in it. A fire at Kennedy Airport had drawn attention to the hazards of flammable foam in furniture; the fire had leapt eight meters between groups of chairs filled with flammable foam and caused more than $1 million in damages.[27]

In another sector, techniques for stress analysis in aeronautics were modified for use in civil engineering. One of the primary applications of the computerized method of analysis was forecasting material fatigue in bridges. The strength of structural materials is decreased by various influences, and the changes are not always visible, so that visual inspection can be only partially effective. In 1972–1973, using the Ames-developed analytical system called Randomdec, the Federal Highway Administration analyzed steel girders to determine the minimum size of a detectable flaw. To test Randomdec in another way a highway overpass near Moffett Field was fitted with a vibration sensor to monitor the effects that traffic and the weather had on the structure. Comparison of the data with earlier tests on the same bridge showed that degradation of the structural elements could be measured efficiently.[28]

In biomedicine, an Ames-developed battery-operated ultrasonic electrocardioscope was tested and enthusiastically endorsed by Stanford University's School of Medicine. The instrument was much smaller than existing equipment, which meant that it could be used under conditions where the bulkier machines would be impractical or impossible. Being battery powered was even more important. In many situations where a patient's heart must be constantly monitored, it is desirable to limit the use of electrical equipment. The new machine cut down on the electrical hazards of continuous monitoring, which could be especially crucial in the case of newborn infants on additional life-support electronic equipment. The Ames electrocardioscope also had the advantage of being simpler to operate and potentially available for use by the patient at home.[29] During 1974, as testing produced optimal results, marketing studies were begun by two major manufacturing companies that were interested in the possibilities of producing the electrocardioscope on a commercial basis.

The bedrest studies that Ames began in the early 1970s led to another somewhat exotic piece of biomedical equipment. A major problem for bedridden patients, especially those who cannot be moved, is keeping clean and comfortable. For hospital staff, bathing a bedridden patient is exhausting, time-consuming, and often only partially satisfactory. In connection with the bedrest studies, Ames developed the idea of a horizontal shower. The patient, lying on a box-like gurney that collected water and channeled it to a drain, was wheeled into a curtained frame that supported a ring of inwardly directed shower heads. The recumbent patient could thereby enjoy a complete shower without extensive equipment.[30]

Some spinoff technology originated with Ames contractors. This was the case with the Optacon device, developed under contract by the Stanford Research Institute in Palo Alto. The Optacon made any printed page available to a blind person. The reader moved a small camera over each line of print in turn. The machine converted the photo-image of the printed page into a vibrating image of the letters that could be interpreted when the reader placed his or her other hand in a small receiver box. Other government agencies sponsored additional research on the device, and at the end of 1976 a California company was investigating its production.[31]

On a less dramatic level, but important in its own right, was a hand tool developed and patented by an Ames employee. A coaxial cable stripper rapidly cut both shielding and insulation from a cable so that connectors could be attached. The tool was put into production in 1976.[32]

Finally, Ames and the California Division of Forestry developed an automatic system for sending fire prediction information to central sites via satellite. A tiny weather station measured and transmitted wind velocity and

194

direction, solar radiation, humidity, and the moisture content of the ground cover in the immediate area. Weighing only 91 kilograms, it could be transported into remote areas and was easily installed. At the end of 1976 the system was being tested in a limited area in California.[33]

The impressive thing about any technology utilization progress report is that it is soon outdated. Thus, these products of Ames research may well be in routine use in a few years, and not seem unique at all. As examples of ways in which Ames has entered the larger context of daily life, however, they will continue to be an imposing assortment of achievements.

In the widest sense, the product of any research institution is the constant advancement of understanding in its areas of investigation. Coupled with that understanding comes expanding use of the knowledge gained. Ames, as we have seen, has done a creditable job of spreading its research brainpower and facilities outward into the local community and the academic community. Imagination has carried Ames ideas into new contexts with practical applications in a variety of areas, enriching both the beneficiaries and the research center itself.

Locally, the center has grown into a role of local activism that complements its more arcane academic contributions and its spinoff technology. Over the years, Ames learned to use its resources to enrich the surrounding community and to foster an awareness of the center's research mission. Needless to say, Ames's more visible presence and its positive and practical help in community education have done a lot to win support for both the research center and for NASA. In the same way, collaboration with the academic community and spinoff technology have underlined the range of NASA's interests and helped to establish it as an agency which does indeed touch large elements of the population. The very recognition of the need to identify this connection is another measure of the distance Ames has come since 1940.

SOURCE NOTES

Chapter 9. Ames in a Larger Context

[1] Seth Anderson interview, 8 Feb. 1982.

[2] De France's determination to avoid conflicts of interest has been commented on by many Ames employees.

[3] According to Life Sciences Director Harold Klein, De France was still reluctant to embark on institutes and seminars with academia in the early 1960s, when life sciences was being established at Ames. The newly recruited life scientists saw this as parochial. Harold Klein interview, 24 Feb. 1982.

[4] The growth of public relations activity can be seen in the Ames *Astrogram* issues throughout the 1960s.

[5] Ames *Astrogram* 7 (no. 17, 10 June 1965): 2.

[6] *Palo Alto Times* editorial of 28 Sept. 1965, reprinted in the Ames *Astrogram* 7 (no. 27, 14 Oct. 1965): 2.

[7] Ames *Astrogram* 8 (no. 14, 28 Apr. 1966): 5.

[8] Director Hans Mark to staff, 30 Nov. 1970.

[9] Ames Dir. of Admin. Arthur Freeman to NASA Hq., Dir. of Procurement, 7 June 1971, enclosing "Summary of Ames Activities." SBFRC 75-A-1324, 021896, RMO 5.

[10] Ibid., p. 1.

[11] Ames *Astrogram* 10 (no. 18, 4 July 1968): 2.

[12] "Users' Guide to University-Related Programs," NASA-Ames Research Center, Jan. 1980, pp. 9–10. University Affairs Office.

[13] "Summary of Ames Activities," p. 5.

[14] Ibid.

[15] Knapp A. Tomberlin interview, 5 Aug. 1982.

[16] Hans M. Mark interview, 20 May 1982.

[17] "Users' Guide to University-Related Affairs," p. 7.

[18] Tomberlin interview.

[19] J. Henry Glazer interview, 9 Aug. 1982.

[20] Ibid.

[21] Ibid.

[22] John W. Boyd interview, 23 July 1982.

[23] "Users' Guide to University-Related Programs," p. 7.

[24] First Plenary Conference on NASA-Ames-University Agreements, 4–5 Feb. 1971, at the University of Santa Clara, pp. 37–38.

[25] Glazer interview, 9 Aug. 1982.

[26] Daniel J. Harnett, statement before the Senate Committee on Aeronautical and Space Sciences, Mar. 1972.

[27] Ibid., app. A.

[28] *Technology Utilization Report, 1973,* NASA SP-5119 (Washington, 1974) pp. 21–22.

[29] Ibid., pp. 34–36.

[30] *Technology Utilization Report, 1974,* NASA SP-5120 (Washington, 1975), p. 76.

[31] *Spinoff 77: An Annual Report,* produced by the NASA Technology Utilization Office, Jan. 1977, p. 64.

[32] "NASA Benefits Briefing Notebook," prepared for the NASA Technology Office under NASA contract NASW-3313, by the Denver Research Institute, Oct. 1978.

[33] *Spinoff 77,* pp. 74–76.

10

RESEARCH CENTER INSTEAD OF AERONAUTICAL LABORATORY

The words *aeronautical laboratory* evoke images of a bygone era. Ames Research Center today bears little resemblance to the institution that was built so hurriedly on the eve of World War II. The changes that together worked such a transformation were separately no more than gradual and rational accommodations to the changing world. The center's leaders actively sought some of the changes; others came unavoidably from increasing size, complexity, and diversity. For the most part, managers made change work in the center's favor. Such an ability is obviously essential in the long term for a successful research institution. The Ames that Smith De France built, outstanding as it was, could not have prospered indefinitely with its original characteristics. Though the body of this book has dealt with many of those changes as they occurred over almost 40 years, a comparison of Ames in 1976 with the Ames of the 1940s might be useful as a summary. Because the introduction of project management was perhaps the most significant single change of all, that topic will also be discussed in this final chapter.

PHYSICAL CHARACTERISTICS

In 1945, after five years of frantic construction, Ames remained unfinished. Indeed, it still bore the appearance of any large-scale construction job. Landscaping was nonexistent. The newly finished 40- by 80-foot wind tunnel loomed at the northwestern boundary, dominating the scene and highly visible from the Bayshore Highway. Much empty space remained; it would gradually be filled up as more and more facilities were built. In 1945 there were 16 buildings on the 0.4 km^2 of the laboratory.[1]

By 1976 the land area had tripled and more than 50 buildings were in use, not counting additions to earlier facilities and temporary accommodations provided by trailers. To the wind tunnels and laboratories had been added ballistic ranges, flight simulators, two libraries, a separate cafeteria, a building to house computer facilities, helium storage tanks, a holding facility for life-sciences animals — an array never dreamed of when the first wind tunnels were constructed. Mud had long since been supplanted by lawns, evergreens, and a maze of sidewalks and roads.

In 1945 the main research tools were wind tunnels, supported by a few research aircraft. Wind-tunnel speeds ranged from 425 km/hr in the 40- by 80-foot wind tunnel to Mach 3.4 in the 1- by 3-foot supersonic tunnel. Facilities looked much like those at Langley or Lewis — which was only to be expected, as all three laboratories dealt strictly with aeronautical research.

By 1976 the divergence of research had made each research center unique. Wind-tunnel speeds now reached Mach 15. Aircraft had long since achieved speeds unimagined in 1945, and research was no longer particularly dedicated to achieving higher speed. Instead, take-off and landing characteristics distinguished some of the research aircraft; others had unusual altitude potential or stability characteristics. Heat had become a crucial issue in research. High-speed aeronautics, merging into astronautics, had encountered and resolved reentry heating problems, and arc-jet facilities made possible high-temperature testing of aerodynamic shapes and materials. Supporting the wind tunnels, ballistic ranges, and simulators in flight research were not only a selection of aircraft, but also computational facilities for the mathematical attack on aerodynamic problems.

In addition to aircraft that supported aeronautical research in traditional ways, Ames also possessed aircraft that were used as laboratories, or platforms from which to conduct experiments. The Convair 990 was used in photographic surveys, as were the high-altitude U-2s. The C-141 Starlifter was an astronomical observatory, bearing a 92-cm telescope. As well as being an object of research, flight had become a tool of research. In addition to the increase in range and sophistication of aeronautical and astronautical research tools, the biological and chemical laboratories used by the Life Sciences Directorate made Ames unique among NASA's research centers. By 1976 Ames could not possibly have been described as an aeronautical laboratory.

PERSONNEL

As with facilities, Ames personnel had become much more diversified as years passed. Originally, researchers had all worked either in wind-tunnel research, flight research, or theoretical aerodynamics. In the shops, machinists and woodworkers made wind-tunnel models to researchers' specifications and test equipment for use in the tunnels and aircraft. A small management staff and a few clerks kept the ratio of "direct labor" to "support labor" high. There were no contractors, hence no contractor personnel, at Ames in 1945. The work force approximated 800, with an operating budget of $8 million.[2] As all veterans would attest, everyone knew everyone else.

In 1976, with approximately 1600 civil servants plus 1200 contractor personnel at Ames,[3] the situation had changed completely. The diversity of research facilities was matched by a diversity in research personnel. To the aeronautical engineers had been added physicists, biologists, chemists, astronomers, geologists, mathematicians, medical doctors, and planetologists. Most of the work done originally by in-house machinists and model builders was now contracted out, to be done off the premises. Contractors had also become responsible for the maintenance of much equipment.

During World War II, Ames had been hard pressed to keep an adequate staff. The personnel shortage was not a question of budgets, but of locating and retaining qualified persons. In the early years most of the Ames staff was drawn from relatively few sources. Some engineers had transferred from Langley while Ames was being built, but many of the research staff had been hired out of graduating university classes, largely from schools west of the Rockies. By the 1970s, however, Ames was more cosmopolitan. Researchers were still hired directly out of school, but the school was as likely to be in the East as the West. Both research and management personnel were hired from other NASA centers; they were also likely to leave Ames for jobs at other NASA installations. In addition to the greater movement of employees within NASA, Ames now gained personnel from industry, university faculties, and the military. The possible sources of personnel had increased immensely, along with the scope of research. If the researchers were no longer as tightly knit professionally as they had once been, that advantage was offset by a wider outlook and a new cosmopolitanism within the organization.

A similar change occurred within management. In 1945 Ames managers came from only one source — Langley. The three top administrators — De France, Jack Parsons, and Arthur Freeman, the administrative officer — had a common background, having spent their whole careers in the NACA. The research division heads — Don Wood, Harvey Allen, and Jack Parsons — were still largely exempted from administrative duties and worked almost full time in research. By 1976 managers came from a variety of sources and brought with them a much wider range of experience. The director had been in management positions in academia and at another national research laboratory. The head of one research directorate had been born and educated in Great Britain; another was a former academic who had built a new university's biology department; a third, while spending almost his entire career at Ames, had nevertheless done research all over the world. The director of administration had had a long and wide-ranging career in industry. Many in management positions had held Sloan fellowships, which gave business and financial training to promising young managers. Reflecting the new career flexibility, management changed greatly over short intervals of time, as some individuals moved on to other government positions, both in NASA and with other agencies. Some retired in mid-career to take up teaching positions. In 1976, though 20-year veterans were not rare in research and management, many of the staff had been at Ames only a few years. The flow of personnel through Ames had increased from a trickle to a stream, widening the center's frame of reference with each arrival and departure.

MANAGEMENT METHODS AND ORGANIZATION

By 1976 Ames had a variety of facilities and personnel because research was no longer conducted within a single discipline. Through the 1950s the center had been concerned only with high-speed and low-speed aeronautics. The problems within the field remained recognizable to anyone working anywhere in aeronautics. In 1943 Harvey Allen, who was to become one of the foremost researchers in high-speed aeronautics, was a major contributor to the design of the 40- by 80-foot wind tunnel that was used only for low-speed work. By 1976, however, even an engineering genius of Allen's competence could not participate technically in all the Ames work. That increase in research range was accompanied by many changes: large budgets, contracting out, intricate relationships with outside organizations, and project management. A long-term Ames researcher and administrator observed, "We not only changed our business totally, but our way of doing it."[4]

Management had remained relatively simple through the middle 1950s. In 1945 De France, with the aid of Jack Parsons, had almost complete autonomy over the laboratory. The posts of assistant director did not yet exist. There were three research divisions. A financial officer was in charge of the accounting records, but De France controlled the budget and decided where the yearly monetary allotment was spent. Because all Ames personnel were civil servants, personnel problems were straightforward. There was a clearly visible line between management and research and an equally clear boundary drawn around Ames — Washington was far away, and management carried on without much interaction with NACA Headquarters. The general philosophy was "Give us the money and leave us alone."[5] If funds were available, Ames usually got its requested financing and was pretty much left alone to use the funds in its own manner.

Financial management presented a very different picture by 1976: more money, more management, more institutional structure. Ames no longer controlled its own budget. Flexibility in the use of available funds had greatly diminished. As Dean Chapman noted in 1982, "In De France's day, he would get some money for [Ames] and the freedom to use it. Today, money doesn't even really come to the center; it comes through program offices for a specific program or project."[6] Bookkeeping had become complicated in the extreme, and by the late 1960s financial management had become a cross that even directorate heads had to bear. Jack Boyd had lived through the slow growth of financial complexity within the research directorates. In the early 1960s, working under assistant director Russell Robinson, Boyd's job had been reasonably straightforward, because directorates were still uninvolved with financial details. In the late 1960s and 1970s, this situation changed dramatically. As a research assistant to Allen during his center directorship and as a technical assistant to Leonard Roberts in the Aeronautics and Flight Systems Directorate, Boyd handled many of the myriad details of financing with which the center and its research directorates had become entangled.[7]

Management also faced several other new duties. One concerned contracts and contractors. Not only did decisions have to be made at various levels in selecting contractors, but their work then had to be monitored, and disagreements and deadlines had to be dealt with. Contractors had to be kept aware of the larger research picture. The Procurement Division was responsible for many of the routine and legal aspects, a function it had not had in 1945. Another consideration was dealing with Headquarters and the other NASA installations on a daily basis. As only one element in an agency that addressed a huge assortment of research and development needs, Ames had become interdependent with the other installations, and with Headquarters, in ways that had not existed previously.

In the old days Ames personnel seldom went to Washington to fight for threatened programs. Decision processes had not involved researchers. By the early 1970s, though, Ames Director Hans Mark depended on physical presence to aid campaigns for programs and funds, and the "red-eye special" flight from San Francisco to Washington was familiar not only to Mark and his directorate heads, but also to researchers who were often called upon to take their causes to the top NASA hierarchy.

That Ames was no longer insular in its affairs was also reflected in the managerial side of new relationships between Ames and numerous other organizations. Project management, as exemplified by the Biosatellite and Pioneer, demanded a new type of management (see below). In addition, however, there were the relationships with the Federal Aviation Administration, the Army Air Mobility Laboratory, and the Advanced Research Projects Agency. On a more individual level were collaborations between Ames researchers and their colleagues in universities and other state and federal agencies. Separate offices sometimes managed these interrelationships, but others were dealt with on lower levels within the directorates themselves.

New research and management demands were reflected, naturally, in the organizational framework of Ames. Comparing the 1945 and 1976 organization charts (app. A) shows only one new research directorate, though the range of research had increased significantly. Most of the change was in the administrative and bureaucratic hierarchy that became unrecognizable by 1945 standards. Not only was there a separate directorate for research support, but the administration directorate had also grown to encompass five divisions. As already observed, new offices that dealt with other agencies, Headquarters, and various elements of the outside world had appeared. Where there had once been only one formalized link — De France — outward to the NACA Washington office, there was, by 1976, an intricate set of relationships extending to other government agencies, industry, the military, and universities.

WORKING CONDITIONS

As the physical aspects of Ames changed over the years, so too did the working atmosphere and the research process. Many long-term Ames employees commented on the changes, the cumulative effects of which were dramatic, though perhaps unlikely to be noted by outside observers.

For example, safety practices became more stringent. In the 1940s and 1950s, Seth Anderson was a flight-research engineer studying stability and control characteristics of various aircraft. In those days, and especially during World War II, problems were attacked more directly, with less regard for formal procedures. Solutions were suggested and tested, and the reports were written up promptly. Sometimes the whole process took only two or three months. Today, similar work might take two years. Though an engineer-observer, not a test pilot, Anderson flew some of the 60 to 70 types of aircraft tested at Ames during the war.

> We didn't have enough pilots, so it was a chance for me to help fly some of these vehicles. It was a more hurried type of testing that today would be considered unsafe; in the early days we went along as observers and engineers to run the test equipment. When [duct] tests were conducted on the P-51 wing in the 16-foot wind tunnel, the actual airplane was mounted in the tunnel with the wing tips cut off. . . . It was tested with one of the engineers in the cockpit at speeds up to 500 mph. [Duct rumble was both an acoustic and a structural problem. Its onset and intensity were most accurately sensed by a person in the cockpit.] We never do that now . . . because of the safety aspects.[8]

204

The circumstances of Ames's birth indeed influenced its early atmosphere, and conservative testing procedures may have been occasionally sacrificed during World War II. Other Ames veterans, commenting on wartime flight testing, noted that urgency was underlined by heavy battle casualites. Risks were relative.[9]

Another interesting change, perhaps more a reflection of personality differences than anything else, was the shift in the day-to-day relationships between researchers and Ames management. Researchers had little contact with De France, who relied on either Parsons or his assistant directors Robinson and Bioletti (after 1950) to keep him in touch with what was going on in the wind tunnels. Though De France was certainly available if one needed to see him, the line of communication from researchers to administration generally did not extend all the way to the director of Ames.

This situation changed under Harvey Allen. Having spent most of his career in research, Allen refused to give it up as director of the center. Because his interests and talents were so diverse, he involved himself in technical discussions in a way De France and Mark did not. Veterans recalled,

> You never used to see De France as a researcher. Harvey used to have areas that he was really interested in, because he did some of it himself [and] never really got out of the research game, so you tended to see Harvey a bit more. [It was] on a peer level though, less of a supervisor.[10]

. . . . .

> Allen spent a sizable fraction of his time just wandering around, sitting down and talking to people about their research, how it was coming along, etc. You'd see him do that in the afternoons when he finished his other work.[11]

With Hans Mark, managerial involvement in the research life of Ames was a conscious policy by which he informed himself of the technical details of work in progress and evaluated researchers and their achievements. It was, as one scientist recalled drily, a far cry from the "kind old founders of Ames. If you were good, you looked forward to the reviews. If you weren't you dreaded them. They were not unlike oral reviews for the Ph.D."[12]

The difference in managerial practice among the three Ames directors illustrates another process that began in the late 1950s and gained momentum over the next 20 years. For better or worse, researchers before 1960 had been successfully insulated from the realities of life. Financial, bureaucratic, and competitive elements of the center's work were of no direct concern to them. Ames veterans varied greatly in their explanations for the shift, as they did when attempting to pin down the change chronologically. All agreed, however, that their jobs had become more complicated and all attributed those changes to financial factors, either growing or shrinking funding. It seems apparent that both the boom of the early 1960s and the subsequent retrenchment after Apollo influenced the Ames mode of operation, making life more difficult for researchers.

Some saw the growth of the NASA budget as the crucial element:

> In the early days, when the total NACA budget was $40 million, there was little scrutiny of how the money was spent, in part because there weren't engineering specialists at Headquarters. We didn't have serious problems in dealing with Headquarters because the research funds were relatively small. When large funding became available for special projects, a much closer rein was needed to justify expenditures.[13]

Another researcher added:

> Early in my career [the 1960s] there was more bureaucracy than later. Progress reports were required by NASA Headquarters, [and we spent a lot of time] giving research talks to Headquarters visitors. That [later] relaxed, and perhaps part of the reason it relaxed was that travel money got scarce.[14]

Contrastingly, some Ames researchers saw the bureaucratic detail and finance problems stemming from cutbacks, rather than from the growth of funds and programs. Interconnected to financing complexity was a gradual shifting of control to NASA Headquarters. As Dean Chapman remembered,

> One of the changes took place beginning in the late 1960s. There was so much money in the Apollo years — there was money to do anything that it was important to do. When the money began to get tight [things changed].
>
> I can remember starting to do something without [a Research Authorization], without [a Research and Technology Objective and Plan]. You'd just do it, then write a report. The only discussion you had as a research worker was with your supervisors. Now you have to work with Headquarters directly, to persuade them to divide the money for this or that project, to specifically earmark the money, etc.[15]

Robert Nysmith, later an administrator at NASA Headquarters, recalled Mark's reviews as pivotal in making the researcher aware of both budget restraints and competitive elements:

> I . . . can't remember worrying about such things under De France and Allen [when I was a researcher]. I figured that those guys knew what they were doing. If I needed a piece of equipment I'd go and cry and beg to my branch chief, and if he [couldn't] get it, [I'd] jury-rig something that would get the job done. I'd worry about a paper I was going to present, or something I [was] trying to figure out, but [not the funding details]. I'm afraid the system now requires the researcher to be more worldly. I get that feeling when I talk to researchers — they're worrying about things I never used to know existed.[16]

Large-scale, time-limited project management with precisely defined goals (such as Pioneer, to be discussed below) did not exist when Ames was founded; but the process by which even the more traditional research was carried on changed in the interval covered by this book. The new complexities — relations with external agencies, cooperation with external researchers, reliance on contract support services, participation of more academic disciplines, additional controls on money, elaborate decision-making methods — changed significantly the way researchers went about their daily activities. One common effect of many of the changes was to decrease the center's self-sufficiency, as a 40-year veteran noted in 1982:

> The center used to be self-contained. If you wanted something made in a shop, we had a shop where you could go get it made. Now, there are large numbers of support service contractors, and shop work is sent out to get done. There are lots of things where it seems to me the center simply can't respond the way it used to.[17]

The use of contractors has changed the relationships Ames has with other organizations and the mode of operation within the center itself. There are two underlying reasons behind the development of contracting at Ames. First, the increased scope of research made it impossible for Ames to produce all the components or to employ permanently all the specialists it needed. Second, financial considerations made contracting necessary. A contractor might — or might not — be able to do a given job cheaper than civil servants could. But contracts are of fixed duration, whereas civil servants are hired indefinitely. Further, Congress usually was more willing to provide money for contracting than to raise civil-service ceilings. The whole question has ramifications that merit reflection.

In much the same vein as Dusterberry, Robert Nysmith described the changed research scene at Ames in terms of the development of shop contracting. His perspective illuminates a series of changed relationships:

> We started undergoing manpower reductions [in the late 1960s]. A conscious decision was made to take the cuts in the support areas and protect the professional positions. As a result the character of research started to change.
>
> One of the fond memories I had as a researcher was that of encountering a problem in my task and seeing the need for a piece of equipment. I'd sit down with a sketch, make up a work order, and take it to the branch chief. He'd sign it, and I'd go off to the . . . head of the machine shop. He'd say, "Yeah, go talk to Joe," and Joe would say, "OK, you want to wait?" or "I'll have it tomorrow morning," or "Why do you want to do that?" Maybe right then and there we'd change the sketch. He'd understand what I wanted it for, and what it was supposed to be used on, and in fact when I went and used it, half the time [the men in the shop] would come over to watch it. [The shop machinists] were an integral part of the research project.
>
> Now . . . the researcher makes up a job order [which is let] out on contract to a job shop. It may take two weeks to a month to get it back, and then it may not be right.

Such delays meant that a researcher had to have several tasks under way at once. Then, when one was stopped by the lack of equipment, the researcher could work on another.[18]

On a larger scale, contracting a great deal of work, especially on major research projects, turned some researchers into contract managers, sometimes costing them their research roles. Dean Chapman noted, "It's in many cases an irreversible process. You can't go back, there's too much to catch up with in research." Research capability in aeronautics was frequently traded for project-management capability, with many of the best researchers becoming space-oriented managers. "Aeronautics was left without a full distribution of good researchers, and though that's shifting now, we still don't have the capability that existed pre-Sputnik, in that there were specialists in aeronautics, men who knew their fields better than the people in industry."[19] Harry Goett, speaking from his experience both at Ames and at Goddard, said much the same thing:

> If you get more money, you also get more people from the outside. You may still be doing good research, but your researchers become program managers, supervisors. And any good researcher, after three years of being a program manager, is out of the research business and is a program manager.[20]

208

As contracting caused the researcher to proceed more often piecemeal, so too did the scope of the research that was undertaken. For the typical job at Ames in 1945, all the workers involved with it were at the laboratory. Even when Ames and Langley were pursuing similar studies, they worked independently, with researchers periodically comparing their respective advances. (An example is the transonic research of 1946–1948, described in chapter 2.) By 1976, however, researchers typically were interacting with colleagues all around the country,[21] and often a research project was a collaborative undertaking with other NASA centers, industry, and the military. The effects were obvious: while professional ties were strengthened and horizons widened, while the range of research involvement was extended, it was also possible for one's own research to be lost in the larger effort. The change almost certainly affected the researcher's perception of his work, though exactly how can scarcely be described precisely. But older Ames personnel noticed:

> There was no question whatsoever that under the NACA, aerodynamics and in-house work done by NACA people was top dog. Then NASA came along, and [Ames] became part of a [much larger] organization . . . and the prestigious stuff moved away from those traditional NACA laboratories and over to the Goddards and Marshalls and Johnsons, who had the money.[22]

The shift to big programs, where the prestige was, also shifted the relationships between Ames and industry and the military. Goett said the NACA

> had a doctor-patient relationship with industry. [If] North American won a contract with the Air Force, within a very short time North American would be up here [asking advice. As we now contract with industry], the situation is reversed. Industry is not going to admit what [it] doesn't know. It becomes a situation of "Give me $10 million and I'll do it."

What happened was that NASA evolved into a developmental agency as much as a research organization.

> When NASA started out, it was the Air Force that had the trucks — the Atlas, the Titan — that we used to launch our payloads. Now NASA is building trucks for the Air Force,[23]

Goett observed drily as he considered the Space Shuttle and its implications. NASA became, instead of a seller of advice, a buyer of goods and services from the very industries it had once advised. Many Ames personnel viewed the change as unfortunate:

> The thing that bothered me [was that] when NASA started you could tell immediately . . . that we were different . . . because we had an operational role instead of just a research role. The minute we [assumed] an operational role, somebody was trying to sell us something, and instead of coming in and telling us what their problems were, they came in and told us what their solutions to [our problems were].[24]

All these changes at Ames — from small to large budgets, administrative simplicity to complexity, self-sufficiency to large-scale interdependence, research to development and operations — are illustrated in the advent of project management. Project management, in a way, is as representative of NASA as basic research was of the NACA. Ames's striking triumph in project management, Pioneer, illustrates many of the contrasts between old and new.

THE PIONEER PROJECTS

Strictly speaking, Pioneer was four separate projects, of which Ames was responsible for all but the first. The process by which Ames acquired the management of Pioneer, the problems involved in project management, and the ways in which Ames successfully directed the missions indicate the different issues that the center faced under NASA.

The first Pioneer project (five vehicles launched between 1958 and 1960) had been planned for the International Geophysical Year by the Advanced Research Projects Agency. Both the Air Force Ballistic Missile Division and the Army Ballistic Missile Agency were assigned execution of the launchings. When NASA was formed, it inherited the probes, which were then launched by the Air Force Ballistic Missile Division (*Pioneer 1, 2, and 5*) and the Army Ballistic Missile Agency (*Pioneer 3* and *4*). Those launched by the Air Force were developed by Space Technology Laboratories, Inc., the company that eventually became TRW Systems Group, the prime contractor for most of the later Pioneers. *Pioneer 3* and *4* were developed by the Jet Propulsion Laboratory as a NASA contractor and launched by the Army.

The first little Pioneers were quite successful. *Pioneer 1,* launched in October 1958, returned data on the Earth's magnetic field and micrometeorites for 48 hours, which was a good record at the time. *Pioneer 3* in December confirmed the existence of the Van Allen radiation belts. *Pioneer 4,* launched in March 1959, and *Pioneer 5,* launched a year later, were NASA's first solar satellites. Both sent back invaluable information on radiation and magnetic fields.

Pioneer 6–9, managed by Ames, were identical spacecraft designed to explore the interplanetary medium, charting the characteristics of the magnetic fields, cosmic rays, high-energy particles, electron density, electric fields, and cosmic dust. Approved in November 1962, the spacecraft were launched between December 1965 and November 1968. TRW Systems Group was the prime contractor. Launched by Thor-Deltas from Kennedy Space Center and tracked by the Jet Propulsion Laboratory with the Deep Space Network, the four vehicles provided Ames with the experience to continue the Pioneer series when interest mounted to explore Jupiter.

Pioneer 10 and *11* were also relatively low-budget interplanetary vehicles. Approved in 1969, these two spacecraft became one of NASA's most interesting and visible projects, conducting investigations of the interplanetary medium beyond Mars, crossing the asteroid belt, and studying the environment and atmosphere of Jupiter. *Pioneer 11* was designed with the flexibility to continue on to Saturn, as it indeed did. TRW Systems Group was again the prime contractor. JPL provided tracking support, while Lewis Research Center and Kennedy Space Center were responsible for launch-vehicle and launch-site support.

Pioneer Venus was approved in 1974 and launched in 1978 to investigate that planet and its environment. *Pioneer Venus* is outside the chronological scope of this narrative, but it too was a logical follow-on mission for Ames and within the tradition of small, relatively inexpensive spacecraft that characterized the previous Pioneers. Goddard Space Flight Center did preliminary studies for the mission, but the mission was reassigned to Ames. Hughes Aircraft Company was the prime contractor.

The process by which Ames became involved in project management illustrates the growth and development of research ideas, the NASA decision-making process, and far-reaching changes in Ames. The narrative of events, once Ames won approval for *Pioneer 6–9,* furnishes a fascinating glimpse of the maze of considerations that constitute project management. It was a world very different from that of a small research laboratory.[25]

In 1958–1959, soon after NASA's inception, Al Eggers, chief of the Vehicle-Environment Division, became interested in the idea of a solar probe. One of Ames's most imaginative researchers, he had also been involved in the lifting-body work of 1956–1957. Eggers, like Harvey Allen, had so many ideas that it was impossible to follow up many of them, but the probe was to be pursued. Charles Hall, then Eggers's assistant, recalled:

> Al was very interested in broadening the research of the group he had. He had no doubt that there would be a solar probe and [wanted to investigate what we] would need to do it. He had people in all the little branches working on various aspects of a solar probe, not just [within] his division, either.[26]

Asking Hall to organize the paper details and to coordinate efforts, Eggers started an informal study group to consider the idea. People from various Ames divisions worked on elements of the problem:

> R. T. Jones, Charles Hermach, John Dimeff, Michel Bader — it was easy to get people from other divisions. We laid out an outline of what we thought the study should be. We finished the study in early 1961, it worked out pretty well and we had had a lot of fun doing it.

At Eggers's suggestion, De France turned the study group into the Solar Probe Committee. At this point, Hall began to push for an attempt to interest NASA in the idea. Though Eggers wondered if refinements to the study were needed, Hall wanted to "see if anyone would let us build this thing. It's one thing to say you can build something on paper, and another to actually go out and build it." The committee, led by Hall, presented its findings to the NASA Headquarters Particles and Fields Committee, which was then meeting at Stanford. That group seemed interested, and Hall and Eggers were urged to take the idea to another Headquarters committee. At this point, as Hall remembered it later, he was aware that Ames was flirting with project management. "When I told Al we should put up or shut up, I think I knew what we were into. When we went to Washington, though, I think De France still thought it was a research deal."

In Washington, after initial committee interest, Hall was able to see Edgar Cortwright, then deputy director of the Office of Space Sciences. Cortwright, while impressed with the preliminary study, said he didn't feel Ames had the management experience to do a solar probe, but suggested a small spacecraft interplanetary project, something the Particles and Fields committee had also been interested in. "He told me Ames was the *last* place he thought would be interested in project management work," Hall observed, "but asked if we'd be interested in the interplanetary project." While still in Washington, Hall met with Cortwright's staff to draft possibilities, assuming Ames approval was forthcoming. Back at Ames, Hall and Eggers received De France's approval to proceed with the interplanetary project.

Over the next few months, a preliminary study was done by Space Technology Laboratories (later TRW Systems Group). The management of the study was informal. "In those days," as Hall recalled, "it wasn't any big deal; you could almost write the contract requirements in a letter." The eventual result was a study document produced by TRW, and the next step was approval to go ahead from NASA Headquarters.

De France heartily endorsed Pioneer, which is somewhat surprising given his conservative outlook. He himself had been out of research for a long period and was of a generation that had never heard of project management. His assistant directors, Harvey Allen and Russell Robinson, feared that project work would rob the rest of the center of manpower and were hesitant about proceeding. De France's approval was crucial. "People are always surprised; they ask me, 'How did you get Pioneer when De France was against it?' He *wasn't* against it, he was for it!" Hall recalled. About to depart for Washington to seek final Headquarters approval, the group met to discuss plans. Associate Director Jack Parsons was there, assuming he'd be standing in for De France, when to everyone's surprise De France announced his intent to go by train and meet the rest of the group there. Hall saw, in retrospect, De France's presence as probably decisive:

> Bob Seamans asked De France, "How does Ames feel about this, Smitty?" and De France said, "Ames is behind it 100%." You know, he was so well respected at Headquarters . . . that when he said 100%, that just about sold the program. So we did get approval based on that meeting.

Ames received tentative approval for Pioneer in June 1962, and final, formal approval in November. Hall was put in charge of the project and set about establishing a project office. In January 1963, to provide more institutional structure to the Pioneer and Biosatellite projects (Ames had acquired the second project also) the Development Directorate was formed under Robert Crane. Within it, both project offices and a new division, Systems Engineering, were established. With an eye to advance planning, Eggers was made the head of another new directorate, that of R&D Analysis and Planning. These new organizational arrangements, as well as the later creation of the Mission Analysis Division under Clarence Syvertson, were effective evidence that Ames was looking to its future in a new way, and that formal advance planning was becoming more and more essential.

The technical and scientific achievements of the Pioneer spacecraft are well documented elsewhere. More pertinent to this study are the management aspects of the project. At first, the Pioneer project office was completely out of the mainstream of activity at Ames. Hall's small group occupied some cubicles in what was then the cafeteria. But Hall insisted that continuous close communication among the project elements, both at Ames and on contract sites, was essential, and one way he accomplished this was by physical proximity. As he recalled, "I had a hard time convincing the Ames contracts people they ought to be in the same building; they didn't want any part of that."

Another initial problem was assembling a staff. Ames researchers, it appeared, had been happy and excited doing feasibility studies for Pioneer, but when it came to becoming part of the formal project, they were less certain they wanted to participate. Hall later explained,

> You know, . . . there was so much enthusiasm during the study, I figured that when we got the go-ahead for the project, people at the lab would beat down the doors. . . . The project was approved, and by God, I didn't hear from anyone! So I started calling up some of these people, and most of them turned me down. They didn't want to do project work. Ames in those days had a very university atmosphere; they didn't want to have their research sullied by the outside world.

Eventually, however, with the support of Bob Crane as assistant director of development, Hall formed a staff, many hired from the outside, and Pioneer became a bona fide project in search of contractors.

It is generally recognized that one of Hall's outstanding characteristics as a project manager was his ability to make a close and constant assessment of contractors and their performance throughout the project. Crane's successor found Hall "extremely thorough and technically knowledgeable on the project; he didn't let things slip through him. . . . He didn't ignore problems, and he kept close tabs on the contractors at all stages."[27]

Before the prime contractor was chosen, Hall and his group had demonstrated that alert pragmatism. While trying to decide among the four main competitors, Hall's team visited the companies on a whirlwind tour from Los Angeles to Ann Arbor and Philadelphia and back. The trip's findings changed the competition order and convinced Hall of the importance of actually visiting potential contractors to observe their operations. One of the competitors

> had top-notch equipment and no one who knew how to work it. Their group was small and very inexperienced, trying to get into the business. I don't really know how you get into the business, [but] it would have been a disaster if we'd picked them.

No matter what the contracting method, or who the contractor was, there were bound to be difficulties at some stage of the relationship. For

214

Pioneer 6-9, proposals were recieved, and after competition the spacecraft contract was awarded to TRW. For *Pioneer 10* and *11,* TRW was selected without competition, using sole-source justification. Both methods have drawbacks in producing accurate cost proposals. Competitive-contract proposals tend to be lower, sole-source contractors may be more realistic in their estimates. On *Pioneer 6-9,* for example, the original proposals based on the preliminary study resulted in a sizable spread between TRW and Hughes Aircraft Company, the principal competitors. Later, added technical details and further refinements in the bidding narrowed the margin and the proposals became almost identical in cost. The initial difference, as Hall observed, was partially a product of the different accounting methods used by the two companies, which made it difficult to assess who had made the more realistic bid. It taught him a valuable lesson.

[Since] TRW and Hughes had different accounting systems, it was impossible to get figures [based on our] system, since they had their own. You have to go along with the contractor's organization to get real data. . . . It's easier to adjust your own thinking than to adjust theirs.

TRW received cost-plus-incentive contracts for *Pioneer 6-9* and *Pioneer 10* and *11.* Costs were $64.3 million for the first four and $94.7 million for the latter two.[28] Overruns were kept to a minimum through a system that provided automatic checks on the various interacting components of the project; but even so, numerous contract changes drove costs up from the original estimates. Still, the two series are examples of economical project management, with controlled costs and sensible trimming of nonessentials that kept a technically sound project relatively inexpensive for what it accomplished.

Like any large NASA project, Pioneer relied on many interdependent elements, including the Deep Space Network, which would track and communicate with the spacecraft around the world via stations from California to Australia. In addition, there were the components of the spacecraft itself, the experimenters' instruments, the launch vehicle, and launch operations. The Pioneer project office sought to participate in all interactions between the various elements and to give close attention to all problem areas. Weekly staff meetings among the organizational elements and periodic reviews by Ames and by NASA Headquarters assured that difficulties were spotted promptly. Spacecraft were reviewed and checked out by the project office at the Redondo Beach, California, factory to eliminate later possible problems at the launch site. Even more important, the project office kept personnel at the spacecraft contractor's facility to stay on top of problems. Because of the constant surveillance, and because of a team of technically

May 1973. Pioneer 17 being unloaded at Cape Kennedy (now Cape Canaveral) prior to launch. (Pioneer 10 had been launched in March 1972.) Note the relatively small size of the Pioneer spacecraft and the reusable packaging protecting it, both typical of Pioneer's thrifty budgeting.

216

alert monitors from the Pioneer office, many potential disasters were averted.

Even so, there were tense periods. On *Pioneer 10,* a potential calamity was discovered when the four radioisotope thermoelectric generators, the sole power source, were tested. *Pioneer 10* was to be the first spacecraft powered solely by these devices, and they were essential to the mission. During the tests, the power source degenerated much more rapidly than anticipated. Hall insisted on a complete investigation, and after a sophisticated series of tests, Teledyne Isotopes, the contractor for the generators, discovered that moisture trapped inside the capsule containing the radioisotope material was affecting the nuclear reaction. Even more serious, the complicated chemical process was causing the protective casing surrounding the radioactive material to become brittle, so that it would shatter under minimal strain. Teledyne, working against time, changed the moisture-absorbing

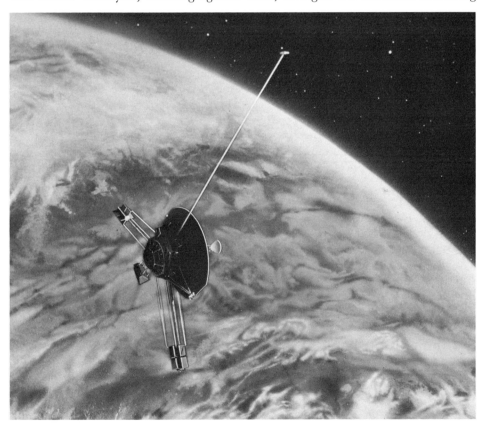

1972. An artist's rendition of Pioneer 10 spacecraft flying over Jupiter's surface. Pioneer 10 reached Jupiter in December 1973 after a flight lasting over 20 months.

217

insulation material, and the crisis was over. As Hall observed, however, such a crisis five months before the scheduled launch date was too close for comfort.

The 50-odd personnel of the Pioneer project office were aided in their task by another element new to Ames. As already noted, because of the technical unknowns and the scope of the project, as well as the financial commitment, much advance planning and selling had to occur. With the first Ames-managed Pioneer series, the task was made somewhat easier because NASA Headquarters, though interested in a solar-probe project, also had interplanetary exploration ideas. Work continued on the planning for the solar probe, with Howard Matthews and others doing advanced studies on possibilities, until the U.S. and Germany agreed to a joint solar mission. Meanwhile, through the efforts of Robert Crane, at the time head of the Development Directorate, Ames acquired the Pioneer Jupiter project. Initial studies had been conducted by Goddard Space Flight Center, but because Goddard was already overcommitted, and because *Pioneer 6–9* were about completed, Ames was assigned the Jupiter project, which would become *Pioneer 10* and *11*. While Hall's office dealt with the demands of that immense undertaking, the Development Directorate, by now under John Foster, planned for the future as it fought to sell *Pioneer Venus* to both Ames management and NASA Headquarters. The system worked well, but in the case of *Pioneer Venus,* obtaining final approval for the project was a lengthy and frustrating process. For Ames, it was another new aspect of large-scale and long-range programs that contrasted strongly to the more traditional mode of funding it was accustomed to. Project management, like increased bureaucracy, brought worldliness into the center.[29]

Even though Pioneer did not interact much with the more traditional research at Ames, the example of project planning, as well as management, forced many outside of Pioneer to become aware of a world where aggressive salesmanship was necessary. In 1975, when Foster retired, the Development Directorate was abolished. Biosatellite no longer existed, and no further large-scale planetary project was envisioned. Pioneer was placed under the Astronautics Directorate, where research and project management rubbed shoulders to the dismay of Astronautics Director Dean Chapman, who estimated that Pioneer and the other projects took 80–90% of his time.[30] The amounts of money involved and the complexity of the interacting elements made project management out of place in the research directorate.

Assessing the Pioneer projects, participants identified many crucial elements in their success. Characteristically, Hall called attention to the technical strengths of the contractors, the project personnel, and the researchers, as well as to the "luck" that produced scheduling miracles and eleventh-hour solutions to near-disasters. Perhaps, too, there was a realistic awareness of the limitations of the project that kept goals and estimates sensible.

218

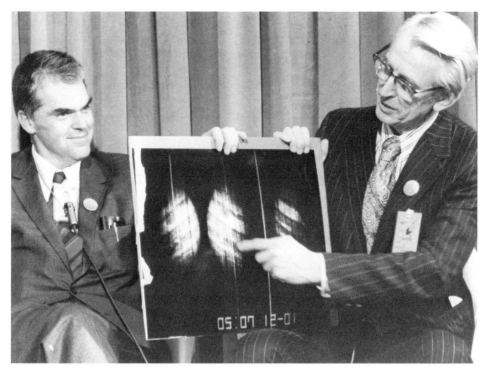

December 1973. Hans Mark, Director of Ames (left), and James Fletcher, NASA Administrator (right), brief the media and visiting scientists during Pioneer 10's encounter with Jupiter.

Foster, naming what he considered the crucial factors for Pioneer's success, added that the science experiments were well planned, that Headquarters support was excellent, and that the contractors were reliable. Assessing Hall's role, Foster, who had urged that Ames enter space research, paid him an observant colleague's compliment: "We used to have a saying, 'We can't give Charlie any more people to help him, because he doesn't have time to do their work!' He knew every system on that thing; his deputies were just extensions of himself."[31]

For some reason, Pioneer seemed to catch the imagination of the country. Perhaps it was the idea of the small spacecraft — and all the Pioneers were relatively small vehicles — being guided and controlled from Earth on a move-to-move basis, instead of being preprogrammed. Perhaps it had to do with the distances *Pioneer 10* and *11* traveled to Jupiter and Saturn, or the suspense of crossing the asteroid belt. Perhaps the media caught the camaraderie of the *Pioneer 10* and *11* team, as a result of Hall's

219

December 1973. Charlie Hall (in striped shirt), Pioneer project manager, and Ames, TRW, and academic members of the Pioneer team reflect their mission's success during Pioneer 10's Jupiter flyby.

stand-up meetings, where a first-thing-in-the-morning exchange of information kept everyone informed during the periods when planetary encounters were imminent. Whatever the reasons, the Pioneer projects added a visibility to Ames that contrasted dramatically to the center's earlier profile as an aeronautical laboratory.

Charlie Hall, remembering his own career as a research engineer, compared research with project management:

> Research is more relaxed, more of an individual activity. You have more control. . . . There is not as much outside pressure. . . . [In project management] there are [frequently] influences over which you have no control but [which] are having very strong influences on your project. You run up and down the wall trying to find out what you have to do to circumvent these influences. . . . Project management is a team effort, so you have to organize the thing so you do work as a team. . . . In research, if you don't

plan right, you just veer off a little to one side or another, it's no big deal. In the project I always felt I was working six months from now; I might not know what was happening today, but I knew what would be happening six months from today, because I had to plan it so I knew we would get there.

... you don't see that type of thinking necessary in research.... In research you don't even have to worry about tomorrow if today's going all right, because whatever happens good today is going to lead you in the right direction tomorrow. In project management you have to stay far ahead, to make sure the [things] you're doing today will get the work done in time....

In both the technical sense and in terms of the interested public, the Pioneer series was a project of which Ames could be proud. Hall, however, perhaps characterized a new Ames, as well as Pioneer, when he reflected on the differences between the older basic research and the newer project management, for the center faced the influences, challenges, and deadlines of the outside in ways unimagined in 1940.

Looking at the institution over a forty-year span, what is striking are the many outward changes that have occurred — physical expansion; research diversity and sophistication; complexity of management; daily intrusion of bureaucracy; desired involvement with other institutions, groups, and agencies; and cooperative projects and programs requiring closely coordinated responsibilities shared among a number of agencies and institutions. Initially, one might suspect that these adaptations to a changing context are what have kept Ames as healthy as it is. Further consideration produces an equally striking observation — in what is perhaps the most essential area, Ames has not changed greatly. From the beginning, the laboratory/research center has had a very strong sense of itself that was supported by the intellectual capability and imagination of its personnel. That, in the final analysis, is the crucial ingredient in the health and productivity of the center, and an ingredient that must be conscientiously protected and encouraged.

SOURCE NOTES

Chapter 10. Research Center Instead of Aeronautical Laboratory

[1] John Parsons, Chief, Construction Div., to Smith De France, May 1945. 74-A-1624, V-4823, SBFRC.

[2] Edwin P. Hartman, *Adventures in Research: A History of Ames Research Center, 1940–1965*, NASA SP-4302 (Washington, 1970), app. A, p. 515.

[3] Ames Personnel Office.

[4] John W. Boyd interview, 23 July 1982.

[5] Ibid.

[6] Dean R. Chapman interview, 28 Apr. 1982.

[7] Boyd interview.

[8] Seth B. Anderson interview, 5 Feb. 1982.

[9] Comments by John Dusterberry and Charles Hall, Jan. 1983.

[10] Robert W. Nysmith interview, 27 May 1982.

[11] Chapman interview.

[12] Dell P. Williams III interview, 27 May 1982.

[13] Anderson interview.

[14] William L. Quaide interview, 27 May 1982.

[15] Chapman interview.

[16] Nysmith interview.

[17] John C. Dusterberry interview, 21 Apr. 1982.

[18] Nysmith interview.

[19] Chapman interview.

[20] Harry J. Goett interview, 3 Dec. 1981.

[21] Quaide interview.

[22] Geott interview.

[23] Ibid.

[24] Interview of Steven E. Belsley by Walter Bonney, 24 Sept. 1974.

[25] I am grateful to John V. Foster and Charles F. Hall for their assistance in providing me with information on the Pioneer projects. From 1969 to 1975, Foster was the director of development, responsible for the Pioneer Project Office at Ames. Charles F. Hall was the Pioneer project manager from 1962 to 1979.

[26] Charles F. Hall interview, 10 Aug. 1982. Subsequent quotations in this chapter, unless otherwise attributed, are from this interview.

[27] John V. Foster interview, 19 July 1982.

[28] J. Richard Spahr and Charles F. Hall, *The Pioneer Projects — Economical Exploration of the Solar System*, NASA TM X-62,481, Ames Research Center, Sept. 1975, p. 1.

[29] Some of the details in the process were described by John Foster, 19 July 1982.

[30] Chapman interview.

[31] Foster interview.

APPENDIX A

ORGANIZATION CHARTS, 1940–1976

The major reorganizations of Ames have been discussed in the text and are illustrated in the organizational charts that follow, but neither the text nor the charts give a complete organizational history. Rather, organizational change has been used to chart other evolutions at Ames: division of authority, new research directions, increasing bureaucracy, and growing interaction with outside agencies.

The first six charts are for the entire laboratory or center. In the early years research was organized around the wind tunnel that a unit used, and the unit was typically named for that facility, e.g., the 16-Foot Tunnel Section. When research became more diversified, units were named for the area of investigation, e.g., the Flight Dynamics and Control Branch. Most of the charts do not go below the directorate or division level. The first five are from Hartman, *Adventures in Research,* pp. 33, 41, 180, 319, and 402. The sixth is taken from a copy of the official chart dated Sept. 1976 in the NASA History Office Archives.

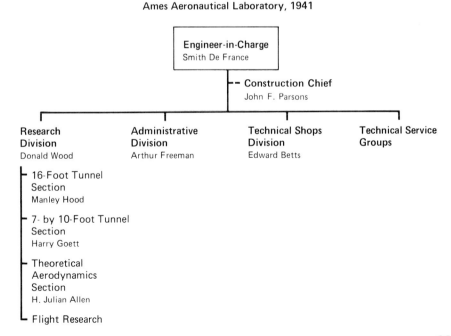

Ames Aeronautical Laboratory, 1941

Ames Aeronautical Laboratory, 1945

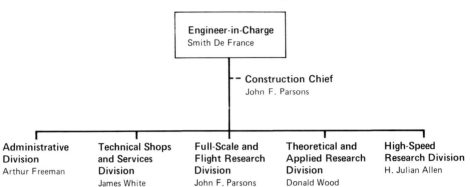

Engineer-in-Charge
Smith De France

- **Construction Chief**
  John F. Parsons

Administrative Division	Technical Shops and Services Division	Full-Scale and Flight Research Division	Theoretical and Applied Research Division	High-Speed Research Division
Arthur Freeman	James White	John F. Parsons	Donald Wood	H. Julian Allen

Ames Aeronautical Laboratory, 1953

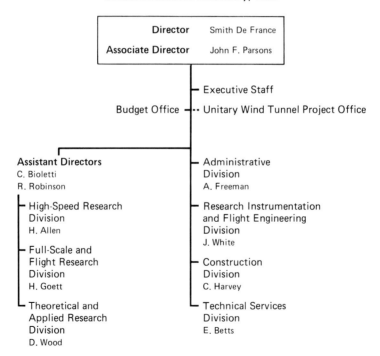

Director   Smith De France

Associate Director   John F. Parsons

- Executive Staff

Budget Office — Unitary Wind Tunnel Project Office

Assistant Directors
C. Bioletti
R. Robinson

- High-Speed Research Division
  H. Allen

- Full-Scale and Flight Research Division
  H. Goett

- Theoretical and Applied Research Division
  D. Wood

- Administrative Division
  A. Freeman

- Research Instrumentation and Flight Engineering Division
  J. White

- Construction Division
  C. Harvey

- Technical Services Division
  E. Betts

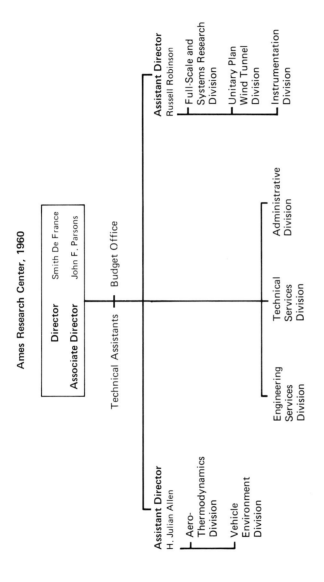

Ames Research Center, 1960

Director	Smith De France
Associate Director	John F. Parsons

Technical Assistants — Budget Office

Assistant Director
H. Julian Allen
- Aero-Thermodynamics Division
- Vehicle Environment Division

- Engineering Services Division
- Technical Services Division
- Administrative Division

Assistant Director
Russell Robinson
- Full-Scale and Systems Research Division
- Unitary Plan Wind Tunnel Division
- Instrumentation Division

225

Ames Research Center, 1964

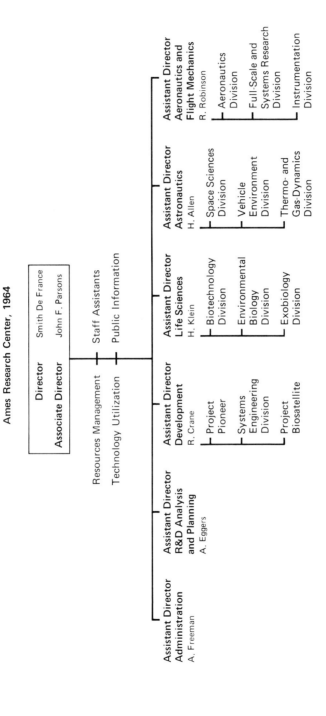

| Director | Smith De France |
| Associate Director | John F. Parsons |

Staff Assistants
Public Information

Resources Management
Technology Utilization

Assistant Director Administration
A. Freeman

Assistant Director R&D Analysis and Planning
A. Eggers

Assistant Director Development
R. Crane
— Project Pioneer
— Systems Engineering Division
— Project Biosatellite

Assistant Director Life Sciences
H. Klein
— Biotechnology Division
— Environmental Biology Division
— Exobiology Division

Assistant Director Astronautics
H. Allen
— Space Sciences Division
— Vehicle Environment Division
— Thermo- and Gas-Dynamics Division

Assistant Director Aeronautics and Flight Mechanics
R. Robinson
— Aeronautics Division
— Full-Scale and Systems Research Division
— Instrumentation Division

226

Ames Research Center, 1976

| Director | Hans Mark |
| Deputy Director | Clarence Syvertson |

Executive Staff

U.S. Army Air Mobility R&D Laboratory Ames Directorate

NASA Inspections Office

F.A.A. Aircraft Simulation Office

Equal Opportunity Program Office

NASA Management Audit Office

Health and Safety Office

Public Affairs Office

Patent Counsel

Chief Counsel

Planning and Analysis Office

Administration Directorate Louis Brennwald

Research Support Directorate Loren Bright

Life Sciences Directorate Harold Klein

- Biomedical Research Division H. Sandler
- Biosystems Division R. Johnson
- Extraterrestrial Biology Division J. Billingham
- Man-Vehicles Systems Research Division A. Chambers

Astronautics Directorate Dean Chapman

- Airborne Missions and Applications Division M. Knutson
- Space Projects Division R. Nunamaker
- Space Sciences Division D. Compton
- Thermo- and Gas-Dynamics Division V. Peterson
- Project Pioneer C. Hall

Aeronautics and Flight Systems Directorate Leonard Roberts

- Aerodynamics Division R. Petersen
- Aircraft Operations Division D. Reese
- Flight Systems Research Division T. Snyder
- Simulation Sciences Division G. Rathert

227

The last five charts show the Life Sciences Directorate during its first 14 turbulent years The major shifts in research can be easily followed. Human-machine integration in its various aspects was a strong element from the beginning. Over the years exobiology lost ground as biomedical research grew. These charts are taken from the historical files of the Life Sciences Directorate.

LIFE SCIENCES DIRECTORATE
October 1962

ASSISTANT DIRECTOR FOR LIFE SCIENCES

- ENVIRONMENTAL BIOLOGY DIVISION
  - Neurobiology Branch
  - Experimental Pathology Branch
  - Physiology Branch
  - Biochemical Endocrinology Branch

- BIOTECHNOLOGY DIVISION
  - Environmental Control Research Branch
  - Man-Machine Integration Branch
  - Human Performance Branch
  - Biomedical Research Branch

- EXOBIOLOGY DIVISION
  - Chemical Evolution Branch
  - Biological Adaptation Branch
  - Life Detection Systems Branch

LIFE SCIENCES DIRECTORATE
January 1964

ASSISTANT DIRECTOR FOR LIFE SCIENCES

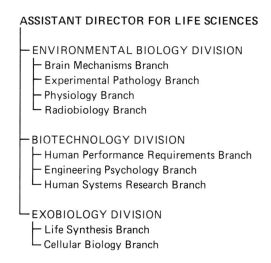

- ENVIRONMENTAL BIOLOGY DIVISION
  - Brain Mechanisms Branch
  - Experimental Pathology Branch
  - Physiology Branch
  - Radiobiology Branch

- BIOTECHNOLOGY DIVISION
  - Life Support Branch
  - Man-Machine Integration Branch
  - Manned-Systems Simulation Branch

- EXOBIOLOGY DIVISION
  - Biochemical Evolution Branch
  - Cellular Biology Branch
  - Life Detection Systems Branch

LIFE SCIENCES DIRECTORATE
December 1966

ASSISTANT DIRECTOR FOR LIFE SCIENCES

- ENVIRONMENTAL BIOLOGY DIVISION
  - Brain Mechanisms Branch
  - Experimental Pathology Branch
  - Physiology Branch
  - Radiobiology Branch

- BIOTECHNOLOGY DIVISION
  - Human Performance Requirements Branch
  - Engineering Psychology Branch
  - Human Systems Research Branch

- EXOBIOLOGY DIVISION
  - Life Synthesis Branch
  - Cellular Biology Branch

LIFE SCIENCE DIRECTORATE
October 1972

DIRECTOR OF LIFE SCIENCES

- BIOMEDICAL RESEARCH DIVISION
  - Biochemical Endocrinology Branch
  - Environmental Physiology Branch
  - Human Studies Branch

- BIOTECHNOLOGY DIVISION
  - Environmental Control Research Branch
  - Man-Machine Integration Branch
  - Neurosciences Branch

- PLANETARY BIOLOGY DIVISION
  - Biological Adaptation Branch
  - Chemical Evolution Branch
  - Life Detection Systems Branch

LIFE SCIENCES DIRECTORATE
September 1976

DIRECTOR OF LIFE SCIENCES

- BIOMEDICAL RESEARCH DIVISION

- BIOSYSTEMS DIVISION
  - Advanced Life Support Project Office

- EXTRATERRESTRIAL BIOLOGY DIVISION
  - Planetary Exploration Office
  - Search for Extraterrestrial Intelligence (SETI) Office

- MAN-VEHICLE SYSTEMS RESEARCH DIVISION
  - Aviation Safety Research Office

230

APPENDIX B

BUDGETS, 1940–1976

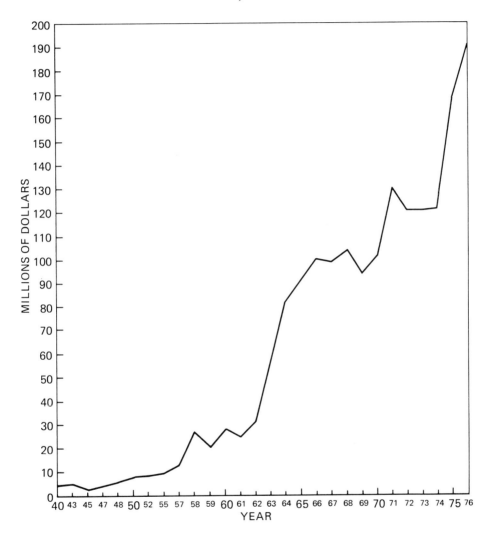

Sources: 1940–1948, *NACA Annual Reports*
1959–1965, *NASA Historical Data Book, 1958–1968, Vol. 1,
NASA Resources,* SP-4012 (Washington, 1976)
1966–1976, Resources Management Office

APPENDIX C

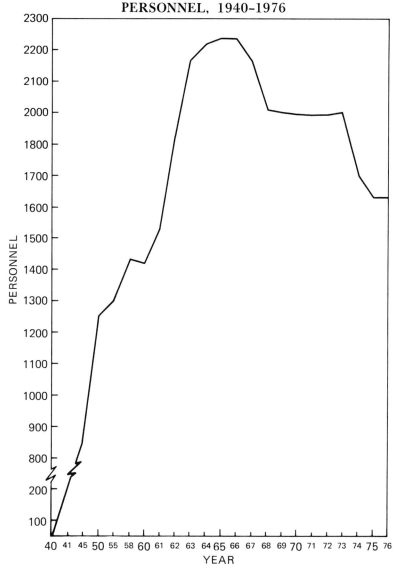

PERSONNEL, 1940–1976

Sources: 1940–1957, Edwin P. Hartman, *Adventures in Research: A History of Ames Research Center, 1940–1965,* NASA SP-4302 (Washington, 1966) (figures are approximate)

1958–1966, *NASA Historical Data Book, 1958–1968, Vol. 1, NASA Resources,* SP-4012 (Washington, 1976)

1967–1976, Resources Management Office

APPENDIX D

SUPPORT CONTRACT WORKERS, 1966–1976

In its early years, Ames had a few contractual arrangements with universities for specific research projects, but contracting was not important to the NACA. With the establishment of NASA, however, contract work grew rapidly, if not so fast as at the manned spaceflight centers.

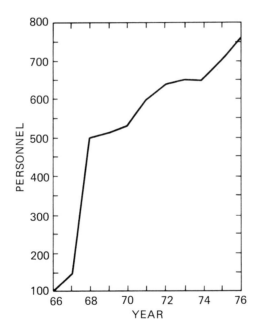

Source: Ames Resources Management Office.

APPENDIX E

CHRONOLOGY OF MAJOR EVENTS IN THE TEXT

1915

The National Advisory Committee for Aeronautics (NACA) founded.

1918

Langley Memorial Aeronautical Laboratory, the NACA's first research establishment, founded at Langley Field, near Hampton, Virginia.

1936

Oct.   Special Committee on the Relation of the NACA to National Defense in Time of War recommended a second laboratory be built.

1938

Dec.   Successor committee on future research needs in the NACA repeated the recommendation for a second laboratory.

1939

Aug.   President signed bill providing for second laboratory.

Sept.   Moffett Field site at Sunnyvale, California, approved for second laboratory.

Dec.   Ground was broken for the new laboratory and first construction began.

1940

Apr.   The new laboratory named after Dr. Joseph Ames, the former chairman of the NACA.

June   Smith J. De France named engineer-in-charge at Ames, though remaining at Langley planning facilities for both Ames and the new engine-research laboratory to be built near Cleveland. Construction at Ames continued, and staff arrived from Langley. Additional aeronautical engineers hired from among recent university graduates.

Aug. Construction of 7- by 10-foot and 16-foot wind tunnels started.

De France arrived at Ames with remainder of Langley transferees.

1941

Oct. Additional appropriations of $6 million approved for Ames.

Dec. After U.S. entry into World War II, activity at Ames became almost entirely devoted to war-related aeronautical problems.

1942

Mar. Construction of the 40- by 80-foot wind tunnel began.

Apr. The Navy took possession of Moffett Field, replacing the Army.

1944

June The 40- by 80-foot tunnel began operation.

1945

Feb. Construction began on two 1- by 3-foot supersonic wind tunnels.

Mar. Sweptback wing, designed to overcome high-speed compressibility effects, tested in Langley wind tunnel.

May Construction began on 6- by 6-foot supersonic wind tunnel at Ames.

July High-Speed Research Division formed under H. Julian Allen.

1947

George Lewis, director of aeronautical research for the NACA, retired. Hugh Dryden succeeded him.

1947

Oct. Capt. Charles Yeager piloted the Bell X-1 to supersonic flight at Muroc.

1950

"Unitary Plan" for national research facilities in aeronautics approved; Ames to build a complex linking one transonic and two supersonic tunnels at a cost of over $27 million.

1952

Harvey Allen proposed blunt-body theory to solve problem of aerodynamic heating of reentry bodies, a major aeronautical research breakthrough.

1957

The International Geophysical Year proclaimed for 1957–1958; it would feature international competition to orbit an artificial satellite.

Oct.   *Sputnik 1* orbited by U.S.S.R., beginning the space race.

1958

Jan.   U.S. Army launched *Explorer 1,* the first American satellite.

Feb.   The Advanced Research Projects Agency established within DoD.

Apr.   Legislation initiated to create NASA.

July   National Aeronautics and Space Act passed.

Oct.   National Aeronautics and Space Administration established; Ames Aeronautical Laboratory became Ames Research Center.

1959

July   Dr. Clark Randt appointed adviser for life sciences by NASA Administrator T. Keith Glennan.

1960

Nov.   Ames named the life-sciences research facility location.

1961

July   Dr. Webb Haymaker named head of the life-sciences research facility.

1962

Oct.   Ames gained Biosatellite Project; Carlton Bioletti named project manager.

Nov.   Ames gained Pioneer project; Charles Hall named project manager.

1965

Feb.   Ames–U.S. Army agreement established Army Aeronautical Research Laboratory at Ames. Ames to furnish facilities and personnel support; Army to furnish personnel to operate one of the 7- by 10-foot wind tunnels.

Oct.   Smith De France retired as director of Ames Research Center, succeeded by Harvey Allen.

Dec.   *Pioneer 6,* the first of the Ames-managed Pioneers, launched.

1966

June   Ames's civil service personnel peaked at 2310.

Dec.   *Biosatellite 1* launched.

1967

July   Ames entered into first consortium agreement with the University of Santa Clara Law School.

Sept.   *Biosatellite 2* launched.

1968

Oct.   Harvey Allen announced his intention to retire.

1969

Feb.   Hans Mark named director of Ames.

1969

June   *Biosatellite 3* launched.

1970

Mar.   A C-141 Starlifter, to be fitted with a 91.5-cm telescope, acquired by Ames as a flying astronomical observatory.

Dec.   Ames acquisition of ARPA's Illiac IV computer system approved.

1971

Sept.   Ames-FAA-DOT agreement provided for use of Ames simulators in qualifying checks of new commercial aircraft.

1972

Jan.   Pioneer Venus project transferred from Goddard Space Flight Center to Ames.

Mar.   *Pioneer 10* to Jupiter launched.

1973

Feb.   Ames became lead center for Earth-observation aircraft; Applications Aircraft and Future Planning Office established.

        Ames–Air Force agreement for development of STOL aircraft.

Apr.   *Pioneer 11* to Jupiter launched.

July   Refurbishment of the 40- by 80-foot wind tunnel began.

1974

Nov.   Design plans for the Quiet Short Haul Research Aircraft completed.

1976

June   Ames named lead center for helicopter research.

APPENDIX F

CHRONOLOGY, 1977–1980

This appendix is a chronology of events in the history of the Ames Research Center subsequent to the period covered in the text and is included to bring the coverage of the volume closer to the date of publication. Events have been selected because of their pertinence to themes and topics developed in the text. Some entries relating to NASA have been included because they would affect Ames in time.

Because these events are not dealt with in the text, considerably more detail is included than was the case for the previous chronology (app. E), and the source is given at the end of each item.

1977

10 Jan. An engineering test model of *Pioneer 10,* the first spacecraft to reach Jupiter, was put on display in the National Air and Space Museum of the Smithsonian Institution in Washington, D.C. Launched on 3 Mar. 1972, the Ames-managed spacecraft reached Jupiter in Dec. 1973, returning the first close-up views of the planet, which was discovered to be a spinning ball of liquid hydrogen with no perceptible surface. Returning a wealth of information about Jupiter's magnetic field, radiation belts, and weather, the spacecraft was then programmed on an escape trajectory out of the solar system. In Feb. 1976 it crossed Saturn's orbit, traveling away from the sun at a speed of 59,200 km/hr. It was expected to reach Pluto's orbit in 1987. (Ames release 77-1; *Astrogram,* 13 Jan. 1977)

14 Jan. Deputy Director Clarence Syvertson was named a fellow of the American Institute of Aeronautics and Astronautics. Joining Ames in 1948, Syvertson did pioneering theoretical research on hypersonic aerodynamics in the early 1950s and on hypersonic vehicles in the late 1950s. He played an important role in the development of the wingless M-2, a manned lifting body that was a precursor to manned maneuverable space vehicles. Head of the Mission Analysis Division at Ames in the early 1960s, Syvertson also headed the Dept. of Transportation–NASA team that produced the Civil Aeronautics Research and Development Study, a foundation for current U.S. aviation R&D. (Ames release 77-3; *Astrogram,* 27 Jan. 1977)

29 Jan.	H. Julian "Harvey" Allen died of a heart attack. A major figure in modern aerospace technology, Allen came to the center as one of the original group of research personnel. He headed the Theoretical Aerodynamics Research Section from 1940 to 1945, when that section evolved into the High-Speed Aerodynamics Division. In the 1940s, Allen developed a general theory of subsonic airfoils that made it possible to calculate accurately the ideal airfoil shape for specified conditions. Low-drag airfoils, such as those used on the Mustang fighter, were much improved with Allen's general theory. His most outstanding accomplishment was the concept of bluntness to reduce the heating of spacecraft reentering the Earth's atmosphere. The discovery resulted in the blunt shapes of ICBM warheads and NASA's space capsules. When the Astronautics Directorate was created from the High-Speed Division, Allen became its first head. From Sept. 1965 to Jan. 1969, he served as Ames's second director. Throughout his years at Ames, he was a friend and mentor to a continuing succession of Ames researchers and other colleagues in the aeronautics profession. (Ames release 77-06; Director's memorandum 77-15; *Astrogram,* 10 Feb. 1977)
3 Feb.	Ames announced that a developmental Spacelab payload typifying payloads planned for Space Shuttle missions in the 1980s was being tested at the research center. Equipment was being readied for a final 7-day simulation of a typical Spacelab mission planned for May 1977 at Johnson Space Center. The payload consisted of 22 experiments to investigate effects of the space environment on humans, frogs, rats, mice, monkeys, and fruit flies. Functions of the heart, red-blood-cell lifetimes, bone and muscle metabolism, body temperature, hormones, and other biomedical factors were to be studied. (Ames release 77-07)
18 Feb.	The first Space Shuttle Orbiter *Enterprise* made its first flight atop a Boeing 747. A prototype of the Orbiter had been tested in the Ames 40- by 80-foot wind tunnel; the craft's thermal protection system was largely a product of research done at Ames. (*Astrogram,* 24 Feb. 1977)
2 Mar.	Ames announced that its Lear Jet equipped with a 30-cm infrared telescope would participate in an international study (Project Porcupine, directed by the Max Planck Institut für Physik

244

und Astrophysik) to study the coupling between the magneto-sphere and ionosphere. An Aries sounding rocket equipped with 11 experiments was to be launched in Sweden. At 450 km altitude, a barium shaped-charge would be ejected. Ionized by sunlight, the visible charge would travel along the Earth's magnetic lines of force, reentering the atmosphere in the Antarctic. The barium trail would be followed by the Lear Jet, equipped with instruments furnished by the University of Alaska. Its flightpath would allow continuous optical coverage of the barium trail against a star background for the first 1,000 seconds after release. The project was to be completed by the end of March. (Ames release 77-14)

3 Mar.   The Ames C-141 Kuiper Airborne Observatory left on its first international expedition. From bases in Australia, the C-141 was to observe the planet Uranus during unique astronomical conditions. On 10–11 Mar. Uranus would move between Earth and a star. The resulting occultation, or blacking out, of starlight would enable the international team of scientists to learn more about Uranus's atmosphere, composition, shape, and size. Investigators included researchers from American and Australian universities. (Ames release 77-13)

10 Mar.   Scientists aboard the Kuiper Airborne Observatory discovered that Uranus possesses equatorial rings, which are apparently composed of rock and ice. Tracking Uranus as it passed in front of a star in the constellation Libra, the telescope lost sight of the star for periods of about 8 seconds at 10 different times. "I think we were looking through a very faint ring system similar to the rings of Saturn," said the leader of the investigation team. "The fact that there were 5 blackouts on either side of the planet suggests rings and not moons, since moons would have been placed around the planet in a more random way." One theory was that the rings are composed of material present during the formation of the solar system that never coalesced into moons; another was that the rings are remnants of a disintegrated moon or moons. (Ames release 77-17; *Astrogram*, 24 Mar. 1977)

14 Mar.   Director Hans Mark announced organizational changes to accommodate Ames's new role as lead center in helicopter research and technology. Created within the Aeronautics and Flight Systems Directorate were the Helicopter Systems Office,

responsible for integrating the various activities in helicopter systems technology; the Helicopter Technology Division, serving as the focal point for helicopter technology development within NASA; and the V/STOL Aircraft Technology Division, restructured from the Research Aircraft Projects Office. The organizational changes reflected the NASA decision of last summer to establish Ames as the lead center for NASA's helicopter activities. By specifying a lead center, NASA hoped to increase research output and to reduce costs. Langley Research Center and Lewis Research Center were to continue to be responsible for key segments of the helicopter activities. Ames would conduct helicopter research using its unique aeronautical facilities: its 40- by 80-foot wind tunnel and flight simulation facilities. Ames would also conduct flight tests with research rotorcraft such as the Tilt Rotor Research Aircraft and Rotor Systems Research Aircraft. Over the next three years 72 positions were to be added to the Ames staff. While Langley's activity in helicopters would be phased down, that center's expected growth in long-haul aircraft technology should minimize any impact on manpower and the local economy. (Ames release 77-19; Director's memorandum 77-20)

24 Mar. The international Infrared Astronomy Satellite (IRAS) Project was approved. IRAS was a cooperative U.S.–Netherlands–U.K. project whose purpose was an infrared survey of the entire celestial sphere. The satellite would consist of a spacecraft to be built by the Netherlands and a large infrared telescope to be built by the U.S. Ames was responsible for the IRAS telescope system, while the overall management of the U.S. part of the project was provided by the Jet Propulsion Laboratory. The Telescope System Project Office was contained within the Space Projects Division of the Astronautics Directorate. (*Astrogram*, 24 Mar. 1977)

14 Apr. NASA awarded two $350,000 contracts to the McDonnell Douglas Corp. and the team of Hughes Aircraft and General Electric for design studies of a vehicle to plunge into Jupiter's atmosphere. The Jupiter Orbiter with Probe mission, requested in NASA's FY 1978 budget, would offer the first opportunity to make *in situ* as well as remote measurements of the planet, its environment, and its satellites. Ames was to manage the probe system. (Ames release 77-20)

246

16 May	*Galileo II,* Ames's Convair 990 flying laboratory, under the joint management of NASA and the European Space Agency (ESA), began a 10-day simulation of a Spacelab mission. A mission specialist and two payload specialists each from NASA and ESA would participate. Spacelab, a major element in the Space Shuttle System, would be located in the cargo bay of the Orbiter and carry facilities and equipment similar to laboratories on the ground. Objectives of the simulation included evaluation of management of payload and mission operations to develop low-cost concepts for Spacelab, studies of interactions between Spacelab personnel and principal investigators on the ground, and the development of minimum training requirements. Another prime concern was to involve the ESA and NASA Spacelab managers in the same roles they would have during an actual Spacelab flight. *Galileo II* was to make six-hour flights on each day of the simulation, and the payload and mission specialists would remain confined throughout the 10-day period to work on the experiment payload and sleep in adjacent living quarters. (Ames release 77-21)

19 May	A critical segment of the Pioneer-Venus mission was successfully tested by dropping the entry probe from an Air Force balloon 27 km above White Sands Missile Range, New Mexico. The test duplicated events just before descent into the planet's dense, hot lower atmosphere, demonstrating deployment of the probe parachute, separation of its heat shield, and separation of the parachute for the final phase of flight down to the surface. The objective of the mission would be to characterize Venus's atmosphere and weather. (Ames release 77-30; *Astrogram,* 16 June 1977)

27 May	Ames Director Hans Mark, nominated for the post of undersecretary of the Air Force, announced that Dep. Dir. Clarence Syvertson was acting director until further notice. Mark was to take up his new post in August. (Director's memorandum 77-66)

10 June	President Carter nominated Dr. Robert A. Frosch to become NASA administrator, succeeding Dr. James C. Fletcher, who resigned 1 May. Frosch was associate director for applied oceanography at the Woods Hole Oceanographic Institution. (*Astrogram,* 16 June 1977)

5 July The new visitor-reception building opened. (Director's memorandum 77-80)

19 July Congress approved $17.7 million for the Jupiter Orbiter and Probe mission in FY 1978. The joint JPL-Ames project was to be the first NASA planetary project undertaken by the Office of Space Science since initiation of the Ames Pioneer-Venus Project in 1972. (*Astrogram,* 28 July 1977)

July-Aug. Two Ames research aircraft, a U-2 and a Lear Jet, were based in the Panama Canal Zone for three weeks conducting studies of atmospheric pollution. Several governmental agencies and universities cooperated in the study, gathering information on how atmospheric pollutants such as halocarbons are carried from low altitudes into the stratosphere, where they may influence the ozone balance. The study, sponsored and planned by Ames, was carried out over a 16-day period with both aircraft making daily flights. Heavily instrumented with sensing and sampling equipment, the aircraft measured atmospheric pollutants at multiple altitudes. The Lear Jet covered altitudes up to 14,000 m, while the U-2 carried the coverage well into the stratosphere at altitudes of 21,300 m. (*Astrogram,* 8 Sept. 1977)

30 Aug. The name of the U.S. Army Air Mobility Research and Development Laboratory was changed to the U.S. Army Research and Technology Laboratories, the directorate at Ames becoming the Aeromechanics Laboratory. The mission of the laboratories remained the same: to plan, develop, manage, and execute R&D programs to provide a firm technical base for superior airmobile systems. Major projects include: (1) The XV-15 Tilt Rotor Research Aircraft, now being flight tested. The aircraft incorporates wingtip-mounted engines, transmissions, and 7.6-m propellers that tilt from a helicopter position for takeoffs, landings, and hovering, to a horizontal position for forward flight. (2) The XH-59A Advancing Blade Concept (ABC), a coaxial, hingeless rotor research helicopter that features stiff, counter-rotating rotor blades rigidly attached to the hubs. The ABC uses only its rotor blade system throughout its entire speed range; no tail rotor is required. (3) The Rotor Systems Research Aircraft, a test vehicle used by the Army and NASA to evaluate a wide variety of existing and future systems. (*Astrogram,* 6 Oct. 1977)

7 Sept.	NASA Headquarters announced civil service manpower adjustments. In spite of overall reductions of 500 positions, Ames was to gain 45 positions for FY 1978. This was a result of the acceleration of the helicopter transfer from Langley Research Center to Ames. (NASA Hq. announcement, 7 Sept. 1977)
14 Sept.	The Space Projects Division was to be reorganized to accommodate its recently assigned responsibility for managing major portions of the infrared telescope for the IRAS project and the atmospheric entry probe of the Jupiter Orbiter Probe mission. Subsequently, the division would consist of the Division Office, the Project Technology Branch, the Jupiter Probe Project Office, and the IRAS Telescope Project Office. The Project Development Branch was abolished. (Director's memorandum 77-124)
12 Oct.	Ames was awarded the Columbus Gold Medal by the city of Genoa, Italy, for the two multibillion-mile Pioneer flights. Acting Director Clarence Syvertson accepted the medal in Italy. (*Astrogram,* 20 Oct. 1977)
14 Oct.	A team of Ames researchers made what may become a major break-through in explaining the origin of life. "Building blocks of life" apparently were collected and organized on the shores of the primordial oceans by "natural catalysts" found widely on Earth. This could be a step in the chemical evolution of the first living organisms. The experiments demonstrated how two basic types of organic molecules (amino acids, the building blocks of proteins, and nucleotides, the building blocks of the DNA molecule) may have been concentrated in the primitive oceans. The work also seemed to show how life-related amino acids were linked together into the chain needed to make living cells, while other amino acids were selectively destroyed. Team leader for the work was Ames's Dr. James Lawless. Also participating was Dr. Nissim Levi, a National Research Council Fellow from Israel, working at Ames. (Ames release 77-43; *Astrogram,* 20 Oct. 1977)
25 Oct.	NASA Hq. announced a reorganization to be effective 8 Nov. The major change affecting Ames was that the center director would report directly to the Administrator. (Director's memorandum 77-144)

25 Oct.	*Galileo II*, Ames's Convair 990 research aircraft, surveyed archaeological sites in Guatemala in an effort to learn more about the Mayan civilization that flourished there centuries ago. Three different types of radar were used to penetrate the dense tropical foliage to different depths, allowing identification of features not readily distinguishable by other means. Signs of roads, stone walls, agricultural terraces, and other man-made structures were sought. The aircraft also carried a scanning infrared sensor to detect differences in vegetation, seeking clues to the extent and type of farming done by the Mayans. The flight was a cooperative effort among Ames, JPL, and researchers at the University of Texas at San Antonio. (*Astrogram,* 17 Nov. 1977)
17 Nov.	Ames announced that measurements made by researchers using a U-2 aircraft suggested that the cosmos may have started serenely, with a powerful but tightly controlled and completely uniform expansion. Using ultrasensitive radio equipment, the research team measured the cosmic microwave background — the radiation left over from the Big Bang, the initial, universe-forming event — and concluded that that event was a smooth process, with matter and energy uniformly distributed and expanding at an equal rate in all directions. Researchers from the Lawrence Livermore Laboratory and the University of California at Berkeley declared, "The big bang, the most cataclysmic event we can imagine, on closer inspection appears finely orchestrated." (Ames release 77-45; *Astrogram,* 1 Dec. 1977)

1978

Jan.	Ames announced the formation of the Stanford-NASA Joint Institute for Surface and Microstructural Research. Manpower and advanced laboratory equipment would be shared by Ames's Materials and Physical Sciences Branch and Stanford's departments of materials science, chemical engineering, and electrical engineering. The agreement formalized and expanded a collaboration that had existed since 1968. Research would continue at both locations, and some Ames equipment was to be transferred to Stanford. (*Astrogram,* 26 Jan. 1978)
Feb.	The Jupiter Orbiter and Probe mission, scheduled for 1982, was formally designated Project Galileo. Scheduled to become the

first planetary spacecraft to be carried aboard the Space Shuttle, *Galileo* was to conduct the most detailed scientific investigation yet of Jupiter and its environment. Ames had project responsibility for the entry probe. (*Astrogram,* 9 Feb. 1978)

24 Feb.   To facilitate the transfer of NASA technology to other potential users, organizational changes were made in the Airborne Missions and Applications Division. The User Applications Branch was renamed the Technology Applications Branch, and the Western Regional Applications Office was established. The new office extended the concept of user-driven transfer of Landsat technology to agencies in 14 western states, including Alaska and Hawaii. (Director's memorandum 79-25)

Mar.   The first XV-15 Tilt Rotor Research Aircraft arrived at Ames. Two aircraft were built under a joint program for Ames and the U.S. Army's Research and Technology Laboratories by Bell Helicopter Textron, Fort Worth, Texas. The aircraft now at Ames had been modified for remote control operation and was to be tested for six weeks in the 40- by 80-foot wind tunnel. Flight testing of the second aircraft would then follow in Texas. Both aircraft would eventually be based at Ames for comprehensive evaluation of the tilt rotor concept, to provide data for terminal area navigation, and to support vertical and short takeoff and landing programs. (*Astrogram,* 6 Apr. 1978)

29 Mar.   A project office was established to modify the 40- by 80-foot wind tunnel. Over the past four years, plans had been drawn to increase the speed of the tunnel to 550 km/hr and to add an 80- by 120-foot test section. The first funding of $19.5 million was received. With growth in size of the project team imminent, a project office to manage the many activities became necessary. Charles A. Hermach was appointed project manager. (Director's memorandum 78-27)

10 Apr.   The Army-NASA-Sikorsky Rotor Systems Research Aircraft (RSRA) made its first flight as a compound helicopter-fixed wing aircraft, taking off from a Wallops Island runway and climbing to 460 m, using both wings and rotor systems for lift. Under contract to NASA and the U.S. Army Research and Technology Laboratories, Sikorsky built two prototypes that were to be tested in 1978. The RSRA had a 14-m wingspan and a five-blade S-61 rotor system powered by two T-58 turboshaft

engines. Two auxiliary TF34 turbofan engines were mounted below the rotor system. (*Astrogram,* 10 Aug. 1978)

30 Apr.　Clarence A. Syvertson, acting director since the resignation of Dr. Hans Mark in August 1977, was named director of the center. Syvertson had been at Ames since 1948, beginning as a research scientist and assistant branch chief. He became chief of the 3.5-Foot Hypersonic Wind Tunnel Branch in 1959, and in 1963 director of the Mission Analysis Division, doing advanced planning for all of NASA. In 1966 he was appointed director of astronautics, and in 1969 deputy director of Ames. He also served as executive director of the Joint DOT-NASA Civil Aviation Research and Development Policy Study to identify future directions for civil aviation development. His work in hypersonic aerodynamics helped to produce the series of prototype lifting bodies that culminated in the M-2. (Ames release 78-16; *Palo Alto Times,* 27 Apr. 1978)

20 May　*Pioneer-Venus 1,* the orbiter, was launched from Kennedy Space Center. The spacecraft was expected to reach Venus in early December, going into an eccentric 24-hr orbit around the planet. The orbiter carried 11 scientific experiments designed to return data about Venus, plus 1 to help pinpoint the sources of gamma-ray bursts from space. The orbiter's S-band telemetry system and X-band beacon would be used for 6 radio-science experiments. *Pioneer-Venus 2,* the probe, with missions complementary to those of the orbiter, was to be launched in early August. The two vehicles were to converge near the planet in early December. (*Astrogram,* 1 June 1978; *Aviation Week and Space Technology,* 27 Feb. 1978)

1 June　*Pioneer Venus 1* was on course toward its orbit around Venus, with most engineering systems checked out and operating normally. Controllers at Ames deployed the craft's 4.3-m magnetometer boom and "despun" the high-data-rate, 1.2-m-diameter dish antenna to center it continuously on Earth. They took pictures of Earth, turned on five of the six interplanetary experiments, made a star map, and checked out power, navigation, and propulsion systems. *Pioneer-Venus 1* measured Earth's protective magnetic envelope, the magnetosphere, as it passed beyond it, as well as charting the solar wind. The next was a first midcourse correction. Launch trajectory was so accurate that a second correction might not be needed. (*Astrogram,* 1 June 1978)

| 15 June | *Pioneer-Venus 1,* on the first leg of its journey toward Venus, detected an extremely powerful burst of gamma rays from somewhere in the universe. Unknown until 1973, gamma-ray bursts have enormous energies and occur about once a month, seemingly from random points in our galaxy or beyond. The spacecraft carried six interplanetary instruments, including a gamma-ray-burst detector, which sensed a two-second pulse of these very high-energy photons just 33 hours after lift-off and 585,000 km from Earth. (*Astrogram,* 15 June 1978) |

| Also in June | Researchers working at Ames apparently discovered a way to account for the formation on Earth four billion years ago of nucleic acids, one of the two most essential components of life. The discovery supplemented earlier work in which the same investigators discovered a mechanism to explain the other critical component of life, protein (see 14 Oct. 1977, above). Their new discovery involved metal clays that would have been common on the shores of primitive bodies of water. When low-concentration solutions of DNA-forming nucleotides are mixed with commonplace metal clays, most clays attract the nucleotides. Furthermore, a clay containing zinc preferentially attracts all six of them. The team consisted of Dr. James Lawless of Ames; Dr. Edward Edelson, a National Research Council Associate; and Lewis Manring, a student at the University of Santa Clara. (*Astrogram,* 29 June 1978) |

| 6 July | The Quiet Short-Haul Research Aircraft (QSRA), built by Boeing under contract to NASA, made its maiden flight in Seattle. The QSRA was a rebuilt de Havilland C-8A Buffalo. With a new wing, tail, and avionics, and four overwing jet engines to provide "upper surface blowing" for high lift, the QSRA was built to develop the technology for future commercial airliners with short take-off and landing capabilities. Ames pilot Jim Martin noted that the aircraft's behavior had been accurately predicted by preflight simulation studies. "I didn't see any surprises. The QSRA simulation at Ames was one of the most accurate simulations I've flown." After more flight testing at Boeing, the aircraft was to be flown to Ames for two years of additional tests. (*Astrogram,* 27 July 1978; *The Boeing News,* 13 July 1978) |

| 17 July | The Life Sciences Directorate was reorganized. The Extraterrestrial Biology Division was renamed the Extraterrestrial Research |

Division, to reflect an expanded role in the development of advanced life-support systems for future space missions. The Advanced Life Support Project Office became the Advanced Life Support Office, with added functions of conducting research into biologically based life support techniques. (Director's memorandum 78-94)

17 July   Ames acquired approximately five acres of land from the Pacific Gas and Electric Company in exchange for an equal parcel of NASA property. The exchange, necessary to accommodate the modifications being made to the 40- by 80-foot wind tunnel, was effected through the General Services Administration. Another parcel was made available to NASA by the Navy through an agreement with the Naval Facilities Engineering Command of San Bruno. (*Astrogram,* 10 Aug. 1978)

3 Aug.   With initial flight testing completed at Boeing Field, the new QSRA was flown to Ames for additional testing before beginning a research program for a short-haul transportation system. High performance of the aircraft was due to the upper-surface-blowing propulsive-lift concept, in which four jet engines were mounted on top of the wing so fan air was directed across the upper surface of the wing and flaps. This significantly increased lift, particularly at lower speeds. In addition, compressed air from the engines was fed through an ejector system to provide boundary layer control blowing at the wing leading edges and ailerons, further enhancing lift and control. Project officials believed the technology could have important ramifications. A QSRA-type aircraft the size of a Boeing 727 transport could carry the same payload at the same speeds as the 727, but could operate from small airports so quietly that it would not be heard in the surrounding community. (Ames release 78-37; *Astrogram,* 24 Aug. 1978)

8 Aug.   *Pioneer-Venus 2* was launched from Kennedy Space Center. The spacecraft was to reach Venus in conjunction with *Pioneer-Venus 1,* an orbiter, in early December. In mid-November *Pioneer-Venus 2* would split into five atmospheric entry craft — four probes and a transporter bus. On 9 Dec., the four probes would begin descent through the planet's dense atmosphere. The transporter bus would burn up in the planet's dense atmosphere, after measuring the composition of the upper atmosphere. (Ames release 78-40; *Astrogram,* 24 Aug. 1978)

17 Aug.	Mission controllers completed a critical course change for *Pioneer-Venus 2,* putting it right on target for encounter with Venus on 9 Dec. 1978. A series of carefully timed rocket thrusts increased the spacecraft's speed by 2.25 m/sec (Ames release 78-40; *Astrogram,* 24 Aug. 1978)
21 Sept.	Final course adjustments for *Pioneer 11's* encounter with Saturn on 1 Sept. 1979 were made by mission controllers at Ames. Its trajectory would bring it to within 30,000 km of Saturn's outer ring. The spacecraft would then swing under the plane of the rings to 25,000 km from the planet's surface. "We're going as close as we dare," said Jack Dyer, chief of mission analysis at Ames. Getting any closer to the ring would risk impact with orbiting fragments. *Pioneer 11* would take the first close-up color pictures of Saturn and its rings and make other first-time measurements of the planet's magnetic field, atmosphere, and other features. (*Astrogram,* 21 Sept. 1978)
25 Sept.	The Life Sciences Experiments Project Office was established within the Biosystems Division of the Life Sciences Directorate. Beginning in 1982, Spacelab missions entirely devoted to life sciences were to be flown under the management of program offices at Headquarters and Johnson Space Center. Project management responsibilities for experiments not involving humans as test subjects were assigned to the new Ames office. (Director's memorandum 78-117)
25 Sept.	Beginning in FY 1979, NASA would provide funds to each center director for new programs not included in the center's budget. The purpose of the Center Director's Discretionary Fund was to stimulate innovative ideas in R&D. The new programs would not be subject to Headquarters approval, though progress was to be reported yearly. No program was to be funded from this source for more than three years; after that time it should be complete or would have to compete for funding in the regular budget. (Director's memorandum 78-145)
26 Sept.	R. T. Jones was awarded the Prandtl Ring Award by the *Deutsche Gesellschaft für Luft- und Raumfahrt* in Darmstadt, Germany. Considered the highest honor in the field of fluid dynamics, the award was presented for Jones's "outstanding contributions in the field of aerodynamics." Over almost 50 years of research, he was responsible for some of the most

far-reaching discoveries made in the field. Most of Jones's work involved the application of abstract mathematics, learned as he went along, to practical flight problems. In the early 1930s, he gained most of his formal education from Max Munk, considered one of the country's most brilliant theorists. In 1934, Jones went to work at Langley Aeronautical Laboratory and remained there until 1946, when he moved to Ames. Jones is most noted for developing the theory of sweepback in this country, the method by which smooth flight at high speeds is made possible. Met with skepticism when Jones first presented the idea in 1944, the sweptback wing became conventional. Not limited to work in aerodynamics, in 1963 Jones left Ames to join Avco Everett Research Laboratory, where he worked on cardiac assist devices and problems of blood flow. He rejoined Ames as a staff scientist in 1970. (*Astrogram,* 8 Apr. 1976, 30 Nov. 1978)

1 Oct.   The Applied Computational Aerodynamics Branch was created within the Thermo- and Gas-Dynamics Division of the Astronautics Directorate. The new branch was to develop user-oriented computer codes for solving practical problems in aerodynamic design. The intent was to bridge the gap between the more basic work in computational technology being done by the Computational Fluid Dynamics Branch and the design codes required by the aerospace industry. (Director's memorandum 78-146)

9 Oct.   Ames announced that the two Pioneer-Venus spacecraft had passed major operational tests. On *Pioneer-Venus 2,* timing and separation systems had been tested for the split-second release of three probes to spread them over Venus's Earth-facing hemisphere 9600 km apart. On *Pioneer-Venus 1,* systems for the essential retrofire and injection-into-orbit maneuver, which takes place behind the planet and out of communication with Earth, had been operated. The spacecraft was to be put into orbit on 4 Dec.; *Pioneer-Venus 2* would enter the atmosphere on 9 Dec. (Ames release 78-48; *Astrogram,* 19 Oct. 1978)

2 Nov.   A brief ceremony marked the start of construction of the 80- by 120-foot wind tunnel. Former Center Director Smith J. De France was present, as was Russell G. Robinson, former director of aeronautics and flight systems, who broke ground for the first construction at Ames in Dec. 1939. The new

addition to the 40- by 80-foot wind tunnel would result in the largest facility of its kind in the world. (Director's memorandum 78-156)

19 Nov.   Final course and attitude corrections were made in the flight of *Pioneer-Venus 2* earlier in the month. The small probes were released on 19 Nov., and final descent was to occur 9 Dec. (*Astrogram,* 14 Dec. 1978)

4 Dec.   *Pioneer-Venus 1* was inserted into orbit around Venus and began radar-mapping Venus's surface. The mapper took one radar scan of the planet each Earth day and would map a belt completely around Venus in 243 days, during which Venus rotates once on its axis. (*Astrogram,* 14 Dec. 1978)

9 Dec.   The four probes of *Pioneer-Venus 2* descended to the surface of the planet, transmitting data as they descended. Unexpectedly, the day probe survived the landing impact and continued to transmit data for 67 minutes. (*Astrogram,* 14 Dec. 1978)

14 Dec.   Ames held a public briefing on the early scientific results of the first phase of the Pioneer-Venus mission. Experimenters revealed that the inert gas argon was found by both orbiter and probe instruments. The unexpected presence of the isotope Argon 36, relatively rare on Earth and Mars, might lead to a total revision of planet-formation theories. The findings could indicate that Venus was formed from very different materials than were Earth and Mars. Data from the four probes indicated that the cloud layer that enshrouds the planet disappears at about 55 km altitude. An immaculately clean atmosphere was found below that level, but the atmosphere was so dense that visibility would be very limited. At 27 km altitude, the large probe's gas chromatograph identified seven substances: neon, nitrogen, oxygen, argon, water, sulphur dioxide, and carbon dioxide. The presence of 97% carbon dioxide and 0.1% water vapor supported the theory that Venus's intense heat results from a greenhouse effect trapping heat from the sun. (*Astrogram,* 14 Dec. 1978)

1979

1 Jan.   John W. Boyd, deputy director of aeronautics and flight systems, was named deputy director of Dryden Flight Research

Center. At Ames since 1947, Boyd had been involved in a variety of research fields. He played an important role in developing and verifying the concept of conical camber for subsonic and supersonic aircraft, theoretical verification of canards as control surfaces for aircraft, experimental verification of the relations between vehicle shapes and problems of entry into planetary atmospheres, and management of aeronautical programs for VTOL and rotorcraft technology studies. (Director's memorandum 78-159; *Astrogram,* 16 Nov. 1978)

19 Jan. The Pioneer Project Office was reorganized to manage the remaining seven active Pioneer spacecraft. A major responsibility was planning and executing *Pioneer 11's* flyby past Saturn in Sept. 1979. The Experiment Systems Branch, Mission Operations Systems Branch, and Spacecraft Systems Branch were abolished, with their remaining functions vested in the Pioneer Project Office. (Director's memorandum 79-15)

1 Feb. A. Thomas Young became deputy director of Ames. Young was formerly director of the Planetary Program in the Office of Space Science at NASA Headquarters. (Director's memorandum 78-167; *Astrogram,* 16 Nov. 1978)

13 Feb. A Small Transport Aircraft Technology Project Team was established at Ames to plan, advocate, and implement an advanced technology project for small transport aircraft. Until recently air service to small communities and on low-density routes was severely constrained by the economic burdens of existing regulations. Deregulation created a rapid growth in this type of service and a strong demand for modern aircraft. The team was created to fill this need. (Director's memorandum 79-30)

Also in Feb. Major findings from *Pioneer-Venus 1* and *2* included the following: (1) The planet's searing atmosphere and surface heat seemed quite certainly to be due to a runaway greenhouse effect. (2) Venus's clouds were in three well defined and distinct layers, and seemed to result from vigorous sulfur-hydrogen-oxygen reactions. (3) Data from the orbiter's first radar map suggested that Venus's topography could be similar to Earth's, with high mountain-like features and extensive areas of relative flatness. The dayside probe found fine dust on the surface at its landing site in the southern hemisphere. (4) Starting at 13 km altitude, the two nightside probes detected a glow that increased as the probes descended. Mass spectrometer evidence for various sulfur compounds near the surface suggested that the mysterious glow could come from chemical fires on the surface or in the very hot and dense lower atmosphere near the surface. (5) The solar wind was interacting with the Venusian atmosphere several times more strongly than expected. (6) The spacecraft had so far identified 10 chemical constituents of the atmosphere and 10 ions in the ionosphere of Venus. (*Astrogram*, 22 Feb. 1979)

Feb.–Mar.   From 22 Feb. to 9 Mar., one of Ames's U-2 high-altitude research aircraft flew several astronomy missions over Peru. The payload was an upward-looking differential microwave radiometer for measuring the sky's background microwave radiation at extremely low temperatures. The measurements obtained were to be used to determine the movement and speed of Earth and our galaxy, the Milky Way, with respect to far distant bodies of the universe. Similar measurements made by the same aircraft in 1976–1977 supported the theory that the Milky Way and Earth are traveling through space at 1.6 billion km/hr. The mission, though accomplished successfully, was not without traumatic moments. Engine trouble with supporting C-130 aircraft, temporarily lost equipment, and the highjacking of the aircraft on which the crew traveled to Peru made the mission a close-run thing. On the return flight, the U-2 was granted an emergency waiver to fly without rescue support aircraft because of more trouble with the second C-130 pressed into service. (*Astrogram*, 22 Mar., 5 Apr. 1979)

30 Mar.   The Pioneer-Venus Team and Project Manager Charles Hall were honored by the National Space Club for outstanding contributions to space science. The Nelson P. Jackson Award, given to the year's most outstanding contributor in the missile, aircraft, and space fields, was given jointly to the NASA Ames Research Center for management of Pioneer-Venus and to Hughes Aircraft Company, which built both spacecraft. Hall, who had managed the Pioneer Projects since their inception in 1962, was awarded the Annual Astronautics Engineer Award. (Ames release 79-13; *Astrogram*, 5 Apr. 1979)

Also in Mar.   One of the two Rotor Systems Research Aircraft (RSRA) was delivered to Ames from Wallops Island after initial flight testing there. The RSRA could be configured to fly as a helicopter or with fixed wings and auxiliary jet engines. It could also be fitted with a variety of experimental and developmental rotor systems for research purposes. The RSRA joined the growing body of short-haul research aircraft based at Ames, including the X-14 jet-powered VTOL aircraft, the Augmentor Wing Jet STOL Aircraft, the Tilt-Rotor Research Aircraft, and the Quiet Short-Haul Research Aircraft. (*Astrogram*, 8 Mar. 1979)

13 Apr. NASA and Soviet life scientists were to cooperate in studying physiological changes in humans resulting from simulated weightlessness. Objectives of the joint study were to improve bedrest test procedures, to standardize physiological measurements and analysis techniques performed on astronauts and cosmonauts, and to reduce test duplication and increase the flow of information between the two groups. Dr. Harold Sandler of Ames was project scientist and Dr. Carter Alexander of JSC was project manager. A five-week study was to be conducted at the Institute of Biomedical Problems in Moscow, beginning in mid-May; a second would follow at Ames in mid-July. (Ames release 79-17; *Astrogram*, 3 May 1979)

23 Apr. The Numerical Aerodynamic Simulation Facility Project Office was established at Ames to pursue the design of a significant advancement in computational capability as part of the NASA FY 1980 program. Ames had previously carried out studies to assess the feasibility of a facility capable of one billion floating point operations per second. On the basis of positive results from those feasibility studies, Ames's proposal to continue work in this field was accepted by NASA Headquarters. (Director's memorandum 79-73)

2 May The Convair 990 research aircraft, *Galileo II,* was to participate in a summer-long international study of the summer monsoon, which annually brings torrential rains to the Asian subcontinent. MONEX (monsoon experiment) was to explore the origin of the monsoon winds in order to improve short-range prediction and understanding of the monsoon's role in global weather patterns. *Galileo II* would operate from bases in Saudi Arabia and elsewhere in the region, in coordination with several other aircraft, ships, and a variety of ground-based facilities. The mission was part of a large-scale atmospheric research program being conducted by the World Meteorological Organization of the United Nations. (Ames release 79-18; *Astrogram*, 31 May 1979)

| 7 May | The infrared instrument aboard the *Pioneer-Venus* orbiter had been returning downgraded data since 14 Feb. Efforts to correct the problem did not succeed, although the instrument functioned successfully long enough to make a thorough infrared survey of Venus. The regulated voltages that powered the instrument were registering 6 to 7 volts instead of the required 10. (Ames release 79-19) |

| 4 June | The Material Science and Applications Office was established within the Thermo- and Gas-Dynamics Division of the Astronautics Directorate. The office would conduct research on the fatigue and fracture mechanics of metal and composite materials subjected to corrosion, while developing accelerated life-testing techniques for such materials. (Director's memorandum 79-95) |

| 11 July | *Pioneer 10* crossed the orbit of Uranus. The seventh planet out, Uranus is 2.9 billion km from the Sun and about 2.7 billion km from Earth. Launched on 3 Mar. 1972 for the first flight beyond Mars and through the asteroid belt, *Pioneer 10* dispelled theories about an asteroid barrier to outer planet exploration. Mission planners used Jupiter's gravity to hurl the spacecraft on an escape trajectory out of the solar system. The spacecraft would next head for Neptune, and then on to the expected limit of radio communications after crossing Pluto's orbit in 1987. (*Astrogram*, 14 June 1979) |

| 15 July | The Tilt Rotor Research Aircraft Project Office was abolished, and the Tilt Rotor Aircraft Office was established. The new office would be responsible for all tilt rotor technology development and demonstration programs, including completion of the XV-15 research aircraft, proof-of-concept flight demonstration and concept evaluation, management of advanced flight experiments, and conduct of the Tilt Rotor Systems Technology Program. David Few was appointed manager of the new office. (Director's memorandum, 30 July 1979) |

| 19 July | Two Soviet medical doctors arrived at Ames to participate in the second phase of the space-medicine study that began in May in Moscow. They were the project manager for the Soviet phase of the study, Valeriy Mikhailov, and one of the principal researchers, Anatole Grigoriev. Previously, Dr. Harold Sandler of Ames and Dr. Carter Alexander of Johnson traveled |

to the Soviet Union for the first phase of the study. (Ames release 79-27; *Astrogram*, 28 June 1979)

24 July   The Tilt Rotor Research Aircraft, one of Ames's new acquisitions, demonstrated in-flight conversion from the helicopter mode to the airplane mode. The flight was made in Texas at Bell Helicopter's Flight Research Center. Bell designed and built the airplane under a joint research program for Ames and the U.S. Army's Research and Technology Laboratories. This is the second tilt rotor aircraft built for the project; the first was flight tested in 1977 and then shipped to Ames for wind-tunnel testing to define the initial flight envelope for flight tests with the second aircraft. (*Astrogram*, 9 Aug. 1979)

1 Aug.   The Helicopter-VTOL Human Factors Office was established within the Man-Vehicle Systems Research Division to study pilot-system performance problems, particularly those dealing with the transfer of information. The office was staffed by both NASA and Army Aeromechanics Laboratory research personnel. (Director's memorandum 79-100)

22 Aug.   A CH-47B Chinook, the Army's medium-lift helicopter, arrived at Ames from Langley. This modified version had one set of conventional flight controls on the left side and a fly-by-wire, variable-stability control system on the right. A research console was mounted in the cargo compartment for in-flight changes in flight-control response. For the next several months the Chinook was to be used to study sideslip performance. (*Astrogram*, 20 Sept. 1979)

Also in   *Pioneer 11* was reoriented to keep the spin axis and antenna
Aug.   pointed toward Earth as it hurtled toward Saturn. With the spacecraft 945 million miles from Earth, controllers at Ames fired two one-second burns of Pioneer's two thrusters, moving the spacecraft 1.1 degree to the left. The spacecraft would soon be maneuvered again to allow the ultraviolet instrument to begin measuring Saturn. *Pioneer 11* had begun to experience the tremendous gravity of Saturn. The planet would pull the spacecraft toward it with increasing speed until at closest approach on 1 Sept., Pioneer would speed past Saturn at 125,000 km/hr. *Pioneer 11* had returned 10 pictures of the planet; as the spacecraft moved closer to the planet, the images would grow larger and clearer, and by 30 Aug., the images should be twice as good as Earth-based photos. (*Astrogram*, 23 Aug. 1979)

262

1 Sept.	Pioneer's encounter with Saturn was completed exactly as anticipated. Traveling at 85,000 km/hr, the spacecraft passed through the ring plane in less than a second. The crossing was dangerous because any impact with debris could have destroyed the spacecraft. One minute after its closest approach, Pioneer disappeared behind Saturn for over an hour, out of radio contact with Earth. After the spacecraft's reappearance, it made another shallow-angle, hazardous ring-plane crossing on its outward journey on the afternoon of 1 Sept. The spacecraft then headed out of the solar system, traveling roughly in the same direction as the solar system is moving through the galaxy. (Director's memorandum 79-161; *Astrogram,* 6 Sept. 1979)
25 Sept.	An unmanned Cosmos biosatellite containing experiments from the USSR, the United States, and other countries was launched in the Soviet Union. Over 40 American scientists from 18 universities and research institutes were involved in the 14 U.S. experiments managed by the Cosmos Project within Ames's Life Sciences Directorate. The major part of the payload consisted of 38 white rats and 60 fertile Japanese quail eggs. They would be in orbit for about three weeks; upon return, data would be shared with other participating countries. The studies were to determine the effects of weightlessness on various physiological processes. This was the first mission by any country to attempt a mammalian breeding experiment. (*Astrogram,* 6 Sept. 1979)
25 Sept.	John Dusterberry was appointed systems integration manager of the 40- by 80-foot wind tunnel modification project. (Director's memorandum 79-157)
Also in Sept.	After a series of workshops at Ames chaired by Dr. Philip Morrison of MIT, scientists recommended an organized program to Search for Extraterrestrial Intelligence. Accordingly, a SETI Project Development Office was formed at Ames. The staff was composed of scientists from Ames and JPL; the project manager was John Billingham of Ames. (*Astrogram,* 20 Sept. 1979)
4 Oct.	Director Clarence Syvertson announced changes in the program planning and review process at Ames. Twice a year organizational directors would present their program plans in five consecutive meetings; each meeting was to be devoted to one directorate. In addition, each Monday morning Syvertson would

review one division's activities. Each division would therefore be reviewed twice a year. (Director's memorandum 79-173)

10 Oct. The Pioneer Project Office was to be gradually phased out over the next three months. The Pioneer-Saturn mission and the Pioneer-Venus missions had been completed, and no future Pioneer projects were planned. A new Space Missions Branch in the Space Projects Division took control of the seven operational Pioneer spacecraft. (Director's memorandum 79-178)

17 Oct. A two-day conference aponsored by the Western Regional Applications Program at Ames met to discuss progress in applying Landsat technology to natural-resource management. The Regional Remote Sensing Conference included over 300 representatives of state and federal agencies, universities, national associations, and private industry. Goddard Space Flight Center and the Earth Resources Laboratory cooperated with Ames in the national test to see if the satellite system could provide more immediate and economical resource information than conventional methods of data collection. (Ames release 79-40; *Astrogram*, 18 Oct. 1979)

24 Oct. Ames announced further findings from *Pioneer 11's* encounter with Saturn on 1 Sept.: (1) Saturn has an 11th moon, discovered in a photo of the outer edge of Saturn's rings and by instrumentation on the spacecraft. Its estimated diameter is 400 km. (2) Saturn has a magnetic field, magnetosphere, and magnetic belts. (3) Low temperatures mean that life on the planet's satellite Titan is unlikely, though still possible. (4) Two new rings were identified. One, named the F ring, is separated from the A ring by a 3,600-km gap called the Pioneer Division. A second ring, the G ring, lies between the orbits of the satellites Rhea and Titan. (5) A feature called the French Division, between the middle and inner visible rings (B and C rings) was seen in Pioneer pictures of the shadow of the rings on Saturn's surface. It was named after French astronomers who first suggested its presence. (6) Substantial particle material was seen in Cassini's Division and in the outer and inner portions of the A ring. The Cassini Division looks empty when viewed from Earth. (7) Preliminary measurements of the ring mass indicated they have a low density and probably are made up largely of ice. (8) Pioneer sustained two micro-meteoroid hits above the rings and three more hits below the rings. (9) Gravity field mea-

surements indicated that Saturn is flattened about 10% at the poles by its rapid rotation. (10) Gravity field analysis and temperature profile measurements suggested that the planet's core is about twice the size of Earth, but is so compressed by Saturn's huge mass that it contains about 11 Earth masses of material, largely iron and rock. (11) Above the core, the planet apparently consists of liquid metallic hydrogen, which does not exist on Earth. (12) More than twice as much heat is radiated into space by Saturn than it absorbs from the Sun. (13) Saturn's magnetic field is 1,000 times stronger than Earth's and 20 times weaker than Jupiter's. (14) Saturn has radiation belts made up of high-energy electrons and protons that are comparable in intensity to those of Earth, but they are completely eliminated by Saturn's rings. The high-energy particles bounce back and forth between Saturn's poles about once a second, until absorbed by ring material. This produces the most radiation-free sector of space yet found in the solar system. (15) Ultraviolet instrumentation may have detected a generalized hydrogen glow or the presence of auroras on Saturn. (Director's memorandum 79-161; Ames release 79-42; *Astrogram*, 15 Nov. 1979)

21 Nov. A University of Iowa team led by Dr. James Van Allen announced more discoveries based on data returned from *Pioneer 11*. A 12th moon of Saturn, a new ring around the planet, and a possible 13th moon had been found. The 12th moon is about 170 km in diameter and lies within the region occupied by Saturn's outer F ring. The moon's period of revolution around Saturn is about 15 hr. The new ring, 8000 km wide, directly adjoins the outer F ring and could be considered an outward extension of it, though it is composed of more tenuous material than the F ring. The discoveries were made by what Van Allen calls "particle-beam astronomy." This means that as high-speed subatomic particles oscillate between Saturn's poles, traveling known paths through the planet's symmetrical magnetic field, they form particle beams much as in a particle accelerator. As the particles are absorbed by moons and ring material, the beam is cut off. Shadows in the beams indicate moons and rings, the size of which can be measured. A 13th moon was suggested by particle-beam measurements, but Van Allen's team was uncertain whether the information indicated another moon or only the changing character of the particles at that location. (Ames release 79-45; *Astrogram*, 29 Nov. 1979)

20 Dec.	Ames celebrated its 40th anniversary with the unveiling of a plaque at the original construction site. Russell Robinson, from the NACA's Washington office, had been at Moffett Field to oversee the initial construction efforts in December 1939 and broke ground for the first building — a construction shack that also provided temporary office space. For the anniversary ceremony Robinson helped Ames Director Clarence Syvertson unveil the commemorative plaque. (*Astrogram*, 27 Dec. 1979)
21 Dec.	The AD-1 oblique-wing research aircraft made its maiden flight at Dryden Flight Research Center. In a 38-min flight the craft reached an altitude of 300 m and a speed of 140 knots. The wing of the craft, which could be moved back as much as 60° while the opposite wing moves forward an equal amount, remained fixed during the flight. After several more flights to demonstrate airworthiness and to gain familiarity with the craft's basic flight behavior, NASA was to use the aircraft to investigate the handling qualities and control characteristics generic to oblique-wing aircraft. The concept, originally developed by R. T. Jones to provide more efficient transonic flight, had undergone extensive wind-tunnel testing at Ames, culminating in the joint Ames-Dryden AD-1 flight research project. (*Astrogram*, 24 Jan. 1980)

1980

1 Jan.	John W. Boyd returned to Ames as associate director after serving as deputy director of Dryden Flight Research Center for a year. He had formerly been deputy director of the Aeronautics and Flight Systems Directorate. (Director's memorandum 79-210; *Astrogram*, 13 Dec. 1979)
31 Jan.	The Shuttle Infrared Telescope Facility study team was established within the Space Projects Division in the Astronautics Directorate. After eight years of preliminary work, the start of design definition studies made a formal team desirable. The work would complement and extend the capability of the Gerard P. Kuiper Observatory and the IRAS project currently under way. The shuttle telescope was to have an aperture of nearly one meter and would be cryogenically cooled. (Director's memorandum 80-15)

Also in Jan.	The Galileo orbiter-probe mission to Jupiter, scheduled for launch in January 1982, had to be revised. The Space Shuttle was not going to be able to lift a payload as heavy as Gailieo so early in Shuttle's operational history. Therefore the Galileo mission would be flown on two spacecraft and launched separately. The Galileo Project Office at Ames would be responsible for development of a new carrier for the probe. Overall management of the mission remained the responsibility of the Jet Propulsion Laboratory, which was also developing the orbiter. (*Astrogram,* 3 Apr. 1980)

1 Feb.	A. Thomas Young, deputy director of Ames, was named director of Goddard Space Flight Center. Jack Boyd became acting deputy director of Ames, as well as retaining his position of associate director. (Director's memorandum 79-196; *Astrogram,* 13 Dec. 1979)

10 Feb.	Following the retirement of Dean Chapman, William Ballhaus was named director of astronautics, moving up from chief of the Applied Computational Aerodynamics Branch. He won the prestigious Lawrence Sperry Award in 1980. (Director's memorandum 80-27 and 79-154; *Astrogram,* 22 Feb. 1980)

12 Feb.	The QSRA resumed its flight program after a 4-month standdown for extensive modification, which included installation of underwing fairings, a speed-hold system, revised spoiler gearing, a new antiskid brake system, and alteration of the horizontal tail. A joint program with the Navy was to begin in April. (*Astrogram,* 22 Feb. 1979)

28 Feb.	The Pioneer Project received special Honor Awards for the successful completion of the Pioneer-Saturn and Pioneer-Venus missions. Deputy Administrator Alan Lovelace was at Ames to help celebrate the event. (*Astrogram,* 24 Jan, 7 Mar. 1980)

29 Feb.	The Pioneer Project Office was closed after 16 years of developing and flying spacecraft to study the Sun and various planets. Responsibility for the continued operation of the active spacecraft, *Pioneer 6–11* and *Pioneer-Venus Orbiter,* was transferred to the Space Missions Branch of the Space Projects Division. Charles F. Hall had been Pioneer project manager since 1963. (Ames release 80-4; Director's memorandum 80-36)

Also in Feb.	The Biomedical Research Division within the Life Sciences Directorate was planning a study to determine if humans aged 55 to 65 could safely ride the Space Shuttle. First briefings were held for the prospective subjects; of the 44 who reported for physicals, 25 were found fit enough to participate in preliminary testing. Final selectees would enter Ames's Human Research Facility for 9 days of controlled observations, 10 days of bedrest, and 5 days of recovery and tests. Dr. Harold Sandler was project scientist. (Ames release 80-7; *Astrogram,* 1 May 1980)
Feb.	An 11-m satellite communications antenna was installed to bring Ames real-time test data from research aircraft flying at Dryden Flight Research Center. The communications path would be from the aircraft to Dryden, to an RCA Satcom, to the new antenna, and to Ames computers almost instantaneously. Flight testing of the Army-NASA Tilt Rotor Research Aircraft later this spring was to provide the first use of the new system. (*Astrogram,* 7 Mar. 1980)
21 Mar.	With the resignation of Loren Bright, Sam White was named director of research support. White had been chief of the Helicopter Technology Division since 1977. (Director's memorandum 80-52; *Astrogram,* 3 Apr. 1980)
Also in Mar.	In the first of a series of investigations, the Vertical Motion Simulator was used to evaluate changes planned for the Shuttle orbiter control system. The modifications concerned the control characteristics of the spacecraft in the atmospheric reentry phase and during landing. The simulator had a greater motion-range capability than any other facility and could therefore more accurately reproduce the motion an astronaut at the controls of the Shuttle would feel on approach, flare, and landing. (*Astrogram,* 3 Apr. 1980)
28 Apr.	The IRAS Project was moved from the Space Projects Division to the Astronautics Directorate. R. R. Nunamaker, who had been temporary manager, returned to his permanent position as chief of the Space Projects Division; D. L. Compton became IRAS Project manager. (Director's memorandum 80-80)
29 Apr.	Richard Peterson, chief of the Ames Aerodynamics Division, was named deputy director of Langley Research Center. (Ames release 80-31; *Astrogram,* 15 May 1980)

Apr.   The Army Aeromechanics Laboratory sponsored a flight-simulator visual-systems workshop in April at Ames to exchange ideas on the psychophysical and engineering aspects of visual simulation systems. The discussions were expected to benefit the design of a ground-based facility to simulate rotorcraft missions, a joint project of the laboratory and Ames. (*Astrogram*, 12 June 1980)

8 May   The shore-based phase of the joint Navy-NASA QSRA flight program was completed. The first objective was to determine the best method of landing a large propulsive-lift aircraft on an aircraft carrier. Repeated landings under various conditions generated data on specific aspects of approach and landing, such as touchdown dispersion and sink rate. If approved, the next phase of the program would involve unarrested landings aboard an aircraft carrier at sea. (*Astrogram*, 29 May 1980)

May   Through data returned by Pioneer-Venus spacecraft, researchers identified major features on the planet. By 18 May the orbiting spacecraft had radar-mapped a belt extending completely around the planet, from 75 degrees North to 63 degrees South latitude, some 93% of Venus's surface. Two huge continent-like features were identified. One, centered at 65 degrees North latitude, is the size of Australia and contains mountains as high as Everest. The other, centered about 5 degrees South, has somewhat lower terrain and is half as large as Africa. The data also show deep rift valleys, rolling plains, high plateaus, and other mountains. Scientists proposed that the northern highland mass be named Ishtar Terra, for Ishtar, the Babylonian goddess of love and war. Aphrodite Terra was proposed as a name for the equatorial upland mass, after the Greek goddess of love, known to the Romans as Venus. (Ames releases 80-47, 80-48; *Astrogram*, 10 July 1980)

May   Ames psychophysiologist Patricia Cowings presented research which she believed might result in a cure for "space sickness," motion sickness in the weightless environment of spaceflight. Working in the Biomedical Research Division, Cowing and associates taught about 50 volunteers how to suppress illness when subjected to an ever-faster-spinning chair. 65% of the volunteers became able to suppress illness symptoms at all speeds; another 20% learned to tolerate significantly higher speeds before becoming sick. By monitoring respiration and heart rate, the subjects learned to recognize when their bodies were operating best. In addition to biofeedback, subjects were taught mental exercises to speed up the learning process. (Ames release 80-32; *Astrogram*, 29 May 1980)

15-28 June A NASA delegation of aeronautics R&D officials visited China in an exchange that would bring members of the Chinese aeronautical establishment to the U.S. in the fall. Each group hoped to become familiar with the other's civil aeronautics program in preparation for exploring prospects for U.S.-Chinese cooperation in this field. The group met Chinese officials in Beijing and toured aeronautical facilities. Ames Director of Astronautics William Ballhaus was among the delegation. (*Astrogram*, 26 June, 24 July 1980)

26 June A project team was established to plan a new flight simulator, the Man-Vehicle Systems Research Facility. Its purpose would be to minimize pilot and ground-control errors in commercial aviation, both present and future, and in air-traffic-control systems. The new facility was expected to cost $8 million and be completed in Dec. 1983. (Director's memorandum 80-60)

June The tie-down test facility for the XV-15 tilt rotor research aircraft, which would permit ground operation of the rotors in all flight configurations, was completed. The helicopter-sized blades were so large that the craft had to be raised before being ground-tested in the airplane mode. The facility used the hydraulic lift of the existing V/STOL hover-test stand with two tie-down towers that were moved into place after the aircraft was elevated. (*Astrogram*, 26 June 1980)

Also in May-June An Ames U-2 took part in a NASA study to find out how volcanic eruptions affect Earth's weather and climate by studying the plumes emitted from Mt. St. Helens, which erupted on 18 May. Data collected for the Aerosol Climate Effects (ACE) program at Ames is the most complete set of observations made of volcanic aerosols in the stratosphere. Aerosols are fine particles, either solid or liquid, suspended in gas; the ACE study began over a year ago to assess the climatic effect of aerosols in the Earth's atmosphere. Five missions were flown in the St. Helens area; preliminary data analysis indicates the volcanic plumes contained a mixture of solid ash particles and sulfuric acid, with proportions varying in different samples. The amount of sulfuric acid found in the stratosphere was several hundred times greater than that found prior to the eruptions; large increases in gaseous sulfur dioxide were also detected.

In addition to the aerosol sampling missions, the U-2 photographed Mt. St. Helens on June 19 at the request of the Washington State Office of Emergency Services. The flight was the result of a month of weather map observations for predictions of skies clear enough to allow the U-2 to photograph the volcanic damage from an altitude of 19,800 m. The photography gave the state the first comprehensive coverage of the damaged area. (*Astrogram,* 24 July 1980, 7 Aug. 1980)

10–13 July   The QSRA made several flights from and landed on the USS *Kittyhawk* at sea — the first time that a four-engine jet transport had operated aboard an aircraft carrier. Both touch-and-go and full-stop landings were made by a team consisting of one Navy pilot and two NASA research pilots. This was the second phase of a joint Navy-NASA program that started in March 1980; data obtained would provide the Navy with a basis for planning airplane and ship procurement. (*Astrogram,* 24 July 1980)

July   Bell Helicopter completed the first phase of the XV-15 tilt rotor research aircraft flight-test program in Texas. Subsequent flights at Dryden Flight Research Center would expand the maneuvering envelope and investigate operational aspects of the tilt rotor for military and civil applications. The second XV-15 was being tested at the Ames tie-down facility, with flight testing planned for late fall 1980. (*Astrogram,* 21 Aug. 1980)

27 Aug.   Ames selected two firms to do system design studies for its Numerical Aerodynamic Simulator, a specialized supercomputer to assist in developing and testing new flight vehicles, as well as doing fluid-flow research in meteorology, gas dynamics, and computational chemistry. The studies were expected to result in a new data processor 40 times faster than existing supercomputers, with a high-speed memory 60 times larger than the current generation of supercomputers. The two contractors were Burroughs Corporation of Paoli, Pennsylvania, and Control Data Corporation of Arden Hills, Minnesota. (Ames release 80-71; *Astrogram,* 11 Sept. 1980)

11 Sept.   Vice Premier Bo Yibo of China visited Ames with 16 other Chinese delegates who were on a month-long visit to the United

271

States. He had been invited to visit a NASA center by Deputy Administrator Alan Lovelace, who headed the NASA delegation to China in June. The Vice Premier was touring the United States to observe the operations of major high-technology firms as part of the reorganization and modernization of China's machine-building industry. (*Astrogram*, 3 Oct. 1980)

12 Sept.   The Augmentor Wing Jet STOL Research Aircraft completed its last research flight at Ames after over eight years of STOL flight research. The joint program between NASA and the Canadian Department of Industry, Trade, and Commerce began in the mid-1960s with a series of model tests in the Ames 40- by 80-foot wind tunnel. The present aircraft was designed around a de Havilland of Canada Buffalo (C-8A) donated to NASA by the USAF. The Boeing Company modified the aircraft, and Rolls Royce and de Havilland designed the propulsion system. A powered elevator, antiskid brakes, and a comprehensive digital avionics research system (called STOLAND) were installed. In 1974 the aircraft was transferred to the Avionics Research Branch, and over the next three years utilized the broad range of capabilities provided by STOLAND to investigate the operational characteristics of powered-lift transports. The first fully automatic landing was made in 1975; later research investigated flightpath tracking and flare-control laws. The aircraft was to be returned to Canada for further exploration of the augmentor concept. (*Astrogram*, 31 Oct. 1980)

16 Sept.   The Ames Basic Research Council was established to evaluate and recommend proposals for the Director's Discretionary Fund, Funds for Independent Research, and to represent Ames on the OAST Research Council at NASA Headquarters. (Director's memorandum 80-172)

17 Sept.   The Aeronautics and Flight Systems Directorate was reorganized to accommodate new program responsibilities, facilities, and research aircraft. The reorganization would permit Ames to be more responsive to the needs of the helicopter program and to give added emphasis to disciplinary research. The Helicopter Technology Division and the V/STOL Aircraft Technology Division were combined to form the Helicopter and Powered Lift Division; the Simulation Sciences Division and the Flight Systems Research Division were combined to form the Flight Systems and Simulation Research Division. (Ames release 80-74; Director's memorandum 80-176)

| Sept. | Ames announced that the 40- by 80-foot wind tunnel would close in July 1981 for approximately one year to complete an $85 million modification project. The power system was to be enlarged and a new 80- by 120-foot test section added. (*Astrogram*, 18 Sept. 1982) |

Sept.

Ames announced that the 40- by 80-foot wind tunnel would close in July 1981 for approximately one year to complete an $85 million modification project. The power system was to be enlarged and a new 80- by 120-foot test section added. (*Astrogram*, 18 Sept. 1982)

30 Oct.

NASA and Army officials of the Tilt Rotor Research Aircraft Project accepted the first XV-15 aircraft in ceremonies at Dryden Flight Research Center. Government flight testing, to be conducted by NASA, Army, and Navy, and Bell Helicopter Textron, would follow to demonstrate and evaluate the tilt-rotor concept. A second aircraft was undergoing ground testing at Ames. (Ames release 80-76; *Astrogram*, 26 Dec. 1980)

31 Oct.

Angelo Guastaferro was named deputy director of Ames. He had been director of the Planetary Division, Office of Space Science, NASA Headquarters. He began his NASA career at Langley Research Center in 1963. (Director's memorandum 80-205; *Astrogram*, 14 Nov. 1980)

4 Nov.

Following the resignation of Leonard Roberts as director of aeronautics and flight systems in September, Thomas Snyder was appointed to the position. Snyder had been chief of the Flight Systems Research Division. (Director's memorandum 80-194; *Astrogram*, 28 Nov. 1980)

18 Nov.

Hughes Aircraft Company was chosen for the negotiation of a contract for the Galileo Probe Carrier Spacecraft; the estimated contract value was $40 million. The spacecraft was scheduled to be launched from the Space Shuttle in Mar. 1984. Upon reaching Jupiter in July 1987, the carrier would release the probe, which would then enter the planet's atmosphere. (Ames release 80-79)

30 Nov.

The Technology Utilization Office was abolished, and its functions were transferred to the Western Regional Applications Office within the Airborne Missions and Applications Division of the Astronautics Directorate. The office was renamed the Western Regional Applications and Technology Utilization Office. (Director's memorandum 80-215)

4 Dec.

Pioneer-Venus 1 completed two years in orbit. Its data led to explanations of the planet-wide circulation of Venus's atmosphere, greenhouse effect, and long-term patterns of cloud circulation, as well as new measurements of atmospheric elements. (Ames releases 80-84, 80-88)

9 Dec.   The parachute system for the Galileo Jupiter atmosphere probe was flight tested at the Naval Weapons Center, China Lake. It was the third and last test of the system; improvements had been made in the parachute after previous tests. (Ames release 80-81)

16 Dec.   *Pioneer 6* completed 16 years of circling the Sun and returning useful data — the longest operating life ever attained by an interplanetary spacecraft. The original specifications called for an operating life of six months; *Pioneer 7, 8,* and *9* were also years beyond their six-month design lives. Together, they made up a network of solar weather stations. (Ames release 80-91)

18 Dec.   Ames researcher Dr. David White proposed a new way of thinking about the origin of life on Earth. He suggested that simple self-replicating chemical systems, rather than complex ones, could have served as the precursors of living cells more than 3.5 billion years ago. The first chemical systems, which were "alive" only in the sense that they could reproduce themselves, may have been far simpler than previously thought. The question raised by the theory was whether some combination of these simple molecules would have the necessary properties to reproduce themselves. (Ames release 80-52)

Dec.   The QSRA completed a comprehensive flight program in which each of 20 experimental test pilots, representing 15 different organizations, made two flights. (*Astrogram,* 12 Dec. 1980)

Dec.   Steelwork for the new test section on the 40- by 80-foot wind tunnel began. The 183-m addition was to culminate in a bell-shaped air intake 110 m wide and 40 m high. (*Astrogram,* 26 Dec. 1980)

274

APPENDIX G

MAJOR PROFESSIONAL AWARDS WON BY AMES PERSONNEL
1940–1980*

1943

William H. McAvoy
 Octave Chanute Award (Institute of the Aeronautical Sciences)

1946

Robert T. Jones
 Sylvanus Albert Reed Award (Institute of the Aeronautical Sciences)

Lewis A. Rodert
 Collier Trophy (National Aeronautical Association)

1947

Laurence A. Clousing
 Octave Chanute Award (Institute of the Aeronautical Sciences)

1948

Smith J. De France
 Presidential Medal of Merit
 Vice President, Institute of the Aeronautical Sciences

Walter G. Vincenti
 Gold Medal Award (Pi Tau Sigma)

*The listed awards reveal only a partial recognition of the many honors achieved by Ames personnel over the years. Because of space constrictions, I have omitted in-house awards from NASA and Ames, which represent perhaps even greater honors, recognition by colleagues for research excellence.

1951

Smith J. De France
    Vice President, Institute of the Aeronautical Sciences

1952

Dean R. Chapman
    Lawrence B. Sperry Award (Institute of the Aeronautical Sciences)

Smith J. De France
    Honorary Doctor of Law Degree, University of California, Los Angeles

1953

Smith J. De France
    Honorary Doctor of Engineering Degree, The University of Michigan

1954

George C. Cooper
    Octave Chanute Award (Institute of the Aeronautical Sciences)
    Arthur S. Flemming Award (Junior Chamber of Commerce,
        Washington, D.C.)

Milton D. Van Dyke
    Fulbright Award for Research
    John Simon Guggenheim Award

1955

H. Julian Allen
    Sylvanus Albert Reed Award (Institute of the Aeronautical Sciences)

Robert T. Jones
    Fellow, American Institute of Aeronautics and Astronautics

William F. Kauffman
    Arthur S. Flemming Award (Junior Chamber of Commerce,
        Washington, D.C.)

Walter G. Vincenti
    Rockefeller Public Service Award

1956

Alfred J. Eggers, Jr.
    Arthur S. Flemming Award (Junior Chamber of Commerce,
    Washington, D.C.)

1957

C. A. Syvertson
    Lawrence B. Sperry Award (Institute of the Aeronautical Sciences)

1958

H. Julian Allen
    Science Trophy (Air Force Association)
    Wright Brothers Lecture Award (American Institute of Aeronautics and
    Astronautics)

Alfred J. Eggers, Jr.
    Outstanding Alumni Award, University of Omaha

1959

Dean R. Chapman
    Rockefeller Public Service Award

Alfred J. Eggers, Jr.
    Arthur S. Flemming Award (Junior Chamber of Commerce,
    Washington, D.C.)

1961

Alfred J. Eggers, Jr.
    Sylvanus Albert Reed Award (American Institute of Aeronautics and
    Astronautics)

1962

Merrill H. Mead
    Alfred P. Sloan Fellowship (M.I.T.)

Walter C. Williams
    Sylvanus Albert Reed Award (American Institute of Aeronautics and
    Astronautics)

1963

John S. White and Rodney C. Wingrove
  Samuel Burka Award (Institute of Navigation)

1964

Evelyn Anderson
  Fourth Annual Federal Women's Award

Smith J. De France
  Career Service Award (National Civil Service League)

Fred J. Drinkwater, III, and Robert C. Innis
  Octave Chanute Award (American Institute of Aeronautics and
    Astronautics)

1965

John W. Boyd
  Alfred P. Sloan Fellowship (Stanford)

Carr H. Neel
  The Award of Excellence (Instrument Society of America)

Rodney C. Wingrove
  Lawrence B. Sperry Award (American Institute of Aeronautics and
    Astronautics)

1966

George E. Cooper
  Admiral Luis de Florez Flight Safety Award (19th Annual International
    Air Safety Seminar, Madrid)

Smith J. De France
  Elder Statesman of Aviation Award (National Aeronautic Association)

Fred J. Drinkwater, III
  Richard Hansford Burroughs Award (Flight Safety Foundation)

278

1967

Loren G. Bright
   Alfred P. Sloan Fellowship (Stanford)

Woodrow Cook
   American Helicopter Society Honorary Fellowship Award

1968

Robert E. Eddy
   Alfred P. Sloan Fellowship (Stanford)

Charles W. Harper
   Wright Brothers Lecture (American Institute of Aeronautics and
      Astronautics)

Kenneth K. Yoshikawa
   Japanese Government Research Award for Foreign Specialists
      (Research Fellowship, National Aerospace Laboratory, Tokyo)

1969

Jerry P. Barrack and Jerry V. Kirk
   Arch T. Colwell Merit Award (Society of Automotive Engineers)

Leonard Roberts
   Alfred P. Sloan Fellowship (Stanford)

1970

Angelo Giovannetti, Jr.
   Alfred P. Sloan Fellowship (Stanford)

Ronald F. Reinisch
   Fellow of the American Institute of Chemists

Ray T. Reynolds
   Fellow, Meteoritical Society

Paul R. Swan
   Congressional Operations Fellowship

1971

George E. Cooper
  Richard Hansford Burroughs Award (Flight Safety Foundation)

Wallace H. Deckert
  Hugh L. Dryden Fellowship (National Space Club)

Alan E. Fayé, Jr.
  Alfred P. Sloan Fellowship (Stanford)

Donald E. Gault
  John Simon Guggenheim Memorial Foundation Fellowship at Max
    Planck Institute for Nuclear Physics, Heidelberg, Germany

Harold Hornby
  Woodrow Wilson Fellowship (Princeton)

Robert T. Jones
  Honorary Ph.D. — Science, University of Colorado

1972

Charles C. Kubokawa
  Japanese Government Research Award for Foreign Specialists
    (Research Fellowship, National Aerospace Laboratory, Tokyo)

Richard H. Peterson
  Alfred P. Sloan Fellowship (Stanford)

Victor L. Peterson
  Alfred P. Sloan Fellowship (M.I.T.)

Thomas Snyder
  Hugh L. Dryden Memorial Fellowship (Stanford)

1973

Wallace H. Deckert
  Hugh L. Dryden Memorial Fellowship (M.I.T.)

David L. Fisher
  Alfred P. Sloan Fellowship (Stanford)

Robert T. Jones
    Fellow, American Academy of Arts and Sciences
    Member, National Academy of Engineering

John H. Wolfe
    AIAA Space Science Award

1974

Dale E. Compton
    Alfred P. Sloan Fellowship (M.I.T.)

Palmer Dyal
    Hugh L. Dryden Memorial Fellowship (University of California,
        Berkeley)

Q. Marion Hansen
    Alfred P. Sloan Fellowship (Stanford)

Hans Mark
    Fellow, American Institute of Aeronautics and Astronautics

NASA/Ames Pioneer 10 Team and TRW Systems Group
    Nelson P. Jackson Aerospace Award (National Space Club)

John H. Wolfe
    Space Science Award (American Institute of Aeronautics and
        Astronautics)

1975

Dean R. Chapman
    Elected to National Academy of Engineers

John C. Dusterberry
    De Florez Training Award (American Institute of Aeronautics and
        Astronautics)

Robert T. Jones
    W. Rupert Turnbull Lecture (Canadian Aeronautics and Space
        Institute)

Robert L. Pike
Alfred P. Sloan Fellowship (Stanford)

Bruce F. Smith
Hugh L. Dryden Memorial Fellowship (University of California, Berkeley)

1976

Jana M. Coleman
Education for Public Management Fellowship (Cornell)

Charles F. Hall
Special Achievement Award (National Civil Service League)

Lado Muhlstein, Jr.
Alfred P. Sloan Fellowship (Berkeley)

C. A. Syvertson
Advanced Management Program (Harvard Business School)

1977

Ames Research Center
Columbus Medal (Genoa, Italy)

Alan B. Chambers
Professional Management Development Fellowship (Harvard Business School)

Dennis Cunningham
Education for Public Management Fellowship (Cornell)

Ray Hicks
SAE Wright Brothers Award

Harvard Lomax
Fluid and Plasmadynamics Award (American Institute of Aeronautics and Astronautics)

James B. Pollack
Arthur S. Flemming Award (Junior Chamber of Commerce, Washington, D.C.)

282

1978

David Chappell
   Robert L. Lichten Award, American Helicopter Society

Phyllis A. Hayes
   Education for Public Management Fellowship (University of Washington)

Robert T. Jones
   Prandtl Ring Award (Dutsche Gesellschaft für Luft- und Raumfahrt)

Paul Kutler
   Lawrence Sperry Award

George T. Lenehan
   Congressional Operations Fellowship

Harvard Lomax
   Fellow, American Institute of Aeronautics and Astronautics

James B. Pollack
   Space Science Award (American Institute of Aeronautics and Astronautics)

Terrill V. Putnam
   Alfred P. Sloan Fellowship (Stanford)

1979

Ames Research Center and Hughes Aircraft
   Nelson P. Jackson Aerospace Award

Charles F. Billings
   Distinguished Service Award *(Aviation Week and Space Technology)*

Patrick M. Cassen
   Newcombe-Cleveland Award (American Association for Advancement of Science)

Dean R. Chapman
   Dryden Lectureship in Research (American Institute of Aeronautics and Astronautics)

Dallas Denery
Hugh L. Dryden Memorial Fellowship (Stanford)

Charles F. Hall
Astronautics Engineer Award (National Space Club)

Robert T. Jones
Honorary Fellow, American Institute of Aeronautics and Astronautics

NASA/Ames Pioneer Venus Team and Hughes Aircraft Company
Nelson P. Jackson Aerospace Award (National Space Club)

Ray T. Reynolds
Newcombe-Cleveland Award (American Association for Advancement of Science)

1980

William F. Ballhaus, Jr.
Lawrence Sperry Award (American Institute of Aeronautics and Astronautics)
Arthur S. Flemming Award (Junior Chamber of Commerce, Washington, D.C.)

Sanford Davis
Hugh L. Dryden Memorial Fellowship (Stanford)

40- by 80-Foot Wind Tunnel Staff
Paul E. Haueter Award, American Helicopter Society

Lawrence G. Lemke
Western Regional Lichten Award

BIBLIOGRAPHIC ESSAY

FEDERAL RECORD CENTER DOCUMENTS

As all federal historians know, there is no lack of documentation within the bureaucracy. Indeed, the problem lies at the other extreme: archival material in federal record centers is overwhelming in quantity, at times also bafflingly difficult to pinpoint in specificity. While I found it relatively easy to locate files on programs, records that were often more helpful — specific offices and divisions, financial records, facilities, personnel — were more difficult to uncover.

Records pertaining to Ames fall into two categories: those that date from the NACA period, from 1938 to 1958, and those that pertain to Ames as part of NASA, from 1958 to the present. The NACA records belong to the National Archives and Records Service; NASA records remain the property of the agency. Both groups of records, however, are found in the San Bruno Federal Record Center, about 24 km south of San Francisco. The records are for the most part open to authorized scholars. The bulk of documentary material used in this book comes from this collection. A useful guide to the Ames records for the NACA period is William H. Cunliffe and Herman G. Goldbeck, "Special Study on the Records of the National Advisory Committee for Aeronautics," July 1973, NN-572-13.

Ames Research Center maintains a current and well organized file on all records retired to San Bruno. By consulting a shelf list at Ames, boxes that looked potentially valuable were requested from the San Bruno Federal Record Center. I found it more efficient to have boxes sent down to Ames itself, since retrieval from the archives sometimes resulted in long waits in its reading room. At Ames, boxes could be examined and those that proved useful could be retained for further work. From over 60 file cartons, I retained about 30 that proved to have useful material. In the early period especially, files that contained useful material were quite clearly differentiated by file-folder title; thus, "General Correspondence, Ames, 1939–1941" and "Construction of Facilities, Ames, 1940–1945," etc., immediately caught my eye. For the NASA period, the proliferation of material seems to have resulted in a shelf list that is more difficult to interpret. One is not sure, when ordering "Jet Propulsion Lab, 1973," exactly what one will receive — will the file document Ames's relations with JPL; will it deal only with JPL's activities; will it document any problems arising in the Ames-JPL relationship, or must one track such issues through correspondence files? These questions, of course, are faced by any historian doing work in any field. For recent federal history, however, the mystery element seems especially acute.

Ames has retired much of its research information and its administrative paperwork. For the most part, these files were not useful for my purposes. I searched instead through files pertaining to policy, organization, relations with Headquarters, personnel regulations, and various technical committees and planning groups. Correspondence files of administrators identified many of the major concerns at Ames during various periods, often providing complete exchanges of correspondence on a particular issue over a period of months or years. Boxes in the NACA series 70-A-1261, 74-A-1624, 75-A-1324, and 76-A-1382 were especially useful. For the NASA period, accession series 255-77-0020, containing 60 cartons, was most useful. The Records Management Office at Ames was extremely helpful in aiding my search and in speeding record retrieval from San Bruno.

RECORDS AT AMES

I was greatly aided in my work by the fact that Ames, with an eye to its recent history, had already collected much information on the 1965–1977 period. Gathered and categorized by Edie Watson Kuhr, an Ames veteran who had been at the center since its early years, the four file drawers of information plus additional publications was a very valuable source that eased my task immensely. Mrs. Kuhr was extremely helpful in pointing me in the right direction.

The Ames Research Center Library contains a number of important holdings pertinent to this study, among them a complete set of NACA *Annual Reports,* containing both financial and administrative information and reports completed during the year. Equally important are a complete set of *Technical Notes, Memoranda,* and *Reports,* the research products for which the NACA existed. NASA continued these series.

NATIONAL ARCHIVES MATERIAL

The National Archives has a small collection of NACA material in the Center for Polar and Scientific Archives, which is in the Main Building. In this collection there were several pertinent files, including transcripts of speeches. In addition, there is an extremely useful biography file (series 3), containing substantial material on William Durand, Smith De France, George Lewis, William Moffett, and Jerome Hunsaker, among others. The material varies widely in quality and quantity; the files on Hunsaker, for example, fill almost 20 correspondence boxes. A useful guide is Sara Powell, "A Preliminary Inventory of the Textual Records of the National Advisory Committee for Aeronautics," June 1967, NM-86. The inventory was not distributed, but can be consulted at either the National Archives or the NASA History Office Archives.

NASA HISTORY OFFICE ARCHIVES

Material in the NASA History Office Archives varies in substance and completeness. There is much that is valuable in the small archives, and the material dates from the NACA's earliest years to the present. The NASA History Office archivist is extremely knowledgeable and helpful.

There is much information on the various NASA offices and field centers, as well as unexpected collections of personal correspondence among key NACA figures. For the early period of Ames's history, I made much use of personal correspondence files. An extensive biography section contains material not only on NACA and NASA personnel, but on others important in aeronautics and astronautics. Interspersed within the biography files are a wealth of photos, in some cases, I am sure, located more easily here than in a larger archive. Some biography files contain the transcripts of interviews obtained by previous historians. These were sometimes invaluable.

ORAL HISTORY INTERVIEWS

If an institution has a distinct atmosphere or personality of its own, and Ames does, that atmosphere comes from its leaders and its personnel. Since I attempted to identify those qualities that distinguish Ames and to analyze their origins, I found one of my most valuable sources to be interviews with past and present members of the Ames staff. In some cases the interview was conducted over several sessions. I usually taped the interviews; if this was not possible I made extensive notes during and after the interview. By talking to many people who were influential in the center's history, I was able to expand the documentation I already had and, in some cases, to fill in gaps of knowledge the documents did not provide. When carefully balanced, documentary evidence and oral history interviews complement each other, providing a blending of perspective between that of the historian and that of the historical participant. Talking with my interviewees gave me a depth of understanding not possible by relying solely on documentary evidence. The interview tapes are now located in the NASA History Office.

GENERAL SOURCES

More general sources used included newspapers, professional journals, and secondary monographic sources. The *San Francisco Chronicle,* the *Palo Alto Times,* and the *San Jose Mercury* proved useful, though in the early years they proved by their omissions that the NACA's profile was indeed low. *Aeronautics and Astronautics,* the journal of the American Institute of Aeronautics and Astronautics, was valuable for its technical information, as was *Aviation Week and Space Technology* for a more general perspective on the field. The annual NASA chronologies, *Aeronautics and Astronautics,* are valuable as references for NASA history; their indexes are both thorough and well organized. Robert L. Rosholt's *An Administrative History of NASA, 1958–1963,* NASA SP-4101 (Washington, 1966) provided good guidance through the maze of early NASA administrative evolutions.

Finally, mention must be made of Edwin P. Hartman's book *Adventures in Research: A History of Ames Research Center, 1940–1965.* Although the present monograph differs in intent and style from Hartman's study, his original research and perspective on Ames was invaluable, providing a firm foundation for later work. Hartman's book, more technically focused than this study, gives a detailed treatment of the major areas of Ames's research during its first 25 years. In many ways, the books complement each other, the present book carrying the narrative past NASA's first years into the present context of research directions and management concerns.

A number of other monographs proved useful. Though not separately discussed here, they are cited in the source notes.

INDEX

Mercury project reentry capsule, 67 ill.
Moffett Field, 4, 5-6

National Advisory Committee for Aeronautics (NACA), 1, 85-86, 116, 125-26. *See also* Ames Aeronautical Laboratory; funding.
    High Speed Panel, 61
    and industry, 2, 4, 5, 21, 22, 23, 36, 41, 46, 52, 53, 62, 83
    and the military, 2, 3-4, 5-6, 8-9, 19, 21, 22-23, 35-36, 39-42, 44, 75, 81-83
    personnel, 24, 71, 79, 115, 119
    Research Airplane Projects Panel, 61, 63
    research contributions, 2, 5, 61, 62-63, 75, 118, 125-26
    and space program, 68, 73, 81, 83, 85, 86-87
    and universities, 4-5, 6-7, 117
    Western Coordination Office, 6, 23, 63-64
National Aeronautics and Space Act of 1958, 86, 190
National Aeronautics and Space Administration (NASA). *See also* Ames Research Center, and Headquarters; funding; National Advisory Committee for Aeronautics.
    and contracting, 118-19, 140
    life sciences program, 92-95, 97, 100-05
    manned spaceflight program, 126, 127
    and the military, 92, 143, 177-78, 254
    Office of Life Science Programs, 94-95, 99, 100
    organization, 87, 95, 100, 101, 118, 125, 273
National Science Foundation, 33, 86
Naval Appropriations Act of 1915, 2
Navy, U.S., 83, 84, 85. *See also* military subheads of Ames Aeronautical Laboratory, Ames Research Center, National Advisory Committee for Aeronautics and National Aeronautics and Space Administration.
Nickle, Ferrill, 51, 57, 126
North American Aviation, 52, 63
Nysmith, Robert, 207, 208

Office of Management and Budget, 59, 150, 156

Parsons, John (Jack), 7, 8, 11 ill., 14, 19, 54, 72, 80 ill., 115, 124, 141, 142, 201, 204, 213
Pioneer missions:
    Pioneer 1, 2, 210
    Pioneer 3, 4, 210-11
    Pioneer 5, 210, 211
    Pioneer 6-9, 144, 211, 274
    Pioneer 10, 211, 217 ill., 218, 219-20, 243, 261
    Pioneer 11, 211, 218, 219-20, 255, 262-63, 264-65

THE AUTHOR

Elizabeth Muenger holds a B.A. in English Literature from Oberlin College and an M.A. and Ph.D. in European History from the University of Michigan. Her research interests include the study of civilian-military relations in Great Britain and Ireland, recent European military history, and the history of technology. Prior to her association with NASA she taught at Stanford University. She is currently the Command Historian at the U.S. Air Force Academy.

THE NASA HISTORY SERIES

HISTORIES

Anderson, Frank W., Jr., *Orders of Magnitude: A History of NACA and NASA, 1915-1980* (NASA SP-4403, 2d ed., 1981).

Benson, Charles D., and William Barnaby Faherty, *Moonport: A History of Apollo Launch Facilities and Operations* (NASA SP-4204, 1978).

Bilstein, Roger E., *Stages to Saturn: A Technological History of the Apollo/Saturn Launch Vehicles* (NASA SP-4206, 1980).

Boone, W. Fred, *NASA Office of Defense Affairs: The First Five Years* (NASA HHR-32, 1970, multilith).

Brooks, Courtney G., James M. Grimwood, and Loyd S. Swenson, Jr., *Chariots for Apollo: A History of Manned Lunar Spacecraft* (NASA SP-4205, 1979).

Byers, Bruce K., *Destination Moon: A History of the Lunar Orbiter Program* (NASA TM X-3487, 1977, multilith).

Compton, W. David, and Charles D. Benson, *Living and Working in Space: A History of Skylab* (NASA SP-4208, in press).

Corliss, William R., *NASA Sounding Rockets, 1958-1968: A Historical Summary* (NASA SP-4401, 1971).

Ezell, Edward Clinton, and Linda Neuman Ezell, *The Partnership: A History of the Apollo-Soyuz Test Project* (NASA SP-4209, 1978).

Ezell and Ezell, *On Mars: Exploration of the Red Planet, 1958-1978* (NASA SP-4214, 1984).

Green, Constance McL., and Milton Lomask, *Vanguard: A History* (NASA SP-4202, 1970; also Washington: Smithsonian Institution Press, 1971).

Hacker, Barton C., and James M. Grimwood, *On the Shoulders of Titans: A History of Project Gemini* (NASA SP-4203, 1977).

Hall, R. Cargill, *Lunar Impact: A History of Project Ranger* (NASA SP-4210, 1977).

Hallion, Richard P., *On the Frontier: Flight Research at Dryden, 1956-1981* (NASA SP-4303, 1984).

Hartman, Edwin P., *Adventures in Research: A History of Ames Research Center, 1940-1965* (NASA SP-4302, 1970).

Levine, Arnold, *Managing NASA in the Apollo Era* (NASA SP-4102, 1982).

Newell, Homer E., *Beyond the Atmosphere: Early Years of Space Science* (NASA SP-4211, 1980).

Roland, Alex, *Model Research: A History of the National Advisory Committee for Aeronautics 1915-1958* (NASA SP-4303, 1985).

Rosenthal, Alfred, *Venture into Space: Early Years of Goddard Space Flight Center* (NASA SP-4301, 1968).

Rosholt, Robert L., *An Administrative History of NASA, 1958-1963* (NASA SP-4101, 1966).

Sloop, John L., *Liquid Hydrogen as a Propulsion Fuel, 1945-1959* (NASA SP-4404, 1978).

Swenson, Loyd S., Jr., James M. Grimwood, and Charles C. Alexander, *This New Ocean: A History of Project Mercury* (NASA SP-4201, 1966).

REFERENCE WORKS

Aeronautics and Space Report of the President, annual volumes 1975-1982.

The Apollo Spacecraft: A Chronology (NASA SP-4009, vol. 1, 1969; vol. 2, 1973; vol. 3, 1976; vol. 4, 1978).

Astronautics and Aeronautics: A Chronology of Science, Technology, and Policy, annual volumes 1961-1976, with an earlier summary volume, *Aeronautics and Astronautics, 1915-1960.*

Dickson, Katherine M., ed., *History of Aeronautics and Astronautics: A Preliminary Bibliography* (NASA HHR-29, 1968, multilith).

Hall, R. Cargill, ed., *Essays on the History of Rocketry and Astronautics: Proceedings of the Third through the Sixth History Symposia of the International Academy of Astronautics* (NASA CP-2014, 2 vols., 1977).

Hall, R. Cargill, *Project Ranger: A Chronology* (JPL/HR-2, 1971, multilith).

Looney, John J., ed., *Bibliography of Space Books and Articles from Non-Aerospace Journals. 1957-1977* (NASA HHR-51, 1979, multilith).

Roland, Alex, *A Guide to Research in NASA History* (NACA HHR-50, 6th ed., 1982, available from NASA History Office).

Skylab: A Chronology (NASA SP-4011, 1977).

Van Nimmen, Jane, and Leonard C. Bruno, with Robert L. Rosholt, *NASA Historical Data Book, 1958-1968,* vol. 1, *NASA Resources* (NASA SP-4012, 1976).

Wells, Helen T., Susan H. Whiteley, and Carrie E. Karegeannes, *Origins of NASA Names* (NASA SP-4402, 1976).

Recent volumes are available from Superintendent of Documents, Government Printing Office, Washington, DC 20402; early volumes from National Technical Information Service, Springfield, VA 22161.

Ames Research Center in August 1980.